Calculus of Variations with Applications

A.S. GUPTA

Emeritus Professor, Department of Mathematics
Indian Institute of Technology Kharagpur

PHI Learning Private Limited

Delhi-110092

2013

₹ 225.00

CALCULUS OF VARIATIONS WITH APPLICATIONS
by A.S. Gupta

ISBN-978-81-203-1120-6

The export rights of this book are vested solely with the publisher.

Tenth Printing ... ... **June, 2013**

Published by Asoke K. Ghosh, PHI Learning Private Limited, Rimjhim House, 111, Patparganj Industrial Estate, Delhi-110092 and Printed by Syndicate Binders, A-20, Hosiery Complex, Noida, Phase-II Extension, Noida-201305 (N.C.R. Delhi).

To
My Parents

CONTENTS

PREFACE

Calculus of variations is one of the most important divisions of theoretical and applied mathematics. Variational principles are of great scientific significance as they provide a unified approach to various mathematical and physical problems and yield fundamental exploratory ideas.

The aim of this book is to give a rigorous and thorough analysis of various aspects of calculus of variations. Although a number of text books are available on the subject, most of them are written at a level which is not easily comprehensible to readers or students at the postgraduate level. An attempt has therefore been made in this book to present the materials in a lucid and coherent manner so that readers with some background in calculus, differential equations and functional analysis can easily grasp them. A large number of examples are worked out to acquaint the reader with the various techniques for solving variational problems.

Another motivation for me in bringing out this book is to arrange the materials in a logically consistent and systematic manner so that it may prove to be useful to students as well as research workers. Further, I have presented the recent developments that have taken place in the field, e.g., stochastic calculus of variations, variational principle for any nonlinear problem and variational inequalities. Finally, it may be noted that although some advanced level books on the subject are available, they deal either with problems of elasticity and heat transfer or with problems of theoretical physics. In this book, in addition to the study of these problems, I have emphasized the investigation of several problems in hydrodynamics and hydromagnetics which have important engineering and technological applications.

I am deeply indebted to my wife Lakshmi and my sister Mrs. N. Sengupta who were a constant source of encouragement while writing this book.

A.S. Gupta

PREFACE

Every problem of the calculus of variations has a solution provided the word "solution" is suitably defined.

—Hilbert

GENERAL INTRODUCTION

The calculus of variations has its origin in the generalization of the elementary theory of maxima and minima of function of a single or more variables. Its object is to find extrema or stationary values of functionals. By a functional we mean a quantity whose values are determined by one or several functions. Thus the domain of a functional is a set of admissible functions, rather than a region of a coordinate space.

A simple example of a functional is the length l between two given points (x_0, y_0) and (x_1, y_1) on a curve $y = y(x)$. This length is given by

$$l[y(x)] = \int_{x_0}^{x_1} \left[1 + \left(\frac{dy}{dx} \right)^2 \right]^{1/2} dx.$$

Another example is the area S of a surface bounded by a given curve C because this area is determined by the choice of the surface $z = z(x, y)$ as

$$S[z(x, y)] = \iint_D \left[1 + \left(\frac{\partial z}{\partial x} \right)^2 + \left(\frac{\partial z}{\partial y} \right)^2 \right]^{1/2} dx\, dy.$$

Here, D is the projection of the area bounded by the curve C on the xy-plane. Similarly, the coordinates of the centre of gravity of a curve, and time of transit between two given points of a curve are examples of functionals, since their values are determined by the choice of the curve.

The aim of calculus of variations is to explore methods for finding the maximum or minimum of a functional defined over a class of functions. Several physical laws can be deduced from concise mathematical principles to the effect that a certain functional in a given process attains a maximum or minimum. Here are some examples of variational principles in several branches of science. In mechanics, we have the principle of least action, the principle of conservation of linear momentum, and the principle of conservation of angular momentum. In addition, we have Fermat's principle in optics, and the principle of Castigliano in the theory of elasticity, apart from some variational principles of classical and relativistic field theory.

The history of the calculus of variations can be traced back to the year 1696 when Johann Bernoulli advanced the problem of the *brachistochrone* (Elsgolts [1]). In this problem, one has to find the curve connecting two given points, A and B, that do not lie on a vertical line, such that a particle sliding down this curve under gravity (in the absence of any resistance) from the point A reaches point B in the shortest time. It is not difficult to see that the line of quickest descent will not be the straight line connecting A and B, though this is the shortest distance between the points. The reason is that the velocity of motion in a straight line builds up rather slowly. However, if we imagine a curve that is steeper near A, a considerable portion of the path will be covered at a greater speed. It turns out that the required path is a cycloid. Apart from Bernoulli, this problem was independently solved by Leibnitz, Newton and L'Hospital. However, the development of calculus of variations as an independent mathematical discipline along with its own methods of investigation was due to the pioneering studies of Euler during the period 1707–1783.

Apart from the problem of brachistochrone described above, three other problems exerted great influence on the development of the subject:

(i) In the problem of geodesics, it is required to determine the line of shortest length connecting two given points (x_0, y_0, z_0) and (x_1, y_1, z_1) on a surface S given by $\phi(x, y, z) = 0$. This is a typical variational problem with a constraint since here we are required to minimize the arc length l joining the two points on S given by the functional

$$ l = \int_{x_0}^{x_1} \left[1 + \left(\frac{dy}{dx} \right)^2 + \left(\frac{dz}{dx} \right)^2 \right]^{1/2} dx $$

subject to the constraint $\phi(x, y, z) = 0$. This problem was first solved by Jacob Bernoulli in 1698, but a general method of solving such problems was given by Euler.

(ii) In the problem of minimal surface of revolution, a curve $y = y(x) \geq 0$ is rotated about the x-axis through an angle 2π. The resulting surface bounded by the planes $x = a$ and $x = b$ has the area

$$ S = 2\pi \int_a^b y \left[1 + \left(\frac{dy}{dx} \right)^2 \right]^{1/2} dx $$

Clearly, the determination of the particular curve $y = y(x)$ which minimizes S constitutes a variational problem.

(iii) In the isoperimetric problem it is required to find a closed line of given length which encloses a maximum area S. The solution of this problem is the circle which was known even in ancient Greece. The problem essentially consists of the maximization of the area A bounded by the closed curve $r = r(\theta)$ of given length l. This means that the functional A given by

$$ A = \frac{1}{2} \int_0^{2\pi} r^2 \, d\theta $$

is maximum subject to

$$ l = \int_0^{2\pi} \left[r^2 + \left(\frac{dr}{d\theta} \right)^2 \right]^{1/2} d\theta. $$

In the following sections, we will present methods for solving a wide variety of variational problems. However, the emphasis will be given to the maxima or minima of the following functionals:

$$\int_{x_0}^{x_1} F(x, y(x), y'(x))\, dx,$$

$$\int_{x_0}^{x_1} F(x, y(x), y'(x), \ldots, y^{(n)}(x))\, dx,$$

$$\int_{x_0}^{x_1} F(x, y_1(x), y_2(x), \ldots, y_n(x), y_1'(x), y_2'(x), \ldots, y_n'(x))\, dx$$

and

$$\iint_D F\left(x, y, z(x, y), \frac{\partial z}{\partial x}, \frac{\partial z}{\partial y}\right) dx\, dy$$

in which the function F is given, and the functions $y(x)$, $y_1(x)$, $y_2(x)$, $\ldots$, $y_n(x)$, $z(x, y)$ are the arguments of the functionals. Further, a prime denotes derivative with respect to x.

CHAPTER 1

VARIATIONAL PROBLEMS WITH FIXED BOUNDARIES

1.1 The Concept of Variation and Its Properties

As already pointed out in the introduction, a variable quantity $I[y(x)]$ is a functional dependent on a function $y(x)$ if to each function $f(x)$ belonging to a certain class of functions C, there is a definite value of I. Thus there is a correspondence between a given function $y(x)$ and a number I.

By the increment or variation δy of the argument $y(x)$ of a functional I, we mean the difference $\delta y (= y(x) - y_1(x))$ between two functions belonging to a certain class. A functional $I[y(x)]$ is said to be continuous if a small change in $y(x)$ results in a small change in $I[y(x)]$. This definition is, however, somewhat imprecise since we have not specified what we exactly mean by the phrase 'a small change in $y(x)$'. In other words, under what conditions should we consider the curves $y = y(x)$ and $y = y_1(x)$ close?

One way of specifying the closeness of $y(x)$ and $y_1(x)$ is to say that the absolute value of their difference given by $|y(x) - y_1(x)|$ is small for all x for which $y(x)$ and $y_1(x)$ are defined. When this happens, we say $y(x)$ is close to $y_1(x)$ in the sense of zero-order proximity. But with this definition, the functional

$$I[y(x)] = \int_a^b F(x, y(x), y'(x))\, dx, \tag{1.1}$$

which occurs in many applications, is seldom continuous due to the presence of the argument $y'(x)$. This necessitates the extension of the notion of closeness of the curves $y = y(x)$ and $y = y_1(x)$ such that both $|y(x) - y_1(x)|$ and $|y'(x) - y_1'(x)|$ are small for all values of x for which these functions are prescribed. We then say that these two curves are close in the sense of first-order proximity. In general, the curves $y = y(x)$ and $y = y_1(x)$ are said to be close in the sense of nth order proximity if $|y(x) - y_1(x)|$, $|y'(x) - y_1'(x)|, \ldots, |y^{(n)}(x) - y_1^{(n)}(x)|$ are small for values of x for which these functions are defined.

Figure 1.1 shows two curves which are close in the sense of zero-order proximity but not in the sense of first-order proximity. Figure 1.2 shows two curves which are close in the sense of first-order proximity. It is clear from the above definitions that if two curves are close in the sense of nth order proximity, then they are certainly, close in the sense of any lower order (say, $(n-1)$th) proximity.

We are now in a position to refine the concept of the continuity of a functional. The functional $I[y(x)]$ is said to be continuous at $y = y_0(x)$, in the sense of nth

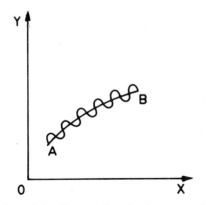

Fig. 1.1 Curves close in the sense of zero-order proximity.

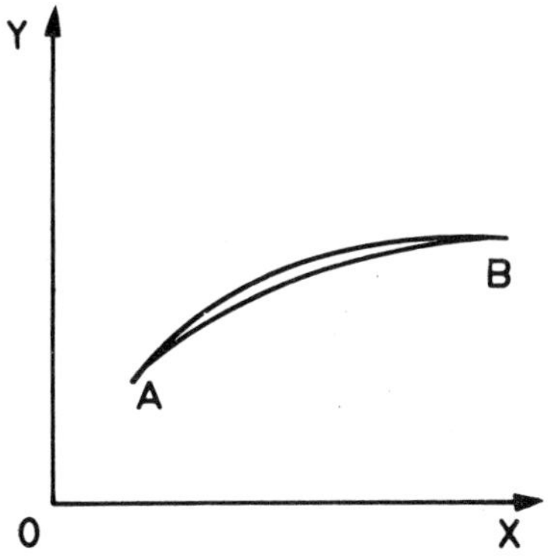

Fig. 1.2 Curves close in the sense of first-order proximity.

order proximity, if given any positive number ε, there exists a $\delta > 0$ such that

$$| I[y(x)] - I[y_0(x)] | < \varepsilon \text{ for } | y(x) - y_0(x) | < \delta$$

$$| y'(x) - y_0'(x) | < \delta, \ldots, | y^{(n)}(x) - y_0^{(n)}(x) | < \delta$$

Example 1. Show that the functional

$$I[y(x)] = \int_0^1 x^3 [1 + y^2(x)]^{1/2} \, dx$$

defined on the set of functions $y(x) \in C[0, 1]$, (where $C[0, 1]$ is the set of all continuous functions on the closed interval $0 \le x \le 1$) is continuous on the function $y_0(x) = x^2$ in the sense of zero-order proximity.

Solution. Put $y(x) = x^2 + \alpha\eta(x)$, where $\eta(x) \in C[0, 1]$ and α is arbitrarily small. Then,

$$I[y(x)] = I[x^2 + \alpha\eta(x)] = \int_0^1 x^3 [1 + (x^2 + \alpha\eta(x))^2]^{1/2} \, dx;$$

Passing to the limit $\alpha \to 0$, we find that,

$$\lim_{\alpha \to 0} I[y(x)] = \int_0^1 x^3 (1 + x^4)^{1/2} \, dx = I[x^2]$$

and this establishes the continuity of the functional on $y_0(x) = x^2$.

It is, however, possible to define the notion of distance $\rho(y_1, y_2)$ between two curves $y = y_1(x)$ and $y = y_2(x)$ (with $x_0 \le x \le x_1$) as

$$\rho(y_1, y_2) = \max_{(x_0 \le x \le x_1)} | y_1(x) - y_2(x) | \tag{1.2}$$

Clearly, with this metric, we can introduce the concept of zero-order proximity. This notion can be extended to the case of nth order proximity of two curves $y = y_1(x)$ and $y = y_2(x)$ (admitting continuous derivatives upto order n inclusive) if one introduces the metric

$$\rho(y_1, y_2) = \sum_{p=1}^{n} \max_{(x_0 \le x \le x_1)} |y_1^{(p)}(x) - y_2^{(p)}(x)| \tag{1.3}$$

Let us now introduce the concept of a linear functional $I[y(x)]$ defined in the normed linear space M of the functions $y(x)$. This functional is said to be linear, if it satisfies

(i) $I[cy(x)] = cI[y(x)]$,

where c is an arbitrary constant,

(ii) $I[y_1(x) + y_2(x)] = I[y_1(x)] + I[y_2(x)]$,

where $y_1(x) \in M$ and $y_2(x) \in M$.

Take, for instance, the functional

$$I[y(x)] = \int_a^b [y'(x) + 2y(x)]\, dx \tag{1.4}$$

defined in the space $C^1[a, b]$, which consists of the set of all functions admitting continuous first order derivatives in $[a, b]$. Clearly, I in (1.4) is a linear functional.

It can, however, be shown that a functional $I[y(x)]$ is linear if (a) it is continuous and, (b) for any $y_1(x) \in M$ and $y_2(x) \in M$, satisfies the condition

$$I[y_1(x)] + I[y_2(x)] = I[y_1(x) + y_2(x)]$$

Let us now define the variation of a functional $I[y(x)]$. The increment ΔI is given by

$$\Delta I = I[y(x) + \delta y(x)] - I[y(x)]$$

which may be written in the form

$$\Delta I = L[y(x), \delta y] + \beta[y(x), \delta y]\, \max |\delta y| \tag{1.5}$$

Here, $L[y(x), \delta y]$ is a functional linear in δy and $\beta[y(x), \delta y] \to 0$ as the maximum value of δy (given by $\max |\delta y|$) $\to 0$. This sort of division of the increment ΔI is analogous to the differential, and the infinitesimal, in the case of a function of a single variable given by

$$\Delta f(x) = f(x + \Delta x) - f(x)$$

$$= A(x)\, \Delta x + \beta(x, \Delta x)\, \Delta x. \tag{1.6}$$

Here, $A(x)\, \Delta x$, known as the differential df, is the principal part of the increment and is linear in Δx. By the same token, the part $L[y(x), \delta y]$ is called the variation of the functional and is denoted by δI.

An alternative definition of the variation δI of a functional I can be given. Consider the functional $I[y(x) + \alpha \delta y]$ for fixed y and δy and different values of the parameter α.

Now using (1.5) the increment ΔI can be written as

$$\Delta I = I[y(x) + \alpha \delta y] - I[y(x)]$$

$$= L[y, \alpha \delta y] + \beta[y, \alpha \delta y] |\alpha|\, \max |\delta y|.$$

The derivative of $I[y(x) + \alpha\,\delta y]$ with respect to α at $\alpha = 0$ is

$$\lim_{\Delta\alpha \to 0} \frac{\Delta I}{\Delta\alpha} = \lim_{\alpha \to 0} \frac{\Delta I}{\alpha} = \lim_{\alpha \to 0} \frac{L[y, \alpha\delta y] + \beta[y, \alpha\delta y] \mid \alpha \mid \max \mid \delta y \mid}{\alpha}$$

$$= \lim_{\alpha \to 0} \frac{L[y, \alpha\delta y]}{\alpha} + \lim_{\alpha \to 0} \frac{\beta[y, \alpha\delta y] \mid \alpha \mid \max \mid \delta y \mid}{\alpha}$$

$$= L[y, \delta y] = \delta I,$$

since by linearity $L[y, \alpha\delta y] = \alpha L[y, \delta y]$ and $\beta \to 0$ as $\alpha \to 0$. Hence the variation of a functional $I[y(x)]$ is equal to

$$\frac{\partial}{\partial\alpha} I[y(x) + \alpha\delta y] \text{ at } \alpha = 0.$$

Definition. A functional $I[y(x)]$ attains a maximum on a curve $y = y_0(x)$, if the values of I on any curve close to $y = y_0(x)$ do not exceed $I[y_0(x)]$. This means that $\Delta I = I[y(x)] - I[y_0(x)] \le 0$. Further, if $\Delta I \le 0$ and $\Delta I = 0$ only on $y = y_0(x)$, we say that a strict maximum is attained on $y = y_0(x)$. In the case of a minimum of I on $y = y_0(x)$, $\Delta I \ge 0$ for all curves close to $y_0(x)$ and a strict minimum is defined in the same way.

Theorem. If a functional $I[y(x)]$ attains a maximum or minimum on $y = y_0(x)$, where the domain of definition belongs to certain class, then at $y = y_0(x)$,

$$\delta I = 0. \tag{1.7}$$

Proof. For fixed $y_0(x)$ and δy, $I[y_0(x) + \alpha\delta y)] = \Psi(\alpha)$ is a function of α and this reaches a maximum or minimum for $\alpha = 0$. Thus $\Psi'(0) = 0$ leading to

$$\frac{\partial}{\partial\alpha} I[y_0(x) + \alpha\delta y]|_{\alpha = 0} = 0, \text{ i.e., } \delta I = 0. \text{ This proves the theorem.}$$

However, when we talk of maximum or minimum, we mean the largest or smallest value of the functional, relative to values of the functional on close-lying curves. But we have already seen that the closeness of curves may be understood in different ways depending on the order of proximity of the curves.

If a functional $I[y(x)]$ attains a maximum or minimum on the curve $y = y_0(x)$ with respect to all curves $y = y(x)$ such that $\mid y(x) - y_0(x) \mid$ is small, then the maximum or minimum is said to be strong.

If, on the other hand, $I[y(x)]$ attains a maximum or minimum on the curve $y = y_0(x)$ with respect to all curves $y = y(x)$ in the sense of first order proximity, i.e., $\mid y(x) - y_0(x) \mid$ and $\mid y'(x) - y_0'(x) \mid$ are both small, then the maximum or minimum is said to be weak. It is quite clear that if a strong maximum (or minimum) of a functional $I[y(x)]$ is attained on the curve $y = y_0(x)$, then a weak maximum (or minimum) is also attained on the same curve. This follows from the fact that if two curves are close in the sense of first-order proximity, then they are definitely close in the sense of zero-order proximity as well.

This theorem can be readily extended to functionals dependent on several unknown functions, or dependent on one or several functions of any number of variables, e.g.,

$$I[y_1(x), y_2(x), \ldots, y_n(x)] \quad \text{or} \quad I[z(x_1, x_2, \ldots, x_m)]$$

or

$$I[z_1(x_1, x_2, \ldots, x_m), z_2(x_1, x_2, \ldots, x_m), \ldots, z_p(x_1, x_2, \ldots, x_m)].$$

The necessary condition for extremum, in all these cases, is still, given by $\delta I = 0$, where the variation δ is defined in exactly the same way as that for a functional $I[y(x)]$.

1.2   Euler's Equation

Let us examine the extremum of the functional

$$I[y(x)] = \int_a^b F(x, y(x), y'(x)) \, dx \tag{1.8}$$

subject to the boundary conditions $y(a) = y_1$ and $y(b) = y_2$, where y_1 and y_2 are prescribed at the fixed boundary points a and b. We assume that $F(x, y, y')$ is three times differentiable. We have already shown that the necessary condition for an extremum of a functional is that its variation must vanish. We shall now apply this condition to (1.8), and assume that the admissible curves on which an extremum is achieved, admits of continuous first-order derivatives. It can be proved, however, that the curve on which an extremum is achieved, admits of a continuous second-order derivative also (see Section 1.9).

Let $y = y(x)$ be the curve which extremizes the functional (1.8) such that $y(x)$ is twice differentiable and satisfies the above boundary conditions (see Fig. 1.3). Let $y = \bar{y}(x)$ be an admissible curve close to $y = y(x)$ such that both $y(x)$ and $\bar{y}(x)$ can be included in a one-parameter family of curves

$$y(x, \alpha) = y(x) + \alpha[\bar{y}(x) - y(x)] \tag{1.9}$$

For $\alpha = 0$, $y(x, \alpha) = y(x)$ and for $\alpha = 1$, $y(x, \alpha) = \bar{y}(x)$.

The difference $\bar{y}(x) - y(x)$ is the variation δy of the function y (see Fig. 1.4) and is similar to the role played by Δx, the increment in x while considering the extrema of a function $f(x)$. Now on the curves of the family (1.9), the functional (1.8) reduces to a function of α, say $\Psi(\alpha)$. Since the extremizing curve $y = y(x)$ corresponds to $\alpha = 0$, it follows that $\Psi(\alpha)$ is extremized for $\alpha = 0$. This implies that

$$\left(\frac{d\Psi}{d\alpha} \right)_{\alpha = 0} = 0, \tag{1.10}$$

where

$$\Psi(\alpha) = \int_a^b F(x, y(x, \alpha), y'(x, \alpha)) \, dx \tag{1.11}$$

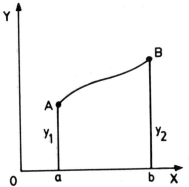

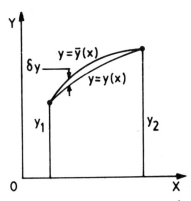

Fig. 1.3 Extremizing curve joining two fixed points.

Fig. 1.4 Extremizing curve and an admissible curve between two fixed points.

Using (1.9) and (1.11), it follows that

$$\Psi'(\alpha) = \int_a^b [F_y(x, y(x, \alpha), y'(x, \alpha))\, \delta y + F_{y'}(x, y(x, \alpha), y'(x, \alpha))\delta y']\, dx \quad (1.12)$$

where a subscript denotes partial derivative with respect to the indicated variable.

Further, the variation $\delta y(= \bar{y}(x) - y(x))$ is a function of x and can be differentiated once, or several times, such that $(\delta y)' = \bar{y}'(x) - y'(x) = \delta y'$. Finally, (1.10) gives from (1.12) the relation

$$\int_a^b [F_y(x, y(x), y'(x))\delta y + F_{y'}(x, y(x), y'(x))\delta y']\, dx = 0 \quad (1.13)$$

Let us integrate the second term by parts subject to the boundary conditions $(\delta y)_a = 0$ and $(\delta y)_b = 0$ (as a consequence of y being fixed at $x = a$ and $x = b$). This gives from (1.13),

$$\int_a^b \left[F_y - \frac{d}{dx} F_{y'} \right] \delta y\, dx = 0 \quad (1.14)$$

In view of the assumptions made on $F(x, y(x), y'(x))$ and the extremizing curve $y(x)$, it follows that $F_y - \frac{d}{dx} F_{y'}$ on the curve $y(x)$ is a given continuous function, while δy is an arbitrary continuous function, subject to the vanishing of δy at $x = a$ and $x = b$.

Before proceeding further, we now prove the following lemma: If for every continuous function $\eta(x)$,

$$\int_a^b \Phi(x)\eta(x)\, dx = 0 \quad (1.15)$$

where $\Phi(x)$ is continuous in the closed interval $[a, b]$, then $\Phi(x) \equiv 0$ on $[a, b]$.

Proof. Assume that $\Phi(x) \neq 0$ (positive, say) at a point $x = \bar{x}$ in $a \leq x \leq b$. By virtue of the continuity of $\Phi(x)$, it follows that $\Phi(x) \neq 0$ and maintains positive sign in a small neighbourhood $x_0 \leq x \leq x_1$ of the point $\bar{x}$. Since $\eta(x)$ is an arbitrary continuous function, we might choose $\eta(x)$ such that $\eta(x)$ remains positive in $x_0 \leq x \leq x_1$ but vanishes outside this interval (see Fig. 1.5). It then follows from (1.15) that

$$\int_a^b \Phi(x)\eta(x)\, dx = \int_{x_0}^{x_1} \Phi(x)\eta(x)\, dx > 0 \qquad (1.16)$$

since the product $\Phi(x)\eta(x)$ remains positive everywhere in $[x_0, x_1]$. The contradiction between (1.15) and (1.16) shows that our original assumption $\Phi(x) \neq 0$ at some point $\bar{x}$ must be wrong and hence $\Phi(x) \equiv 0$ on $[a, b]$.

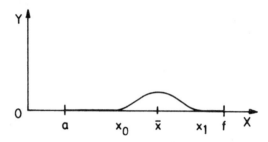

Fig. 1.5   A continuous function which is positive in an interval but vanishes outside.

Invoking this fundamental lemma, and from (1.14) we conclude, that

$$F_y - \frac{d}{dx} F_{y'} = 0 \qquad (1.17)$$

on the extremizing curve $y = y(x)$. This equation is known as Euler's equation and the integral curves of this equation are known as extremals. It should be noted that the functional (1.8) can attain an extremum only on extremals. On expanding (1.17) we find that

$$F_y - F_{xy'} - F_{yy'}y' - F_{y'y'}y'' = 0 \qquad (1.18)$$

which is, in general, a second-order differential equation in $y(x)$ (although sometimes it may reduce to a finite equation). The two arbitrary constants appearing in the solution $y(x)$ are determined from the boundary conditions $y(a) = y_1$ and $y(b) = y_2$.

It should be emphasized, however, that the existence of the solution of (1.17) satisfying the above boundary conditions cannot always be taken for granted, and even if a solution exists, it may not be unique. However, in many problems, the existence of a solution is evident from the geometrical or physical significance of the problem. Hence in such cases, if the existence of solution of Euler's equation is unique, then this solution will provide the solution of the variational problem.

Example 2.   Test for an extremum the functional

$$I[y(x)] = \int_0^1 (xy + y^2 - 2y^2 y')\, dx, \quad y(0) = 1, y(1) = 2.$$

Solution.   Here Euler's equation is

$$x + 2y - 4yy' - \frac{d}{dx}(-2y^2) = 0$$

which reduces to $y = -x/2$. Clearly, this extremal cannot satisfy the boundary conditions $y(0) = 1$, $y(1) = 2$. Thus an extremum cannot be achieved in the class of continuous functions.

Example 3.   Test for extremum the functional

$$I[y(x)] = \int_0^{\pi/2} (y'^2 - y^2)\, dx, \quad y(0) = 0, \quad y(\pi/2) = 1$$

Solution.   In this case Euler's equation is

$$-y - \frac{d}{dx}(y') = 0$$

and its general solution is $y = C_1 \cos x + C_2 \sin x$. Using the boundary conditions, we find that $C_1 = 0$, $C_2 = 1$. Thus the extremum can be achieved only on the curve $y = \sin x$.

In the problems cited above, Euler's equation is readily integrable. But this is not always possible. In what follows that we consider some cases, where Euler's equation admits of integration.

(i)   In this case F in (1.8) is a function of x and y only. Then the Euler equation reduces to $F_y(x, y) = 0$. This finite equation, when solved for y, does not involve any arbitrary constant. Thus, in general, it is not possible to find y satisfying the boundary conditions $y(a) = y_1$, and $y(b) = y_2$ and as such this variational problem does not, in general, admit of a solution. Example 2 cited above is an illustration of such a problem.

(ii) F in (1.8) depends only on x and y'. Here Euler's equation becomes

$$\frac{d}{dx} F_{y'}(x, y') = 0 \qquad\qquad (1.19)$$

which has an integral $F_{y'}(x, y') = C_1$, a constant. Since this relation does not contain y, it can be solved for y' as a function of x. Another integration leads to a solution involving two arbitrary constants which can be found from the boundary conditions.

Example 4.   Find the extremum of the function

$$t[y(x)] = \int_{x_0}^{x_1} \frac{(1 + y'^2)^{1/2}}{x}\, dx$$

Solution. Before we embark on the solution, it may be noticed that the functional t may be recognized as the time spent on translation along the curve $y = y(x)$ from one point to another, if the rate of motion $v = (ds/dt)$ is equal to x. This is due to the fact that $ds = (1 + y'^2)^{1/2} \, dx$.

Since the functional is independent of y, Euler's equation leads to

$$y' = C_1 x (1 + y'^2)^{1/2}. \tag{1.20}$$

This may be integrated by introducing $y' = \tan t$, t being a parameter. Then (1.20) gives $x = (1/C_1) \sin t = \bar{C}_1 \sin t$. Then

$$dy = \tan t \, dx = \bar{C}_1 \sin t \, dt, \tag{1.21}$$

which on integration leads to

$$y = -\bar{C}_1 \cos t + C_2$$

Elimination of t from the expressions for x and y then gives the extremals as

$$x^2 + (y - C_2)^2 = \bar{C}_1^2,$$

which is a family of circles.

(iii) F in (1.8) is dependent on y and y' only. In this case Euler's equation reduces to

$$F_y - F_{yy'} - F_{y'y}y'' = 0 \tag{1.22}$$

But

$$\frac{d}{dx}(F - y'F_{y'}) = F_y y' + F_{y'}y'' - y''F_{y'} - F_{yy}y'^2 - F_{y'y}y''y'$$

$$= y'(F_y - F_{yy}y' - F_{y'y}y'')$$

Thus by virtue of (1.22), Euler's equation has the first integral

$$F - y'F_{y'} = C_1 \tag{1.23}$$

where C_1 is a constant. This equation may be integrated further after solving for y' and separation of variables.

Example 5. Find the curve joining given points A and B which is traversed by a particle moving under gravity from A to B in the shortest time (ignore friction along the curve and the resistance of the medium). This is known as the Brachistochrone problem to which we have alluded before.

Solution. Fix the origin at A with x-axis horizontal and y-axis vertically downward. The speed of the particle ds/dt is given by $(2gy)^{1/2}$, g being the acceleration due to gravity. Thus the time taken by the particle in moving from $A(0, 0)$ to $B(x_1, y_1)$ is

$$t[y(x)] = \frac{1}{\sqrt{2g}} \int_0^{x_1} \frac{\sqrt{1 + y'^2}}{\sqrt{y}} \, dx;$$

$$y(0) = 0, \quad y(x_1) = y_1 \tag{1.24}$$

Although the integral is improper, it is convergent. Since the integrand is independent of x, a first integral of Euler's equation is given by (1.23), which gives, on simplification, the relation

$$y(1 + y'^2) = C_1 \tag{1.25}$$

Put $y' = \cot t$, t being a parameter. Then (1.25) gives

$$y = \frac{C_1}{2}(1 - \cos 2t) \tag{1.26}$$

Now,

$$dx = \frac{dy}{y'} = \frac{2C_1 \sin t \cos t \, dt}{\cot t} = C_1(1 - \cos 2t) \, dt$$

which gives, on integration, the equation

$$x - C_2 = \frac{C_1}{2}(2t - \sin 2t) \tag{1.27}$$

Putting $2t = t_1$ and remembering that $y = 0$ at $x = 0$, we find that $C_2 = 0$. Thus (1.26) and (1.27) give the desired extremals in the parametric form

$$x = \frac{C_1}{2}(t_1 - \sin t_1), \quad y = \frac{C_1}{2}(1 - \cos t_1)$$

which is a family of cycloids with $C_1/2$ as the radius of the rolling circle. In fact, C_1 is determined by the fact that the cycloid passes through $B(x_1, y_1)$.

Example 6.   Find the curve with fixed boundary points such that its rotation about the axis of abscissae give rise to a surface of revolution of minimum surface area.

Solution.   The area of the surface of revolution (Fig. 1.6) is

$$S[y(x)] = 2\pi \int_{x_1}^{x_2} y\sqrt{1 + y'^2} \, dx$$

where the end points A and B of the curve $y = y(x)$ have x-coordinates x_1 and x_2. Since the integrand is a function of y and y' only, a first integral of Euler's equation is

$$y\sqrt{1 + y'^2} - \frac{yy'^2}{\sqrt{1 + y'^2}} = C_1$$

which reduces to $y/\sqrt{1 + y'^2} = C_1$. To integrate this equation, we put $y' = \sinh t$. Then, clearly,

$$y = C_1 \cosh t, \quad dx = \frac{dy}{y'} = C_1 \, dt \tag{1.28}$$

The second equation of (1.28) gives on integration the relation

$$x = C_1 t + C_2 \quad \text{with } y = C_1 \cosh t \tag{1.29}$$

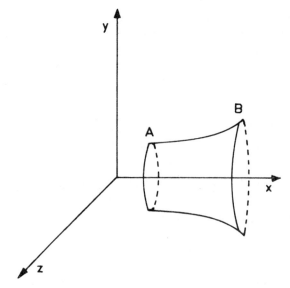

Fig. 1.6   Surface of revolution with minimum surface area.

The elimination of t from (1.29) gives as extremals

$$y = C_1 \cosh \frac{x - C_2}{C_1}$$

which constitutes a two-parameter family of catenaries. The constants C_1 and C_2 are determined from the conditions, that the given curve passes through the given points A and B.

As a last example of the extremum of a functional, we consider the following problem of gas dynamics.

Example 7.   To determine the shape of a solid of revolution moving in a flow of gas with least resistance.

Solution.   Referring to Fig. 1.7, assume that the gas density is sufficiently small such that the gas molecules are mirror reflected from the surface of the solid. The component of the gas pressure normal to the surface is

$$p = 2\rho v^2 \sin^2 \theta \tag{1.30}$$

where ρ, v and θ denote the density of the gas, the velocity of the gas relative to the solid, and the angle between the tangent at any point of the surface with the direction of flow.

The pressure given by (1.30) is normal to the surface and one can write down the force component along the x-axis acting on a ring PQ of width ds ($= \sqrt{1 + y'^2}\, dx$) and radius $y(x)$ in the form

$$dF = 2\rho v^2 \sin^2 \theta \cdot [2\pi y \sqrt{1 + y'^2}] \sin \theta\, dx \tag{1.31}$$

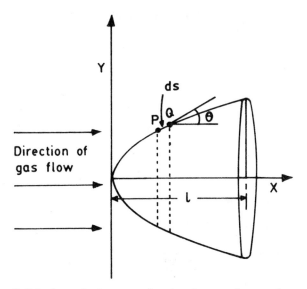

Fig. 1.7   Solid of revolution experiencing least resistance in a gas flow.

Hence the total force along the x-direction is

$$F = \int_0^l 4\pi\rho v^2 \, \sin^3 \theta \cdot \sqrt{1 + y'^2} \, y \, dx \qquad (1.32)$$

To make further progress, we assume

$$\sin \theta = \frac{y'}{(1 + y'^2)^{3/2}} \approx y'$$

where the slope y' is taken to be small. Thus from (1.32), the total resistance experienced by the body is

$$F = 4\pi\rho v^2 \int_0^l y'^3 y \, dx \qquad (1.33)$$

The problem now is to find $y = y(x)$ for which F is minimum. Thus (1.33) constitutes a variational problem with the boundary conditions

$$y(0) = 0, \qquad y(l) = R \qquad (1.34)$$

Since the integrand in (1.33) depends on y and y' only, a first integral of Euler's equation is

$$y'^3 - 3 \frac{d}{dx} (yy'^2) = 0 \qquad (1.35)$$

Multiplying (1.35) by y' and integrating, we get

$$y'^3 y = C_1^3,$$

C_1 being a constant. One more integration gives

$$y = (C_2 x + C_3)^{3/4} \tag{1.36}$$

Using the boundary conditions (1.34), we obtain

$$C_2 = \frac{R^{4/3}}{l}, \qquad C_3 = 0$$

Thus the required function $y(x)$ is given by

$$y(x) = R\left(\frac{x}{l}\right)^{3/4}$$

If F in (1.8) is linear in y' such that

$$F(x, y, y') = M(x, y) + N(x, y)y'$$

then Euler's equation reduces to

$$\frac{\partial M}{\partial y} - \frac{\partial N}{\partial x} = 0,$$

which is a finite equation, and not a differential equation. Thus the curve defined by the above equation does not, in general, satisfy the boundary conditions at $x = a$ and b. Clearly, in this case the variational problem (1.8) does not have (in general) a solution in the class of continuous functions. The reason for this lies in the fact, that, when the above equation holds in some domain of the xy-plane, then the integral

$$I[y(x)] = \int_a^b F(x, y, y') \, dx = \int_a^b (M \, dx + N \, dy)$$

becomes independent of the path of integration. Thus the functional is the same on all admissible curves leading to a meaningless variational problem.

1.3   Variational Problem for Functionals of the Form

$$\int_a^b F(x, y_1(x), y_2(x), \ldots, y_n(x), y_1'(x), y_2'(x), \ldots, y_n'(x)) \, dx,$$

where the function F is differentiable three times with respect to all its arguments.

To find the necessary conditions for the extremum of the above functional, we consider the following boundary conditions for $y_1(x), y_2(x), \ldots, y_n(x)$:

$$y_1(a) = Y_1, \, y_2(a) = Y_2, \, \ldots, \, y_n(a) = Y_n \tag{1.37a}$$

$$y_1(b) = Z_1, \, y_2(b) = Z_2, \, \ldots, \, y_n(b) = Z_n \tag{1.37b}$$

where $Y_1, Y_2, \ldots, Z_1, Z_2 \ldots$ are constants.

We vary only one of the functions $y_j(x)$ ($j = 1, 2, \ldots, n$), keeping the others fixed. Then the above functional reduces to a functional dependent on, say, only one of the functions $y_i(x)$. Thus the function $y_i(x)$ having a continuous derivative must satisfy Euler's equation

$$F_{y_i} - \frac{d}{dx} F_{y_i'} = 0$$

where the boundary conditions on $y_i(x)$ at $x = a$ and $x = b$ are utilized from (1.37a) and (1.37b).

Since this argument applies to any function $y_i(x)$ ($i = 1, 2, ..., n$), we obtain a system of second-order differential equations

$$F_{y_i} - \frac{d}{dx} F_{y_i'} = 0 \qquad (i = 1, 2, ..., n). \tag{1.38a}$$

These define, in general, a $2n$-parameter family of curves in the space $x, y_1, y_2, ..., y_n$ and provide the family of extremals for the given variational problem.

Let us illustrate the above principle by considering a problem from optics.

Example 8. Derive the differential equations of the lines of propagation of light in an optically non-homogeneous medium with the speed of light $C(x, y, z)$.

Solution. According to well known Fermat's law, light propagates from one point to another point along a curve, for which, the time T of passage of light will be minimum.

If the equation of the desired path of the light ray be $y = y(x)$ and $z = z(x)$, then clearly,

$$T = \int_{x_1}^{x_2} \frac{ds}{C} = \int_{x_1}^{x_2} \frac{\sqrt{1 + y'^2 + z'^2}}{C(x, y, z)} \, dx \tag{1.38b}$$

where ds is a line element on the path.

Using (1.5), one gets the system of Euler's equations

$$\frac{\sqrt{1 + y'^2 + z'^2}}{C^2} \frac{\partial C}{\partial y} + \frac{d}{dx}\left[\frac{y'}{C\sqrt{1 + y'^2 + z'^2}} \right] = 0$$

$$\frac{\sqrt{1 + y'^2 + z'^2}}{C^2} \frac{\partial C}{\partial z} + \frac{d}{dx}\left[\frac{z'}{C\sqrt{1 + y'^2 + z'^2}} \right] = 0$$

which determine the path of the light propagation.

It should be noted, however, that in the above form, the principle cannot always be applied. Let P_1 be the centre of a hemispherical mirror. The length of the path of the ray emerging from P_1 and reflected by the mirror at its pole p to a point P_2 on the straight line pP_1 will be longer than the path P_1QP_2, consisting of two rectilinear segments QP_2 and P_1Q, corresponding to a reflection by the mirror at a point Q distinct from p. This difficulty can be circumvented by removing from the formulation the specific mention of fixed end points. A better formulation is as follows: A curve can represent the path of a ray of light if and only if, each point P on Γ, is an interior point of a segment P_1P_2 of Γ which possesses the property that the integral (1.38b) for T taken along the segment P_1P_2 of Γ has a smaller value than that taken along any other curve of light from a point source $P_1(t_1, x_1, y_1, z_1)$. After a given time T_0, such a disturbance will be seen on a surface $F(T_0)$ which, according to Fermat's principle, is such that each point $P_2(t_2, x_2, y_2, z_2)$ is joined to P_1 by an extremal for which the integral (1.38b) takes the value T_0, this value being common to all points of $F(T_0)$. The surface $F(T_0)$ is a wave front and for various values of T_0, a succession or family of such wave fronts is obtained.

One can show that the family of wave fronts corresponding to the emission from a point source at P_1 is identical to the family of concentric geodesic spheres centred at P_1, a problem of the calculus of variations and determined by the integral (1.38b).

Remark 1.   Certain interesting results follow if we consider the problem of propagation of a light ray in an inhomogeneous two-dimensional medium with the velocity of light, proportional to y (see Fig. 1.8). In this case the light rays are the extremals of the functional

$$I[y(x)] = \int_a^b \frac{(1 + y'^2)^{1/2}}{y} \, dx$$

Here the integral of Euler's equation gives $y(1 + y'^2)^{1/2} = \bar{C}_1$, whose integration leads to

$$(x + C_2)^2 + y^2 = \bar{C}_1^2$$

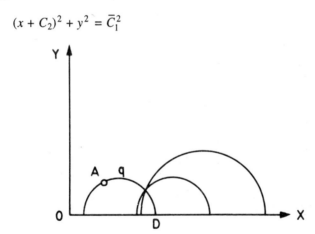

Fig. 1.8   Path of light ray propagation in an inhomogeneous medium.

This is a family of circles centred on the x-axis. The desired extremal is the one which passes through given points. This problem has a unique solution, since only one semicircle centred on the x-axis, passes through any two points lying in the upper half plane.

Consider the curve q. The optical path length q is the time $T(q)$, during which the curve is traversed with velocity of light $v(x, y) = y$. It may be shown that one end of the part *AD* of the semicircle *q*, which lies on the *x*-axis, has an infinite optical path length. Hence we call the points on the *x*-axis as infinite points. We shall consider the semicircles with centres on the *x*-axis to be straight lines, and the optical path lengths of the arcs of such semicircles, to be their lengths, and the angles between the tangents to the semicircles at their intersections to be the angles between such straight lines. Thus we derive a flat geometry in which many of the postulates of ordinary geometry remain valid. For example, only one straight line can be drawn through two points (only one semi-circle centred on the *x*-axis can be drawn through two points on the semicircle). Two straight lines will be deemed as parallel if they have a common point at infinity (i.e., two semicircles touch each other at a certain point *B* lying on the *x*-axis as shown in Fig. 1.9). Further it is possible to draw through a given point *A*, not lying on the straight line *q*, two straight lines q_1 and q_2 parallel to *q*.

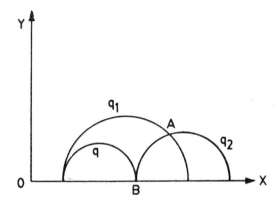

Fig. 1.9   Optical path in an inhomogeneous medium.

We have thus obtained an interesting new geometry, which is called the *Poincare model of Lobachevskian geometry* in the plane.

Remark 2.   The foregoing remarks at once lead to the question of the possibility of drawing an extremal through just any two points with distinct abscissae. An answer to this question can sometimes be found from the following theorem due to Bernstein [14] (proof omitted):
  Consider the equation

$$y'' = F(x, y, y').$$ (1.38c)

If F, F_y and $F_{y'}$ are continuous at each end point (x, y) for every finite y' and if there exist a constant $k > 0$ and functions

$$\alpha = \alpha(x, y) \geq 0, \qquad \beta = \beta(x, y) \geq 0$$

bounded in every finite portion of the plane such that

$$F_y(x, y, y') > k, \qquad |F(x, y, y')| \leq \alpha y'^2 + \beta,$$

then one and only one integral curve $y = \phi(x)$ of (1.38c), passes through any two points (a, A) and (b, B) of the plane, with distinct abscissae $(a \neq b)$.

Consider, for example, the functional

$$I = \int e^{-2y^2} (y'^2 - 1) \, dx$$

Its Euler equation is

$$y'' = 2y(1 + y'^2)$$

Since $F(x, y, y') = 2y(1 + y'^2)$, we have

$$F_y = 2(1 + y'^2) \geq 2 = k \text{ and, further,}$$

$$|F(x, y, y')| = |2y(1 + y'^2)| \leq 2 |y| y'^2 + 2 |y|$$

so that $\alpha = \beta = 2 |y| \geq 0$. Hence by Bernstein's theorem, there exists an extremal through any two points with distinct abscissae.

On the other hand, it can be shown that it is not possible, to draw an extremal of the functional

$$I[y(x)] = \int [y^2 + \sqrt{1 + y'^2}] \, dx$$

through just any two points of a plane having distinct abscissae.

1.4   Functionals Dependent on Higher-Order Derivatives

Let us now consider the extremum of a functional of the form

$$\int_a^b F(x, y(x), y'(x), \dots, y^{(n)}(x)) \, dx, \tag{1.39}$$

where we assume F to be differentiable $n + 2$ times with respect to all its arguments. The boundary conditions are taken in the form

$$y(x_0) = y_0, y'(x_0) = y_0', \dots, y^{(n-1)}(x_0) = y_0^{(n-1)}, \tag{1.40a}$$

$$y(x_1) = y_1, y'(x_1) = y_1', \dots, y^{(n-1)}(x_1) = y_1^{(n-1)}. \tag{1.40b}$$

This implies that at the boundary points the values of y together with all their derivatives upto the order $n - 1$ (inclusive) are prescribed. We further assume that the extremum of the functional I is attained on a curve $y = y(x)$ which is differentiable $2n$ times, and any admissible comparison curve $y = \bar{y}(x)$ is also $2n$ times differentiable. It is clear that both $y = y(x)$ and $y = \bar{y}(x)$ can be included in a one-parameter family of curves

$$y(x, \alpha) = y(x) + \alpha[\bar{y}(x) - y(x)]$$

such that $y(x, \alpha) = y(x)$ for $\alpha = 0$ and $y(x, \alpha) = \bar{y}(x)$ for $\alpha = 1$.

Now on the curves of the above family, the functional (1.39) reduces to a function of α, say, $\Psi(\alpha)$. Since the extremizing curve corresponds to $\alpha = 0$, we must have $\Psi'(\alpha) = 0$ at $\alpha = 0$. This gives, as in Section 1.2, for an extremum, the relation

$$\left[\frac{d}{d\alpha} \int_a^b F(x, y(x, \alpha), y'(x, \alpha), \ldots, y^{(n)}(x, \alpha)) \, d\alpha \right]_{\alpha = 0}$$

$$= \int_a^b (F_y \, \delta y + F_{y'} \, \delta y' + \ldots + F_{y^{(n)}} \, \delta y^{(n)}) \, dx = 0 \tag{1.41}$$

Integrate by parts the second term on the right-hand side once and the third term twice, yielding

$$\int_a^b F_{y'} \, \delta y' dx = [F_{y'} \, \delta y]_a^b - \int_a^b \left(\frac{d}{dx} F_{y'} \right) \delta y \, dx$$

$$\int_a^b F_{y''} \, \delta y'' \, dx = [F_{y''} \, \delta y']_a^b - \left[\left(\frac{d}{dx} F_{y''} \right) \delta y \right]_a^b + \int_a^b \left(\frac{d^2}{dx^2} F_{y''} \right) \delta y \, dx$$

and so on. The last term on the right-hand side of (1.41) can be written by successive integration by parts as

$$\int_a^b F_{y^{(n)}} \, \delta y^{(n)} \, dx = [F_{y^{(n)}} \, \delta y^{(n-1)}]_a^b - \left[\left(\frac{d}{dx} F_{y^{(n)}} \right) \delta y^{(n-2)} \right]_a^b$$

$$+ \ldots + (-1)^n \int_a^b \left(\frac{d^n}{dx^n} F_{y^{(n)}} \right) \delta y \, dx$$

By virtue of the boundary conditions (1.40a) and (1.40b), the integrated parts in all the above expressions on the right side vanish. Thus from (1.41), we find that on the extremizing curve

$$\int_a^b \left(F_y - \frac{d}{dx} F_{y'} + \frac{d^2}{dx^2} F_{y''} - \ldots + (-1)^n \frac{d^n}{dx^n} F_{y^{(n)}} \right) \delta y \, dx = 0$$

for an arbitrary choice of δy. Due to conditions of continuity imposed on F, the first factor in the foregoing integral is a continuous function of x in $[a, b]$. Thus invoking the fundamental lemma of Section 1.2, the function $y = y(x)$, which extremizes I satisfies

$$F_y - \frac{d}{dx} F_{y'} + \frac{d^2}{dx^2} F_{y''} - \ldots + (-1)^n \frac{d^n}{dx^n} F_{y^{(n)}} = 0 \tag{1.42}$$

which is known as the Euler-Poisson equation.

Clearly this is a differential equation of the order $2n$ and hence its solution involves $2n$ arbitrary constants. These are found by using the $2n$ boundary conditions (1.40a) and (1.40b).

Example 9.   Determine the extremal of the functional

$$I[y(x)] = \int_{-l}^{l} \left(\frac{1}{2} \mu y''^2 + \rho y \right) dx$$

subject to

$$y(-l) = 0, \qquad y'(-l) = 0, \qquad y(l) = 0, \qquad y'(l) = 0.$$

Solution.   This variational problem arises in finding the axis of a flexibly bent cylindrical beam clamped at the ends. If the beam is homogeneous, ρ and μ are constants. Then Euler-Poisson's equation (1.42) becomes

$$\rho + \frac{d^2}{dx^2}(\mu y'') = 0$$

whose solution satisfying the prescribed boundary conditions is

$$y = -\frac{\rho}{24\,\mu}(x^4 - 2l^2 x^2 + l^4)$$

1.5   Functionals Dependent on Functions of Several Independent Variables

In the variational problems, considered so far, Euler's equations for determining extremals, are ordinary differential equations. We now extend this to the problem of determining the extrema of functionals involving multiple integrals leading to one or more partial differential equations. Consider, for example, the problem of finding an extremum of the functional

$$J[u(x, y)] = \iint_G F(x, y, u, u_x, u_y)\, dx\, dy \tag{1.43}$$

over a region of integration G by determining u which is continuous and has continuous derivatives upto the second order, and takes on prescribed values on the boundary of G. We further assume that F is thrice differentiable.

Let the extremizing surface be $u = u(x, y)$ so that an admissible one-parameter surface is taken as

$$u(x, y, \alpha) = u(x, y) + \alpha \eta(x, y)$$

where $\eta(x, y) = 0$ on the boundary of G. Then the necessary condition for an extremum is the vanishing of the first variation

$$\delta J = \left(\frac{\partial}{\partial \alpha} J[u + \alpha \eta] \right)_{\alpha = 0}$$

This implies from (1.43)

$$\iint_G (F_u \eta + F_{u_x} \eta_x + F_{u_y} \eta_y)\, dx\, dy = 0 \tag{1.44}$$

which may be again transformed by integration by parts. We assume that the boundary Γ of G admits of a tangent, which turns piecewise continuously. Then using the familiar Green's theorem, we have

$$\iint_G (\eta_x F_{u_x} + \eta_y F_{u_y})\, dx\, dy = \int_\Gamma \eta(F_{u_x}\, dy - F_{u_y}\, dx)$$

$$- \iint_G \eta\left(\frac{\partial}{\partial x} F_{u_x} + \frac{\partial}{\partial y} F_{u_y}\right) dx\, dy$$

Thus from (1.44),

$$\iint_G \left[F_u - \frac{\partial}{\partial x} F_{u_x} - \frac{\partial}{\partial y} F_{u_y}\right]\eta\, dx\, dy + \int_\Gamma \eta(F_{u_x}\, dy - F_{u_y}\, dx) = 0.$$

Since $\eta = 0$ on Γ and the above relation holds for any arbitrary continuously differentiable function η, it follows from above that by using the generalization of the fundamental lemma of Section 1.2 that

$$F_u - \frac{\partial}{\partial x} F_{u_x} - \frac{\partial}{\partial y} F_{u_y} = 0 \tag{1.45}$$

The extremizing function $u(x, y)$ is determined from the solution of the second-order partial differential equation (1.45) which is known as *Euler-Ostrogradsky equation*. If the integrand of a functional J contains derivatives of order higher than two, then by a straightforward extension of the above analysis, we may derive a modified Euler-Ostrogradsky equation for determining extremals. For example, in the case of the functional

$$J[u(x, y)] = \iint_G F(x, y, u, u_x, u_y, u_{xx}, u_{xy}, u_{yy})\, dx\, dy$$

we get the equation for extremals as

$$F_u - \frac{\partial}{\partial x} F_{u_x} - \frac{\partial}{\partial y} F_{u_y} + \frac{\partial^2}{\partial x^2} F_{u_{xx}} + \frac{\partial^2}{\partial x \partial y} F_{u_{xy}} + \frac{\partial^2}{\partial y^2} F_{u_{yy}} = 0$$

Example 10. Find the Euler-Ostrogradsky equation for

$$I[u(x, y)] = \iint_D \left[\left(\frac{\partial u}{\partial x}\right)^2 + \left(\frac{\partial u}{\partial y}\right)^2\right] dx\, dy$$

where the values of u are prescribed on the boundary Γ of the domain D.

Solution. It clearly follows from (1.45) that the equation for extremals is

$$\nabla^2 u = \frac{\partial^2 u}{\partial x^2} + \frac{\partial^2 u}{\partial y^2} = 0, \tag{1.46}$$

which is the well known Laplace's equation. Thus we see that the variational problem is analogous to the solution of (1.46), subject to given values of u on Γ. This is the familiar Dirichlet problem of mathematical physics.

Example 11.   Find the surface of a minimum area, stretched over a given closed space curve C, enclosing the domain D in the xy plane.

   Solution.   The problem here is the determination of extremals of the functional

$$S[z(x, y)] = \iint_D (1 + z_x^2 + z_y^2)^{1/2} \, dx \, dy.$$

   In this case, Euler-Ostrogradsky equation gives

$$z_{xx}(1 + z_y^2) - 2z_x z_y z_{xy} + z_{yy}(1 + z_x^2) = 0$$

which is the equation of minimal surfaces. The above equation signifies that at each point of the surface, the mean curvature vanishes. It is known that soap bubbles stretched on a given contour C is a physical realization of minimal surfaces. In fact here the surface tension of the soap bubble tends to keep the surface area minimum. However it is easy to see that, if the curve C is a plane curve, then the above problem gives the minimal surface as a plane surface.

Example 12.   Find the extremizing function for

$$J[z(x, y)] = \iint_D \left[\left(\frac{\partial^2 z}{\partial x^2} \right)^2 + \left(\frac{\partial^2 z}{\partial y^2} \right)^2 + 2 \left(\frac{\partial^2 z}{\partial x \partial y} \right)^2 - 2zf(x, y) \right] dx \, dy$$

where $f(x, y)$ is a known function.

   Solution.   The extremizing function $z(x, y)$ clearly satisfies the equation

$$\frac{\partial^4 z}{\partial x^4} + 2 \frac{\partial^4 z}{\partial x^2 \partial y^2} + \frac{\partial^4 z}{\partial y^4} = f(x, y),$$

which arises in the problem of deflection of a clamped plate in the theory of elasticity. In the special case $f(x, y) \equiv 0$, the above equation reduces to the well known *biharmonic equation*

$$\nabla^2 \nabla^2 z = 0.$$

Example 13.   Discuss the following equilibrium problem of a membrane. Suppose a membrane at rest covers a region D of the x-y plane (with boundary Γ), and it is subject to an external force of surface density $f(x, y)$. Further, the boundary of the membrane (supposed to be freely movable above Γ) is acted on by an external force of linear density $p(s)$ and the boundary is tied to its rest position by elastic forces characterized by a modulus of elasticity of linear density $\sigma(s)$, the arc length s being measured along Γ.

Solution.   Let the deformation of the membrane normal to the equilibrium plane be denoted by $u(x, y)$. We suppose that this deformation is small in the sense that higher powers of u, u_x and u_y are negligible as compared with lower ones. Then the potential energy of the membrane (which is proportional to a change in area, the factor of proportionality being μ) is given by

$$I[u] = \iint_D \left[\frac{1}{2} \mu (u_x^2 + u_y^2) + fu \right] dx\, dy + \int_\Gamma \left[p(s)u + \frac{1}{2} \sigma(s) u^2 \right] ds$$

For equilibrium, this functional must be an extremum subject to the condition that the functions $u(x, y)$ are continuous in the closed domain D and possess continuous, first and piecewise continuous, second derivatives in the interior of D.

Let $u = u(x, y)$ be the required extremal and $v = u(x, y) + \varepsilon \eta(x, y)$ be a neighbouring surface.

It is easy to see that with $\mu = 1$,

$$2I[u + \varepsilon \eta] = 2I[u] + 2\varepsilon \left[\iint_D \{ \nabla u \cdot \nabla \eta + \eta f \}\, dx\, dy \right.$$

$$\left. + \int_\Gamma \eta(p + u\sigma)\, ds \right] + 0(\varepsilon^2)$$

Hence the necessary condition of extremum given by

$$\lim_{\varepsilon \to 0} [I(u + \varepsilon \eta) - I(u)] / \varepsilon = 0$$

leads to

$$\iint_D (\nabla u \cdot \nabla \eta + \eta f)\, dx\, dy + \int_\Gamma \eta(p + u\sigma)\, ds = 0.$$

Now by divergence theorem,

$$\iint_D (\eta \nabla^2 u + \nabla u \cdot \nabla \eta)\, dx\, dy = \int_\Gamma \eta \nabla u \cdot n\, ds$$

Hence the above necessary condition becomes

$$\iint_D \eta(- \nabla^2 u + f)\, dx\, dy + \int_\Gamma \eta[\nabla u \cdot n + p + u\sigma]\, ds = 0$$

Thus Euler's equation for this problem is

$$\nabla^2 u = f(x, y)$$

with the natural boundary condition

$$\frac{\partial u}{\partial n} + \sigma(s)u + p(s) = 0$$

1.6   Variational Problems in Parametric Form

In many variational problems, it is more convenient and sometimes necessary to make use of a parametric representation of a line as follows:

$$x = \phi(t), \quad y = \Psi(t) \text{ for } t_0 \le t \le t_1 \tag{1.47}$$

Consider the functional

$$J[x(t), y(t)] = \int_{t_0}^{t_1} F(t, x, y, \dot{x}, \dot{y}) \, dt, \tag{1.48}$$

where the integration is along the line (1.47) and a dot denotes derivative with respect to t. In order that the values of the functional (1.48) depend only on the line, and not on the parametrization (which can be accomplished in a number of ways), it is both necessary and sufficient that the integrand in (1.48) does not contain t explicitly and that it is homogeneous of the first degree in $\dot{x}$ and $\dot{y}$. Thus

$$F(x, y, k\dot{x}, k\dot{y}) = kF(x, y, \dot{x}, \dot{y}), \quad k > 0. \tag{1.49}$$

Take, for example,

$$I[x(t), y(t)] = \int_{t_0}^{t_1} \phi(x(t), y(t), \dot{x}(t), \dot{y}(t)) \, dt,$$

where ϕ satisfies the homogeneity condition (1.49). Let us now consider a new parametric representation

$$\tau = \zeta(t)(\dot{\zeta}(t) \neq 0), \quad x = x(\tau), \quad y = y(\tau).$$

Then

$$\int_{t_0}^{t_1} \phi(x(t), y(t), \dot{x}(t), \dot{y}(t)) \, dt = \int_{\tau_0}^{\tau_1} \phi(x(\tau), y(\tau), x_\tau(\tau)\dot{\zeta}(t), y_\tau(\tau)\dot{\zeta}(\tau)) \frac{d\tau}{\tau}.$$

But since ϕ is a homogeneous function of first degree in $\dot{x}$ and $\dot{y}$,

$$\phi(x, y, \dot{x}_\tau \dot{\zeta}, \dot{y}_\tau \dot{\zeta}) = \dot{\zeta}\phi(x, y, \dot{x}_\tau, \dot{y}_\tau).$$

This gives from the above equation

$$\int_{t_0}^{t_1} \phi(x, y, \dot{x}_t, \dot{y}_t) \, dt = \int_{\tau_0}^{\tau_1} \phi(x, y, \dot{x}_\tau, \dot{y}_\tau) \, d\tau.$$

Thus the integrand remains unchanged with a change in the parametric representation.

For example, the area bounded by a closed curve given by $\int_{t_1}^{t_2} (x\dot{y} - y\dot{x}) \, dt$ is a functional which can be put in the form

$$I[x(t), y(t)] = \int_{t_1}^{t_2} \Phi(x, y, \dot{x}, \dot{y}) \, dt,$$

where Φ is a homogeneous function of degree one in $\dot{x}$ and $\dot{y}$. Thus to find extremals for I, one has to solve Euler's equations

$$\Phi_x - \frac{d}{dt} \Phi_{\dot{x}} = 0, \quad \Phi_y - \frac{d}{dt} \Phi_{\dot{y}} = 0 \tag{1.50}$$

However, these equations are not independent, because these must be satisfied by a certain solution $x = x(t)$, $y = y(t)$, and any other pairs of functions with a different parametric representation of the same curve, which, in the case of Euler's equations being independent, would conflict with the theorem of existence and uniqueness of a solution of a system of differential equations. Thus we conclude that in (1.50), any one equation is a consequence of the other and to find the extremals, one has to solve any one of the equations (1.50) along with the equation $\dot{x}^2 + \dot{y}^2 = 1$, which shows that the arc length of the curve is taken as the parameter.

The Weirstrassian form of Euler equations (1.50) is

$$\frac{1}{r} = \frac{\Phi_{x\dot{y}} - \Phi_{y\dot{x}}}{\Phi_1 (\dot{x}^2 + \dot{y}^2)^{3/2}} \tag{1.51}$$

where r is the radius of curvature of the extremal and Φ_1 is the common value of the ratios

$$\phi_1 = \phi_{\dot{x}\dot{x}}/\dot{y}^2 = \phi_{\dot{y}\dot{y}}/\dot{x}^2 = -\phi_{\dot{x}\dot{y}}/\dot{x}\dot{y}$$

For example, in finding the extremals of

$$I[x(t), y(t)] = \int_{t_0}^{t_1} [(\dot{x}^2 + \dot{y}^2)^{1/2} + a^2(x\dot{y} - y\dot{x})] \, dt$$

we first notice that the integrand $\Phi(x, y, \dot{x}, \dot{y})$ is homogeneous of degree one. Using Weirstrass form of Euler equations, we find that

$$F_{x\dot{y}} = a^2, \quad F_{y\dot{x}} = -a^2, \quad F_1 = \frac{1}{(\dot{x}^2 + \dot{y}^2)^{3/2}} \tag{1.52}$$

give $1/r = 2a^2$, which shows that the extremals are circles.

1.7 Some Applications to Problems of Mechanics

Hamilton's Principle

One of the most fundamental and important principles of mechanics and mathematical physics is the principle of least action due to Hamilton (William Rowan Hamilton (1805–1865), an Irish mathematician, also known for his invention of quaternions). Using this principle one can deduce the basic equations governing many physical phenomena. Let us formulate the principle for a dynamical system of particles and begin by considering the case of a single particle.

We consider a particle of mass m moving in a force field. If the position vector of the particle with respect to a fixed origin is denoted by **r**, then by Newton's law of motion, the path of the particle is governed by the equation

$$m \frac{d^2\mathbf{r}}{dt^2} = \mathbf{f} \tag{1.53}$$

where $\mathbf{f}$ is the force acting on the particle.

Now consider any other path $\mathbf{r} + \delta\mathbf{r}$ on the proviso that the true path and the varied path coincide at two distinct instants $t = t_1$ and $t = t_2$. This demands that

$$\delta\mathbf{r}\,|_{t_1} = \delta\mathbf{r}\,|_{t_2} = 0 \tag{1.54}$$

At any intermediate time t, we examine the true path $\mathbf{r}$ and varied path $\mathbf{r} + \delta\mathbf{r}$. Taking the dot product of variation $\delta\mathbf{r}$ into (1.53) and integrating the result with respect to time over the interval (t_1, t_2), we get

$$\int_{t_1}^{t_2} \left(m \frac{d^2\mathbf{r}}{dt^2} \cdot \delta\mathbf{r} - \mathbf{f} \cdot \delta\mathbf{r} \right) dt = 0 \tag{1.55}$$

Integrating the first term in (1.55) by parts, and by using (1.54) we find that

$$m \int_{t_1}^{t_2} \frac{d^2\mathbf{r}}{dt^2} \cdot \delta\mathbf{r}\, dt = m \left[\frac{d\mathbf{r}}{dt} \cdot \delta\mathbf{r} \, \Big|_{t_1}^{t_2} - \int_{t_1}^{t_2} \frac{d\mathbf{r}}{dt} \cdot \delta\left(\frac{d\mathbf{r}}{dt} \right) dt \right]$$

$$= -\delta \int_{t_1}^{t_2} \frac{m}{2} \left(\frac{d\mathbf{r}}{dt} \right)^2 dt = -\delta \int_{t_1}^{t_2} T\, dt$$

where T is the kinetic energy $\frac{1}{2}m(d\mathbf{r}/dt)^2$ of the particle. Substitution of the above relation in (1.55) then gives

$$\int_{t_1}^{t_2} (\delta T + \mathbf{f} \cdot \delta\mathbf{r})\, dt = 0 \tag{1.56}$$

This is Hamilton's principle in its most general form, for a single particle. Now consider the case when the force field $\mathbf{f}$ having components (X, Y, Z) is conservative which implies that

$$\mathbf{f} \cdot d\mathbf{r} \ (= X\, dx + Y\, dy + Z\, dz)$$

is the differential of a single-valued function $\Phi(x, y, z)$. This function is called the force potential and its negative, say V, is the potential energy of the particle. Thus

$$\mathbf{f} \cdot \delta\mathbf{r} = \delta\Phi = -\delta V$$

and its substitution in (1.56) gives

$$\delta \int_{t_1}^{t_2} (T - V)\, dt = 0 \tag{1.57}$$

which is Hamilton's principle. This states that the motion is such that the integral of the difference between the kinetic and potential energies is stationary for the actual path. The difference T-V is known as the Lagrangian function. It can be shown further that this integral is a minimum for the true path, as compared with any neighbouring path having the same terminal configurations, at least over a sufficiently short time interval.

From Hamilton's principle, one can derive another important principle, known as Hertz's principle. This states that a particle (or a system) moving on a surface without external forces acting on it, follows a geodesic line.

A line q is called the geodesic on a surface if at each point of q, the principal normal coincides with the normal to the surface. As an example of Hertz's principle, we may note that a point on a spherical surface moves along a great circle if it is not acted by external forces. Similarly, a point on a cylindrical surface moves along a helix under the same circumstances.

By topological methods in variational problems (Lyusternik [2]), one can show that on any smooth closed surface, there are at least three closed geodesic lines. For example, an ellipsoid has three symmetry planes, and the ellipses, along which these three planes cut the ellipsoid, are closed geodesics.

If the force field is non-conservative (e.g., a dissipative system), the potential energy function does not exist, but (1.56) still holds and $\mathbf{f} \cdot \delta\mathbf{r}$ is the work done by the force $\mathbf{f}$ in a small displacement $\delta\mathbf{r}$. The foregoing study can be easily extended to a system of N particles by summation and to a continuous system by integration. Thus for N particles, the kinetic energy is

$$T = \sum_{k=1}^{N} \frac{1}{2} m_k \left(\frac{d\mathbf{r}_k}{dt} \right)^2$$

and the total work done by the forces is $\sum_{k=1}^{N} \mathbf{f}_k \cdot \delta\mathbf{r}_k$.

In fact, the principle applies equally well to a general dynamical system consisting of a system of particles and rigid bodies.

Let us now apply the above principle to derive the equation of vibration of a rectilinear bar. A displacement from the equilibrium position $u(x, t)$ will be a function of x (measured along the bar in the undisturbed position) and time t. Thus the kinetic energy of the bar of length l is

$$T = \frac{1}{2} \int_0^l \rho \left(\frac{\partial u}{\partial t} \right)^2 dx$$

We assume that the bar is slightly extensible. The potential energy of an elastic bar with a constant curvature is proportional to the square of the curvature. Thus the differential dV of the potential energy of the bar is

$$dV = \frac{1}{2} k \left[\frac{\partial^2 u}{\partial x^2} \bigg/ \left[1 + \left(\frac{\partial u}{\partial x} \right)^2 \right]^{3/2} \right]^2 dx$$

k being a constant. Thus the potential energy of the entire bar, whose axis-curvature is variable, is

$$U = \frac{1}{2}k \int_0^l \left[\frac{\partial^2 u}{\partial x^2} \bigg/ \left[1 + \left(\frac{\partial u}{\partial x} \right)^2 \right]^{3/2} \right]^2 dx$$

According to our assumption of slight extensibility, the deviations of the bar from the equilibrium position are small, and the term $(\partial u/\partial x)^2$ may be ignored. Now by Hamilton's principle, the integral

$$\int_{t_1}^{t_2} \int_0^l \left[\frac{1}{2}\rho \left(\frac{\partial u}{\partial t} \right)^2 - \frac{1}{2}k \left(\frac{\partial^2 u}{\partial x^2} \right)^2 \right] dx \, dt$$

will be an extremum for fixed terminal times t_1 and t_2. The Euler-Ostogradsky equation then gives

$$\frac{\partial}{\partial t} \left(\rho \frac{\partial u}{\partial t} \right) + \frac{\partial^2}{\partial x^2} \left(k \frac{\partial^2 u}{\partial x^2} \right) = 0$$

which is the governing equation for displacement $u(x, t)$.

In a similar manner it can be shown that the differential equation for the displacement $u(x, t)$ of a highly flexible and almost inextensible homogeneous string from its equilibrium position is

$$\frac{\partial^2 u}{\partial t^2} = \frac{T}{\rho} \cdot \frac{\partial^2 u}{\partial x^2}$$

where T and ρ denote the tension and the line density of the material of the string.

There is an important generalization of the above equation, when the string is acted on by a uniformly distributed linear restoring force, directed towards the equilibrium position. This leads to adding a term of the form $-ku$ (k being a positive constant) to the right-hand side of the above equation. The new equation is known as the *Klein-Gordon equation* which, in its general form, is given by

$$\frac{1}{c^2} \frac{\partial^2 u}{\partial t^2} = \nabla^2 u - ku, \quad c^2 = T/\rho$$

1.8   Variational Problems Leading to an Integral Equation or a Differential-Difference Equation

Thus far we have been concerned with variational problems involving functionals formed by integrating a certain differential expression in the argument function. But more general classes of functionals are often encountered in variational problems. Let us consider the functional

$$I[\phi] = \iint K(s, t)\phi(s)\phi(t) \, ds \, dt + \int [\phi(s)]^2 \, ds - 2 \int \phi(s)f(s) \, ds,$$

which we want to extremize. Here $K(s, t)$ is a given continuous function with $K(s, t) = K(t, s), f(s)$ is a given continuous function of s and $\phi(s)$ is the unknown continuous function. All integrations are confined to the interval $a \le s \le b$, $a \le t \le b$. We replace ϕ by $\phi + \varepsilon\zeta$ and consider $I(\phi + \varepsilon\zeta) = \Psi(\varepsilon)$. The variation δI given by $[d\Psi/d\varepsilon]_{\varepsilon=0}$ is obtained after some transformation as

$$2 \int_a^b \zeta(t) \left[\int_a^b K(s, t)\phi(s)\, ds + \phi(t) - f(t) \right] dt.$$

Hence the requirement $\delta I = 0$ for an extremum leads to Fredholm integral equation

$$\int_a^b K(s, t)\phi(s)\, ds + \phi(t) = f(t).$$

as Euler equation for the problem.

Let us next consider another functional

$$I[\phi] = \int_{-\infty}^{\infty} [p(x)\,(\phi'(x))^2 + 2\phi(x + 1)\,\phi(x - 1) - \phi^2(x) - 2\phi(x)f(x)]\, dx$$

which is to be extremized. Here the argument function is continuous and has a piecewise continuous derivative in the entire interval $-\infty < x < \infty$. Now

$$\delta I = \left[\frac{d}{d\varepsilon} I(\phi + \varepsilon\zeta) \right]_{\varepsilon=0}$$

$$= 2 \int_{-\infty}^{\infty} \zeta(x)\, [-(p\phi')' + \phi(x + 2) + \phi(x - 2) - \phi(x) - f(x)]\, dx$$

Now the vanishing of δI for arbitrary ζ gives

$$(p\phi')' - \phi(x + 2) - \phi(x - 2) + \phi(x) + f(x) = 0$$

which is a differential-difference equation for the argument function $\phi(x)$.

1.9 Theorem of du Bois-Reymond

It may be recalled that in deriving Euler's equation for the functional (1.8), it was assumed that the admissible functions admit of continuous first order derivative. However, a variational problem with integrand $F(x, y, y')$ is also meaningful when y' is required to be only piecewise continuous.

Consider first an actual minimum problem, such that $y(x)$ is that function with continuous first and second derivatives, which renders I in (1.8) a minimum. Then it can be shown that $y(x)$ yields a minimum if we expand the class of functions to include functions y^* which need not have second derivatives. In fact, according to Weirstrass approximation theorem, we can approximate the function y^* by a polynomial $p(x)$ and y^* by the derived polynomial $p'(x)$ as closely as we like, where $p(x)$ satisfies the boundary conditions $p(a) = y_1$ and $p(b) = y_2$ as in Section 1.2. Then clearly $I[p(x)]$ differs arbitrarily little from $I[y^*]$. But since

$p(x)$ is an admissible comparison function with continuous second derivatives, $I[p(x)] \geq I[y(x)]$ and therefore $I[y^*(x)] \geq I[y(x)]$. This proves the result.

We next prove our assertion in Section 1.2 that if in this variational problem $y(x)$ is the extremizing function (satisfying the boundary conditions) admitting first order continuous derivative, then $y(x)$ admits of a continuous second derivative also provided that $F_{y'y'} \neq 0$. This is the theorem of du Bois Reymond (see Courant and Hilbert [3a]).

We first prove the following lemma: If $\phi(x)$ is a piecewise continuous function in $[a, b]$ and if

$$\int_a^b \phi(x)\eta(x)\, dx = 0$$

holds for arbitrary continuous function $\eta(x)$ satisfying the condition

$$\int_a^b \eta(x)\, dx = 0, \tag{1.59}$$

then $\phi(x)$ is a constant.

To prove this lemma, we first note that the relation (1.58) is clearly satisfied for constant ϕ. We now fix a constant C such that $\int_a^b (\phi - C)\, dx = 0$ for the given ϕ. Then from (1.58) and (1.59), we have $\int_a^b (\phi - C)\eta\, dx = 0$. Setting $\eta = \phi - C$ in this relation gives $\int_a^b (\phi - C)^2\, dx = 0$ and this proves the lemma. This result can be generalized in the following manner: If $\phi(x)$ is a piecewise continuous function satisfying $\int_a^b \phi\eta\, dx = 0$ for all continuous functions $\eta(x)$ such that

$$\int_a^b \eta\, dx = 0, \int_a^b x\eta\, dx = 0, \ldots, \int_a^b x^n \eta\, dx = 0$$

then ϕ is a polynomial of nth degree.

To prove du Bois-Reymond's theorem we note from (1.13) that the relation

$$\int_a^b [F_y\zeta + F_{y'}\zeta']\, dx = 0$$

holds for any continuously differentiable function $\zeta(x)$, satisfying $\zeta(x_0) = \zeta(x_1) = 0$. Putting $F_y = A'$, $F_{y'} = B$, we obtain, after integration by parts, the relation

$$\int_{x_0}^{x_1} (A'\zeta + B\zeta')\, dx = \int_{x_0}^{x_1} \zeta'(B - A)\, dx = 0$$

We select an arbitrary function $\zeta' = \eta$ which is continuous and satisfies

$$\int_{x_0}^{x_1} \eta\, dx = \zeta(x_1) - \zeta(x_0) = 0$$

Applying the previous lemma, we obtain

$$B - A = F_{y'} - \int_{x_0}^{x_1} F_y \, dx = c \tag{1.60}$$

where c does not depend on x. Equation (1.60) takes the place of Euler's equation.
Now since $\int_{x_0}^{x_1} F_y \, dx$ is differentiable with respect to x, it follows from (1.60) that
$F_{y'}$ also is differentiable. Hence Euler's equation

$$\frac{d}{dx} F_{y'} - F_y = 0$$

holds. Now if F is twice continuously differentiable with respect to its arguments, and further $F_{y'y'} \neq 0$ is satisfied, it follows that the piecewise continuous function y' is also continuous and has a continuous derivative. Because, if $F_{y'y'} \neq 0$, y' may be expressed as a continuously differentiable function $\phi(x, y, F_{y'})$. Further by virtue of (1.60), $F_{y'}$ is a continuous function of x and y' is also continuous. Hence the arguments y and $F_{y'}$ of ϕ are continuously differentiable and hence $y' (= \phi)$ is also continuously differentiable. This establishes Du Bois-Reymond's theorem which can be easily extended to an integrand of the form $F(x, y, y', \ldots, y^{(n)})$ by using the generalization of the above lemma.

1.10   Stochastic Calculus of Variations

We have already seen in Section 1.7 that in classical mechanics the dynamical laws of motion are represented by a variational principle given by Hamilton's principle of least action. In particular, for a dynamical system with f degrees of freedom, the possible motion is given by a flow in R^f which makes the functional

$$J = \int_a^b L(x(t), \dot{x}(t)) \, dt$$

stationary. Here $L \in C^1 \, (R^{2f} \to R)$ is the Lagrangian of the system, $x \in C^2 \, ([a, b] \to R^f)$ is the flow and $\dot{x}$ is the velocity dx/dt. In this case, Newton's dynamical law follows from the Euler-Lagrange equation

$$\frac{d}{dt}\left(\frac{\partial L}{\partial \dot{x}}\right) - \frac{\partial L}{\partial x} = 0$$

for the functional J.

In quantum mechanics, the dynamical law is given by Schrödinger equation

$$ih \frac{\partial \Psi}{\partial t} = \left(-\frac{h^2}{2m} \nabla \cdot \nabla + V\right)\Psi,$$

where h is the Planck constant divided by 2π, $\Psi \in L_2 \, (R^f \to C)$. Here L_2 is the space of square integrable functions in the Lebesgue sense. Motion of this system is determined by a one-parameter unitary flow in a Hilbert space $L_2(R^f \to C)$ generated by Schrödinger equation.

It has been opined that the dynamical law in quantum mechanics is radically different from that in classical mechanics. In particular there is no least action principle analogous to that of Hamilton in quantum mechanics, although Schwinger [4] derived a weak version of the principle.

Recently, Yasue [5] developed a theory of stochastic calculus of variations, which might be regarded as a generalization of the ordinary calculus of variations, to stochastic processes.

We now give, following Yasue, a brief exposition of this principle. Let (Ω, A, Pr) be a probability space, where Ω is a certain non-empty set, A is a σ-algebra of subsets of Ω and Pr is a probability measure defined on A. A mapping x from an open time interval I into a Hilbert space $H = L_2\,((\Omega, Pr) \to R^f)$ is called a stochastic process of second order in R^f if $t \to x(t)$ is continuous from I into H. Now let $P = \{p_t\}_{t \in I}$ and $F = \{f_t\}_{t \in I}$ be an increasing family and a decreasing family of σ-algebras, respectively, such that $x(t)$ is p_t-measurable and f_t-measurable.

If

$$Dx(t) = \lim_{h \to 0+} E\left[\frac{x(t+h) - x(t)}{h}\,\bigg|_{p_t}\right]$$

exists as a limit in H for each t in I and $t \to D\,x(t)$ is continuous from I into H, then the stochastic process is said to be mean forward differentiable. Further, if

$$D_* x(t) = \lim_{h \to 0+} E\left[\frac{x(t) - x(t-h)}{h}\,\bigg|_{f_t}\right]$$

exists, we say that $x(t)$ is mean backward differentiable. In the above definitions, $E[\cdot \mid B]$ denotes the conditional expectation with respect to a σ-algebra $B \subset A$. Further, Dx and D_*x are said to be mean forward and backward derivatives.

We now denote, by $C^1(I \to H)$, the totality of mean forward and backward differentiable stochastic processes of the second order adapted to P and F. The completion of C^1 in the norm

$$\vert\vert\vert\, x\, \vert\vert\vert = \sup_{t \in I} (\Vert x(t) \Vert_H + \Vert Dx(t) \Vert_H + \Vert D_* x(t) \Vert_H)$$

is also denoted by $C^1(I \to H)$, where $\Vert \cdot \Vert_H$ is the norm of H.

Let $L \in C^1(R^{3f} \to R)$ and we consider a functional defined on $C^1(I \to H)$,

$$J_{ab} = E\left[\int_a^b L(x(t), Dx(t), D_* x(t))\, dt\right]$$

where E denotes the expectation and $a, b \in I$ with $a < b$. A functional J defined on $C^1(I \to H)$ is said to be differentiable at $x \in C^1(I \to H)$ if

$$J(x+z) - J(x) = dJ(x, z) + R(x, z)$$

Here dJ is a linear functional of $z \in C^1(I \to H)$ and $R(x, z) = 0\ (\Vert z \Vert)$. The linear functional dJ on $C^1(I \to H)$ is called the variation of the functional J at $x \in C^1(I \to H)$.

Kunio Yasue made some regularity assumptions on $x \in C^1(I \to H)$ and $L \in C^1(R^{3f} \to R)$, viz. $\partial L/\partial Dx(t)$ is adapted to F and mean backward differentiable, and $\partial L/\partial D_*$ is adapted to P and mean forward differentiable. A stochastic process $x \in C^1(I \to H)$ satisfying these regularity assumptions is said to be L-adapted. Kunio Yasue then proved the following theorem of stochastic calculus of variations (proof omitted): The functional J_{ab} given above is differentiable at any L-adapted process $x \in C^1(I \to H)$, and its variation is given by

$$dJ_{ab} = E\left[\int_a^b \left[\frac{\partial L}{\partial x(t)} - D_*\left(\frac{\partial L}{\partial Dx(t)}\right) - D\left(\frac{\partial L}{\partial D_* x(t)}\right)\right] z(t)\, dt\right]$$

$$+ E\left[\left(\frac{\partial L}{\partial Dx(t)} + \frac{\partial L}{\partial D_* x(t)}\right) \cdot z(t)\,\Big|_a^b\right]$$

An L-adapted process $x \in C^1(I \to H)$ is called a stationary point or an extremal of the functional J_{ab} if it destroys the differential at x, i.e., $dJ_{ab} = 0$.

We now state the following fundamental theorem: A necessary and sufficient condition, for an L-adapted process to be an extremal of the functional J_{ab} given before with fixed end points $x(a) = x_a$ and $x(b) = x_b$ is that it satisfies

$$\frac{\partial L}{\partial x(t)} - D_*\left(\frac{\partial L}{\partial Dx(t)}\right) - D\left(\frac{\partial L}{\partial D_* x(t)}\right) = 0 \tag{1.61}$$

almost surely (a.s.), where x_a and x_b belong to H.

To prove this theorem we note that since $z(a) = z(b) = 0$,

$$dJ_{ab} = E\left[\int_a^b \left[\frac{\partial L}{\partial x(t)} - D_*\left(\frac{\partial L}{\partial Dx(t)}\right) - D\left(\frac{\partial L}{\partial D_* x(t)}\right)\right] z(t)\, dt\right].$$

It suffices to show that for a stochastic process of second order y,

$$E\left[\int_a^b y(t)\, z(t)\, dt\right] = 0$$

for any $z \in C^1(I \to H)$ iff $y = 0$ (a.s.). Assume $y(u) > 0$ (a.s.) for $u \in (a, b)$. Then by continuity $y(t) > C > 0$ (a.s.) in a neighbourhood of u; $a < u - d < t < u + d < b$, $d > 0$. But since $z \in C^1(I \to H)$ is arbitrary, we may choose a mean square differentiable process z such that $z(t) = 0$ (a.s.) for $a \leq t \leq u - d$, $u + d \leq t \leq b$, $z(t) > 0$ (a.s.) for $u - d < t < u + d$ and $z(t) = 1$ (a.s.) for $u - \frac{d}{2} < t < u + \frac{d}{2}$. Then $\int_a^b y(t) \cdot z(t)\, dt \geq Cd > 0$ (a.s.) and we get a contradiction. This proves the theorem.

To give an example, we consider a Markov process $x \in C^1(I \to H)$ and L is given by

$$L(x, Dx, D_* x) = L_1(Dx, D_* x) - V(x)$$

$$= \frac{1}{2}\left(\frac{1}{2} m \,|Dx|^2 + \frac{1}{2} m \,|D_* x|^2\right) - V(x)$$

where m is the particle mass and L_1 and V correspond to the kinetic and potential energy. Here the Euler equation (1.61) becomes

$$\frac{m}{2}[DD_* x + D_* Dx] = -\nabla V(x)$$

almost surely, which might be regarded as the generalization of Newton's dynamical law to a stochastic process.

1.11 Supplementary Remarks

Variational Principle for the Equation $y''(x) = f(x, y, y')$

It can be shown that any equation of the above form is a Euler equation for some functional

$$I[y(x)] = \int F(x, y, y')\, dx.$$

This can be established by seeking the functional for which the Euler's equation

$$F_y - F_{y'x} - F_{y'y}\, y' - F_{y'y'}\, y'' = 0$$

coincides with the above second-order differential equation. This means that there must be an identity with respect to x, y, y'

$$F_y - F_{y'x} - F_{y'y}y' - F_{y'y'} \cdot f(x, y, y') \equiv 0.$$

Differentiating this with respect to y', we get

$$F_{y'y'x} + F_{y'y'y}\, y' + F_{y'y'y'} \cdot f + F_{y'y'} \cdot f_{y'} = 0.$$

Setting $u = F_{y'y'}$, we obtain the partial differential equation (PDE)

$$\frac{\partial u}{\partial x} + y'\frac{\partial u}{\partial y} + f\frac{\partial u}{\partial y'} + f_{y'} \cdot u = 0.$$

Hence finding the functional, that is, finding the function $F(x, y, y')$, reduces to the solution of the above PDE, and to subsequent quadrature.

Existence of an Extremum

We conclude this chapter by pointing out a characteristic difficulty in the solution of variational problems. In problems involving ordinary maxima or minima of a function, the existence of a solution is guaranteed by the fundamental theorem of Weirstrass. However variational problems, even if they are meaningfully formulated, may not have solutions. This stems from the fact that it is not, in general, possible to choose the domain of admissible functions as a 'compact set' for which the principle of point of accumulation holds.

For definiteness, let us consider the functional

$$I[y(x)] = \int_a^b [P(x)y'^2 + Q(x)y^2]\,dx \tag{1.62}$$

with the boundary conditions

$$y(a) = y(b) = 0. \tag{1.63}$$

To fix ideas we also assume an integral constraint

$$\int_a^b y^2\,dx = 1. \tag{1.64}$$

We suppose that $P(x)$ and $Q(x)$ are continuous in $[a, b]$ with $P(x) > 0$. It then follows from (1.62) that

$$I[y] \geq \int_a^b Q(x)y^2\,dx \geq \min_{a \leq x \leq b} Q(x) \int_a^b y^2\,dx = \min_{a \leq x \leq b} Q(x).$$

Thus the above functional is bounded below. Now, even if the least value of $I[y]$ is not attained, we can construct a sequence of functions $Y_n(x)$ satisfying (1.63) and (1.64) such that $\lim_{n \to \infty} I[y_n(x)]$ is equal to the greatest lower bound. Such a sequence is known as the minimizing sequence for the functional I.

If a minimizing sequence $\{Y_n(x)\}$ (or its subsequence) is convergent (say, uniformly convergent) to a limit function $Y(x)$, then the functional attains a minimum value for $y = Y(x)$. In fact, we have

$$\int_a^b Y^2\,dx = \lim_{n \to \infty} \int_a^b Y_n^2(x)\,dx = 1$$

$$\int_a^b Q(x)Y^2(x)\,dx = \lim_{n \to \infty} \int_a^b Q(x)Y_n^2(x)\,dx.$$

But

$$\int_a^b P(x)Y'^2(x)\,dx \leq \lim_{n \to \infty} \int_a^b P(x)Y_n'^2(x)\,dx.$$

The last result may appear somewhat strange because one may think that the left hand side equals the right hand side. However, there are cases when the right hand side exceeds the left hand side. Both possibilities are demonstrated in Figs. 1.10(a) and 1.10(b).

Thus we have

$$I[Y] \leq \lim_{n \to \infty} I[Y_n(x)]$$

The sequence $\{Y_n(x)\}$ being a minimizing sequence, we conclude that the quantity $I[Y]$ is the least value and the existence of a minimum is therefore established.

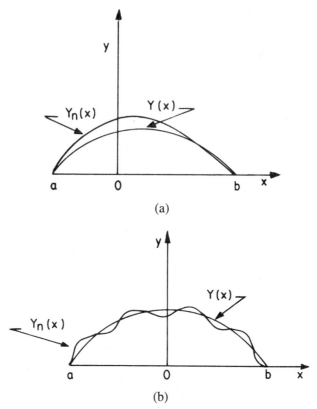

Fig. 1.10 (a) The minimizing function $Y_n(x)$ and limit function $Y(x)$ in the case when the left side of the above inequality equals the right side, and (b) The minimizing function $Y_n(x)$ and limit function $Y(x)$ in the case when the left side of the above inequality is less than the right side.

Conditions for the existence of a convergent sequence $\{Y_n(x)\}$ involve the concept of compactness, which plays a vital role in these and many other problems. A set M of points (elements) of a normed space R (or a more general metric space (R)) is said to be compact in (R), if every infinite sequence of points belonging to M has at least one convergent subsequence. Using this notion we may rephrase the Bolzano-Weirstrass theorem as: every bounded set of points belonging to a finite-dimensional Euclidean space is compact. But every unbounded set of a finite-dimensional Euclidean space is noncompact.

An important feature of infinite-dimensional spaces is that their bounded subsets are not necessarily compact, and therefore, the investigation of these spaces presents difficulties. For example, the sequence of functions $\sin x$, $\sin 2x$, $\sin 3x$, ... is bounded, but noncompact as a subset of the space $C[a, b]$ for fixed a and b. This is due to the fact that the values of $\sin nx$, $n = 1, 2, 3, \ldots$ oscillate between -1 and 1 with increasing frequency as $n \to \infty$ and, therefore, the subsequences of this sequence do not converge uniformly. But it is also possible to prove that every minimizing sequence $\{Y_n\}$ mentioned above is not only bounded, but also compact in the space $C[a, b]$ because, in this case, the absence of uniformly convergent subsequences would imply that there is a subsequence of the number sequence $\left\{ \int_a^b Y_n'^2 \, dx \right\}$, which increases indefinitely and hence the sequence $I\{Y_n\}$ becomes unbounded as well. These properties ensure the existence of a uniformly convergent subsequence of the sequence Y_n, whose limit function $Y(x)$ renders the functional minimum.

An alternative approach to the above problem of existence is due to Tonelli (see Young [6]) and is based on the notion of semi-continuity. A function $F(P)$, defined in a set of P, in which limits have a meaning, is said to be lower semi-continuous at P_0, if it satisfies the following conditions: (a) $F(P)$ is extended real-valued, i.e., its values are real with the possible addition of $+\infty$ and $-\infty$, (b) $F(P_0)$ is defined and $F(P_0) \neq -\infty$, (c) $F(P_0) \leq \lim \inf F(P)$ as $P \to P_0$. If these conditions are satisfied for each P_0 of the set, we say that $F(P)$ is lower semi-continuous.

Now consider the variational problem for the functional

$$I[C] = \int_a^b f(x, y(x), y'(x)) \, dx$$

where C is a curve $y = y(x)$ joining two given points a and b. Then it was shown by Tonelli that $I[C]$ is lower semi-continuous for C belonging to any class K of curves of uniformly bounded lengths situated in a cube if $f(x, y(x), y'(x))$ is convex in $y'(x)$. Further $I[C]$ attains its minimum in K if K is closed.

The link between the proof of existence based on compactness and Tonelli's approach lies in the fact that a closed bounded set in a finite-dimensional space is compact and the well known Weirstrass principle (valid for a continuous function on a closed compact set) remains valid for a lower semi-continuous function, defined on a sequentially compact closed set.

The general scheme presented above involves most of the basic techniques for solving variational problems. These schemes reduce to testing that the functional is bounded below, selecting a minimizing sequence, and proving the compactness of the sequence in an appropriately chosen function space.

There is yet another way of overcoming the difficulty of not having a convergent minimizing sequence, to ensure the existence of an extremum as suggested by Young [6]. It adapts the idea of L. Schwartz for constructing a dual space, and embedding the original space (of admissible curves in our variational problem) into its dual. To fix ideas, consider the problem of minimizing a functional

$$\int F(\mathbf{x}(t), \mathbf{x}'(t), t), \, dt, \ t_1 \leq t \leq t_2,$$ where $\mathbf{x}(t)$ varies along a parametrized arc Γ of finite length. In this context F and Γ are elements of dual spaces. Let the function F belong to some normed space B, so that $\int_\Gamma F \, dt \equiv \langle F, \Gamma \rangle$ clearly defines a linear functional in the dual space B^*. Defining the operation $\oplus$ as union of arcs, we have $\langle F, (\Gamma_1 \oplus \Gamma_2) \rangle = \langle F, \Gamma_1 \rangle + \langle F, \Gamma_2 \rangle$ and $\langle F, c\Gamma \rangle = c \langle F, \Gamma \rangle = \langle cF, \Gamma \rangle$ for any real number c. We see that this functional is indeed bilinear and bounded.

Thus Γ is an element of B^*. Now following the ideas of L. Schwartz, one can define weak convergence in B^*. Such weak limits are called generalized arcs. However the limitations of this approach are similar to those of the theory of distributions.

From the foregoing discussion, it may appear that the non-existence of solution owes its origin to the lack of compactness or closure properties of the family of admissible solutions of a variational problem. However, an entirely different reason for nonexistence of solutions of a variational problem, may also arise.

We pose the following question: When are the initial or boundary conditions well-posed (see ref. [3b]) for a certain class of boundary value problems, involving differential equations? This well-posedness in the sense of Hadamard implies that the solution exists, is unique and depends continuously on the initial/boundary data. Thus, if a differential system is not well-posed, the corresponding variational problem is also not well-posed. The third requirement above, which is particularly incisive, is necessary, if the mathematical formulation in the form of differential equations is to describe observable natural phenomena. Data in nature cannot be assumed to be rigidly fixed. The mere process of measuring them involves small errors. Thus a poor mathematical modelling of a real life problem may lead to ill-posed differential system so that the corresponding variational problem may also be ill-posed, as the following example due to Caratheodory shows.

A variational problem leads to the following Euler-Lagrange equation as the necessary condition for the existence of an extremum

$$y_t = (1 + x_t^2)^{1/2}$$

with the boundary conditions

$$x(0) = y(0) = 0, \quad x(1) = y(1) = 1.$$

It can be shown that the above boundary value problem is not well-posed so that no differentiable solution satisfies the above system.

A simple geometrical example of non-existence of solution can be given as follows: Two points of the x-axis are to be joined by the shortest possible line of continuous curvature which is perpendicular to the x-axis at the end-points. Clearly this problem has no solution. In fact, the length of such a line is always greater than that of the straight line, joining the two end points, but it may approximate this length as closely as desired. Hence there exists a greatest lower bound, but no minimum for admissible curves.

We may now sum up the foregoing considerations about the existence of an extremum in a variational problem. The characterization of such an extremum, in the absence of an existence proof, may turn out to be a nonsense, as in the following example of Oscar Perron. Let us assume that there exists a largest positive integer N. Thus $N \geq n$ for any positive integer n. If $N > 1$, then clearly $N^2 > N$. But $N \geq N^2$ by our hypothesis leads to $N^2 = N$. This gives $N = 1$. Although there is nothing wrong in the proof, the nonsense arises from our original assumption of the existence of a largest positive integer. One may arrive at a similar nonsense if necessary or sufficient conditions for the extremum of a functional are derived, without first checking whether such an extremum is attained in the class of admissible functions. This has a bearing on a basic difficulty arising in the modelling of a physical phenomenon. The existence of solutions in a mathematical model must realistically reflect our physical experience.

PROBLEMS

1. Test for an extremum the functional

$$I[y(x)] = \int_0^1 (xy + y^2 - 2y^2 y') \, dx, \, y(0) = 1, \, y(1) = 2.$$

Ans.   An extremum is not achieved on the class of continuous functions.

2. Find the extremals of the functional

$$I[y(x)] = \int_{x_0}^{x_1} \frac{(1 + y^2)}{y'^2} \, dx.$$

Ans. $y = \sinh (C_1 x + C_2)$

3. Find the extremals of the functional

$$I[y(x)] = \int_{x_0}^{x_1} (2xy + y'''^2) \, dx.$$

Ans. $y = \dfrac{x^7}{7!} + C_1 x^5 + C_2 x^4 + C_3 x^3 + C_4 x^2 + C_5 x + C_6.$

4. Find the Euler-Ostrogradsky equation for the functional

$$I[u(x, y, z)] = \iiint_D \left[\left(\frac{\partial u}{\partial x} \right)^2 + \left(\frac{\partial u}{\partial y} \right)^2 + \left(\frac{\partial u}{\partial z} \right)^2 + 2uf \right] dx \, dy \, dz.$$

Ans. $\dfrac{\partial^2 u}{\partial x^2} + \dfrac{\partial^2 u}{\partial y^2} + \dfrac{\partial^2 u}{\partial z^2} = f(x, y, z).$

APPENDIX A

VARIATIONAL FORMULATION FOR A DISSIPATIVE SYSTEM

It may be noted that it is possible to introduce a formalism (Morse and Feshbach [7]) which will enable us to carry on calculations for dissipative systems, as though they constitute conservative systems. The method is to consider simultaneously with the dissipative system (i.e., one with friction) a system with negative friction (which may be regarded as the mirror image of the original dissipative system) such that the energy drained from the dissipative system is absorbed by the mirror image system. Thus the total energy is conserved and we can define a Lagrange function.

Consider the one-dimensional oscillator with friction, governed by the equation of motion

$$m\ddot{x} + R\dot{x} + Kx = 0.$$

Using the variational technique, we wish to derive this equation from a suitable Lagrange function. To this end, we construct the formal expression as

$$L = m\dot{x}\dot{x}^* - \frac{1}{2}R(x^*\dot{x} - x\dot{x}^*) - Kxx^*,$$

which may be regarded as the Lagrange function in the variables x and x^*. The variable x^* refers to the mirror-image oscillator with negative friction. The above L gives the two momenta as

$$p = m\dot{x}^* - \frac{1}{2}Rx^*, \quad p^* = m\dot{x} + \frac{1}{2}Rx,$$

which have very little to do with the actual momentum of the oscillator. Lagrange's equations for the two systems are

$$m\ddot{x}^* - R\dot{x}^* + Kx^* = 0, \quad m\ddot{x} + R\dot{x} + Kx = 0,$$

where the equation for x is precisely the one with which we started. The other equation involves the negative frictional term $-R\dot{x}^*$.

The Hamiltonian is

$$H = p\dot{x} + p^*\dot{x}^* - L = \frac{1}{m}\left(p + \frac{1}{2}Rx^*\right)\left(p^* - \frac{1}{2}Rx\right) + Kxx^*.$$

Since x^* increases in amplitude as fast as x decreases, H will remain constant.

Although this technique is not very satisfactory even if an alternative method of solution is known, it will still be necessary for studying dissipative system, involving equation of the diffusion type given by

$$\nabla^2 \Psi = a^2 \frac{\partial \Psi}{\partial t}.$$

Here Ψ is the density of a diffusing fluid and a^2 is the diffusion coefficient (assumed constant). Let $\Psi*$ refer to the density of the mirror-image system. We construct the Lagrange function L as

$$L = - (\nabla\Psi \cdot \nabla\Psi*) - \frac{a^2}{2}\left(\Psi* \, \frac{\partial\Psi}{\partial t} - \Psi \, \frac{\partial\Psi*}{\partial t} \right)$$

so that the canonical momentum densities are

$$p = \frac{\partial L}{\partial \dot\Psi} = - \frac{1}{2}a^2 \, \Psi*, \quad p* = \frac{1}{2}a^2 \, \Psi.$$

The Euler equations corresponding to L above are

$$\nabla^2\Psi = a^2 \, \frac{\partial\Psi}{\partial t}, \quad \nabla^2\Psi* = - a^2 \, \frac{\partial\Psi*}{\partial t},$$

where the first equation is the diffusion equation with which we started.

APPENDIX B

EKELAND'S VARIATIONAL PRINCIPLE

We have already seen in Section 1.11 that a functional bounded below attains its infimum if it has some type of continuity in a topology that renders compactness, to the domain of the said functional. However, in some situations of interest in applications, this is not the case. Take, for instance, the functionals (defined in an infinite-dimensional Hilbert space) which are continuous in the norm topology, but not in the weak topology. Such problems can be tackled by Ekeland variational principle (Figueiredo [8]). This principle has found a variety of applications in different fields of analysis. We state Ekeland's principle (weak form) as follows: Let (X, d) be a complete metric space. Let further $\Phi : X \rightarrow RU \{+ \infty\}$ be lower semi-continuous and bounded below. Then for a given $\varepsilon > 0$, there exists $u_\varepsilon \in X$ such that

$$\Phi(u_\varepsilon) \le inf_X \, \Phi + \varepsilon$$

$$\Phi(u_\varepsilon) < \Phi(u) + \varepsilon d(u, u_\varepsilon)$$

for every $u \in X$ with $u \ne u_\varepsilon$.

A stronger version of Ekeland's principle is as follows: Let (X, d) be a complete metric space and $\Phi : X \rightarrow RU \{+ \infty\}$ be a lower semi-continuous function which is bounded below.

Let $\varepsilon > 0$ and $\bar{u} \in x$ be given so that

$$\Phi(\bar{u}) \le inf_X \Phi + \frac{\varepsilon}{2}.$$

Then for a given $\lambda > 0$, there exists $u_\lambda \in X$, such that

(i) $\Phi(u_\lambda) \le \Phi(\bar{u})$,

(ii) $d(u_\lambda, \bar{u}) \leq \lambda$,

(iii) $\Phi(u_\lambda) < \Phi(u) + \dfrac{\varepsilon}{\lambda} d(u, u_\lambda)$

for every $u \neq u_\lambda$.

The proof of both the versions is omitted.

APPENDIX C

INVARIANCE OF EULER'S EQUATION

Suppose a functional

$$I[y(x)] = \int_a^b F(x, y, y')\, dx$$

is transformed by replacing the independent variable or by a simultaneous replacement of the desired function and the independent variable. Then, the extremals of the functional are found from Euler equation for the transformed integrand. Herein lies the principle of the invariance of Euler's equation.

If $x = x(u, v)$, $y = y(u, v)$ and

$$\begin{vmatrix} x_u & x_v \\ y_u & y_v \end{vmatrix} \neq 0,$$

then

$$\int F(x, y, y')\, dx = \int F\left[x(u, v), y(u, v), \frac{y_u + y_v v'_u}{x_u + x_v v'_u}\right](x_u + x_v v'_u)\, du$$

$$= \int \Phi(u, v, v'_u)\, du.$$

Now the extremals of the original functional are determined from Euler's equation

for $\displaystyle\int \Phi(u, v, v'_u)\, du$, i.e.,

$$\frac{\partial \Phi}{\partial v} - \frac{d}{du}\left(\frac{\partial \Phi}{\partial u'}\right) = 0.$$

Take, for instance, the problem of finding the extremals of the functional

$$I[y] = \int_0^{\ln 2} (e^{-x} y'^2 - e^x y^2)\, dx.$$

Its Euler equation is

$$y'' - y' + e^{2x} y = 0.$$

While its solution poses some problem, a substitution

$$x = \ln u, \qquad y = v$$

reduces the functional to

$$I_1[v] = \int_1^2 (v'^2 - v^2)\, du.$$

Its Euler equation $v'' + v = 0$ readily gives rise to the solution

$$v = C_1 \cos u + C_2 \sin u.$$

A passage to original coordinates gives the required solution for extremals as

$$y = C_1 \cos (e^x) + C_2 \sin (e^x).$$

CHAPTER 2

VARIATIONAL PROBLEMS WITH MOVING BOUNDARIES

2.1 Functional of the Form $I[y(x)] = \int_{x_1}^{x_2} F(x, y, y')\, dx$

In the problems discussed so far, we have taken the boundary points (x_1, y_1) and (x_2, y_2) in the functional

$$I\,[y(x)] = \int_{x_1}^{x_2} F(x, y, y')\, dx \qquad\qquad (2.1)$$

as fixed. Let us now consider the case when one or both the boundary points can move. This means that the class of admissible curves is extended because, in addition to the comparison curves with fixed boundary points, we have to admit curves with variable boundary points.

It is clear that if on a curve $y = y(x)$, an extremum is attained in a problem with moving boundary points, then surely enough the extremum is all the more attained on a restricted class of curves with common (fixed) boundary points. Thus the curves $y = y(x)$ on which extremum of the above functional is attained in a moving boundary problem must be solutions of the Euler equation

$$F_y - \frac{d}{dx}\, F_{y'} = 0$$

so that these curves must be extremals.

In the problem with fixed boundary points, the two constants in the solution of Euler's equation are determined from the two boundary conditions at the fixed points at (x_1, y_1) and (x_2, y_2). But in a moving boundary problem, one or both of these conditions are missing, and the arbitrary constants in the general solution of Euler's equation have to be obtained from the vanishing of the variation δI, which is the necessary condition for extremum.

For the sake of simplicity, let us assume that one of the boundary points (x_1, y_1) is fixed while the other boundary point (x_2, y_2) can move and pass to the point $(x_2 + \delta x_2, y_2 + \delta y_2)$. Since, as shown above, the extremum in a moving boundary problem is attained only on extremals, i.e., on solutions $y = y(x, C_1, C_2)$ of Euler's equations, from now on we consider the values of the functional I on such curves. Thus, $I\,[y(x, C_1, C_2)]$ reduces to a function of the parameters C_1 and C_2 and of the limits of integration. We shall call the admissible curves $y = y(x)$ and $y = y(x) + \delta y(x)$ close if $|\,\delta y\,|$ and $|\,\delta y'\,|$ are also small.

The extremals passing through (x_1, y_1), form a pencil of extremals $y = y(x, C_1)$. The functional $I [y(x, C_1)]$ on the curves of this pencil becomes a function of C_1 and x_2. If the curves of the pencil $y = y(x, C_1)$ do not intersect in the neighbourhood of the extremal (see Fig. 2.1), then $I [y(x, C_1)]$ may be considered as a single-valued function of (x_2, y_2). This is because the specification of (x_2, y_2) determines the extremal of the pencil uniquely, and hence determines the value of the functional.

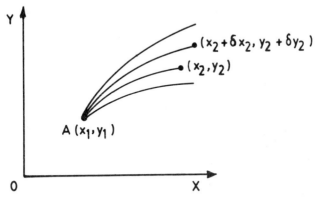

Fig. 2.1 A pencil of extremals through a given point.

Let us determine the variation of the functional $I [y(x, C_1)]$ when the boundary point moves from (x_2, y_2) to $(x_2 + \delta x_2, y_2 + \delta y_2)$. Thus the increment ΔI is given by

$$\Delta I = \int_{x_1}^{x_2+\delta x_2} F(x, y + \delta y, y' + \delta y') \, dx - \int_{x_1}^{x_2} F(x, y, y') \, dx$$

$$= \int_{x_1}^{x_2} [F(x, y + \delta y, y' + \delta y') - F(x, y, y')] \, dx$$

$$+ \int_{x_2}^{x_2+\delta x_2} F(x, y + \delta y, y' + \delta y') \, dx. \tag{2.2}$$

Using the mean value theorem, the second term on the right-hand side of (2.2) can be written as

$$\int_{x_2}^{x_2+\delta x_2} F(x, y + \delta y, y' + \delta y') \, dx = [F]_{x_2+\theta \cdot \delta x_2} \cdot \delta x_2 \tag{2.3}$$

where $0 < \theta < 1$. But by virtue of the continuity of F, we may write

$$F|_{x_2+\theta \cdot \delta x_2} = F|_{x_2} + \varepsilon \tag{2.4}$$

where ε is an infinitesimal such that $\varepsilon \to 0$ as $\delta x_2 \to 0$ and $\delta y_2 \to 0$. Thus by (2.3) and (2.4) we have

$$\int_{x_2}^{x_2+\delta x_2} F(x, y + \delta y, y' + \delta y') \, dx = F|_{x=x_2} \cdot \delta x_2 + \varepsilon \, \delta x_2 \tag{2.5}$$

Using Taylor's theorem we now transform the first term on the right side of (2.2) as

$$\int_{x_1}^{x_2} [F(x, y + \delta y, y' + \delta y') - F(x, y, y')]\, dx$$

$$= \int_{x_1}^{x_2} [F_y(x, y, y')\, \delta y + F_{y'}(x, y, y')\, \delta y']\, dx + R$$

where R is an infinitesimal of the order higher than that of δy or $\delta y'$. Further, the linear part on the right side of the above integral can be, after integration by parts, reduced to

$$[F_{y'}\, \delta y]_{x_1}^{x_2} + \int_{x_1}^{x_2} \left(F_y - \frac{d}{dx} F_{y'} \right) \delta y\, dx.$$

Since the values of the functional I are taken only on the extremals, the integral in the second term of the above expression vanishes since $F_y - \dfrac{d}{dx} F_{y'} \equiv 0$ and the expression then becomes

$$(F_{y'}\, \delta y)_{x=x_2}$$

since $(\delta y)_{x_1} = 0$. Note that $(\delta y)_{x_2}$ is not equal to δy_2 since δy_2 is the increment of y_2 when the boundary point is displaced to $(x_2 + \delta x_2, y_2 + \delta y_2)$. But $(\delta y)_{x_2}$ is the increment of the ordinate at the point x_2 when passing from the extremal joining (x_1, y_1) and (x_2, y_2) to the one joining (x_1, y_1) and $(x_2 + \delta x_2, y_2 + \delta y_2)$ as shown in Fig. 2.2.

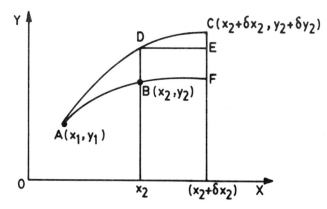

Fig. 2.2 Extremizing curve and a neighbouring curve through a given point.

It is evident from Fig. 2.2 that $BD = (\delta y)_{x_2}$ and $FC = \delta y_2$. Further, $EC = y'(x_2) \cdot \delta x_2$ and hence $BD = FC - EC$ gives

$$(\delta y)_{x_2} \approx \delta y_2 - y'(x_2) \cdot \delta x_2$$

This equality is valid within the infinitesimals of higher order. Thus

$$\int_{x_1}^{x_2} [F(x, y + \delta y, y' + \delta y') - F(x, y, y')]\, dx \approx F_{y'}|_{x=x_2} \cdot (\delta y_2 - y'(x_2)\, \delta x_2).$$

Finally, using (2.5) and the above relation in (2.2), we obtain

$$\delta I = F|_{x=x_2} \cdot \delta x_2 + F_{y'}|_{x=x_2} \cdot (\delta y_2 - y'(x_2)\delta x_2)$$
$$= (F - y'F_{y'})|_{x=x_2} \cdot \delta x_2 + F_{y'}|_{x=x_2} \cdot \delta y_2 \tag{2.6}$$

By virtue of the fact that δx_2 and δy_2 are independent, the necessary condition for the extremum $\delta I = 0$ then gives

$$(F - y' F_{y'})|_{x=x_2} = 0,$$
$$F_{y'}|_{x=x_2} = 0 \tag{2.7}$$

Cases, however, arise when δx_2 and δy_2 are not independent. For example, if the boundary point (x_2, y_2) moves along the curve

$$y_2 = \phi(x_2), \tag{2.8}$$

then $\delta y_2 = \phi'(x_2) \cdot \delta x_2$. Thus from (2.6), we get

$$[F + (\phi' - y') F_{y'}]_{x=x_2} \cdot \delta x_2 = 0.$$

Since δx_2 is arbitrary, we must have

$$[F + (\phi' - y') F_{y'}]_{x=x_2} = 0, \tag{2.9}$$

which provides the condition at the free boundary. This is known as the transversality condition. The conditions (2.8) and (2.9) suffice to determine the extremals of the pencil $y = y(x, C_1)$ on which an extremum may be attained. A condition similar to (2.9) obtains if the boundary point (x_1, y_1) moves along another prescribed curve $y_1 = \Psi(x_1)$.

There is one simple case when the transversality condition (2.9) reduces to the orthogonality condition. Consider the case when F in (2.1) is given by $A(x, y) \cdot (1 + y'^2)^{1/2}$, where $A(x, y)$ does not vanish at the movable boundary point x_2. In this case (2.9) reduces to

$$A(x, y) \cdot (1 + \phi'y')/(1 + y'^2)^{1/2} = 0 \text{ at } x = x_2.$$

Since $A(x, y) \neq 0$ at $x = x_2$, we have $y' = -1/\phi'$ at $x = x_2$, which is the orthogonality condition.

Example 1. Find the shortest distance between the parabola $y = x^2$ and the straight line $x - y = 5$.

Solution. The problem is to find the extremum of the functional

$$I[y(x)] = \int_{x_1}^{x_2} (1 + y'^2)^{1/2}\, dx$$

subject to the condition that the left end of the extremal moves along $y = x^2$ while the right end moves along $x - y = 5$. Thus the transversality condition (2.9) gives

$$[(1 + y'^2)^{1/2} + (2x - y')y'(1 + y'^2)^{-1/2}]_{x=x_1} = 0, \tag{2.10}$$

$$[(1 + y'^2)^{1/2} + (1 - y')y'(1 + y'^2)^{-1/2}]_{x=x_2} = 0. \tag{2.11}$$

Since the general solution of Euler's equation for the above functional is $y = C_1 x + C_2$ (where C_1 and C_2 are constants), it follows that $y' = C_1$. Further, both the end points lie on the extremal $y = C_1 x + C_2$, hence we must have

$$C_1 x_1 + C_2 = x_1^2, \tag{2.12}$$

$$C_1 x_2 + C_2 = x_2 - 5. \tag{2.13}$$

Replacing y' in (2.10) and (2.11) by C_1 and solving the resulting equations along with (2.12) and (2.13), we get

$$C_1 = -1, \quad C_2 = \frac{3}{4}, \quad x_1 = \frac{1}{2}, \quad x_2 = \frac{23}{8}.$$

Thus the required extremal is $y = -x + \frac{3}{4}$ and the shortest distance between the given parabola and the straight line is

$$L = \int_{1/2}^{23/8} (1 + 1)^{1/2}\, dx = \frac{19\sqrt{2}}{8}.$$

Example 2. Using only the basic necessary condition $\delta I = 0$, find the curve on which an extremum of the functional

$$I[y(x)] = \int_0^{x_1} \frac{(1 + y'^2)^{1/2}}{y}\, dx, \quad y(0) = 0$$

can be achieved if the second boundary point (x_1, y_1) can move along the circumference $(x - 9)^2 + y^2 = 9$.

Solution. Denoting the integrand of the functional by F, the extremals are clearly the integral curves

$$F - y'F_{y'} = \text{constant}$$

or Euler equation. This gives

$$1 + y'^2 = C/y^2, \quad C = \text{constant}.$$

Its solution is the two-parameter family of circles

$$(x - C_1)^2 + y^2 = C_2^2. \tag{2.14}$$

The boundary condition $y(0) = 0$ leads to $C_1 = C_2$. Further, since the integrand is of the form $A(x, y) (1 + y'^2)^{1/2}$, the transversality condition at the movable boundary point (x_1, y_1) reduces to the orthogonality condition. Thus the required extremal will be the arc of a circle belonging to (2.14) which is orthogonal to $(x - 9)^2 + y^2 = 9$ (see Fig. 2.3).

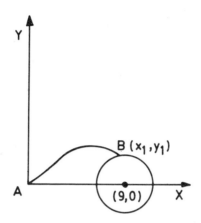

Fig. 2.3 Extremizing curve satisfying the orthogonality condition.

Since $B(x_1, y_1)$ lies on both circles, we must have

$$x_1^2 - 18x_1 + y_1^2 = -72, \qquad x_1^2 - 2C_1x_1 + y_1^2 = 0$$

which gives

$$x_1(C_1 - 9) = -36 \tag{2.15}$$

In view of orthogonality of the two circles at (x_1, y_1), the tangent to (2.14) at B passes through the centre $(9, 0)$ of the given circle. This yields

$$(9 - C_1)x_1 = 9C_1. \tag{2.16}$$

Solving (2.15) and (2.16), we find that $C_1 = 4$ and $x_1 = 36/5$ so that the required extremals (2.14) are the arcs of the circles $y = \pm (8x - x^2)^{1/2}$.

2.2 Variational Problem with a Movable Boundary for a Functional Dependent on Two Functions

Consider the functional

$$I[y(x), z(x)] = \int_{x_1}^{x_2} F(x, y(x), z(x), y'(x), z'(x)) \, dx. \tag{2.17}$$

Let the point $A(x_1, y_1, z_1)$ corresponding to the lower limit in the above integral be fixed, and let the other point $B(x_2, y_2, z_2)$ move in an arbitrary manner, or along a given curve or surface.

It is clear that the extremum can be attained only on the integral curves of Euler equations

$$\frac{\partial F}{\partial y} - \frac{d}{dx}\left(\frac{\partial F}{\partial y'}\right) = 0, \quad \frac{\partial F}{\partial z} - \frac{d}{dx}\left(\frac{\partial F}{\partial z'}\right) = 0.$$

The general solution of these equations contains four arbitrary constants. Since the boundary point $A(x_1, y_1, z_1)$ is fixed, it is possible to eliminate two arbitrary constants. The other two constants have to be determined from the necessary condition $\delta I = 0$ for extremum, where δI is the variation of I. This variation may be computed in precisely the same way as in Section 2.1. Hence, $\delta I = 0$ gives

$$\delta I = (F - y'F_{y'} - z'F_{z'})_{x=x_2} \cdot \delta x_2 + (F_{y'})_{x=x_2} \cdot \delta y_2 + (F_{z'})_{x=x_2} \cdot \delta z_2$$

$$= 0 \tag{2.18}$$

for an extremum.

If the variations δx_2, δy_2 and δz_2 are independent, then (2.18) gives

$$[F - y'F_{y'} - z'F_{z'}]_{x=x_2} = 0, \quad [F_{y'}]_{x=x_2} = 0, \quad [F_{z'}]_{x=x_2} = 0.$$

If the boundary point (x_2, y_2, z_2) moves along some curve $y_2 = \phi(x_2)$, $z_2 = \Psi(x_2)$, then $\delta y_2 = \phi'(x_2) \cdot \delta x_2$ and $\delta z_2 = \Psi'(x_2) \cdot \delta x_2$. Thus from (2.15) we have

$$[F + (\phi' - y')F_{y'} + (\Psi' - z')F_{z'}]_{x=x_2} \cdot \delta x_2 = 0.$$

Since δx_2 is arbitrary, we have

$$[F + (\phi' - y')F_{y'} + (\Psi' - z')F_{z'}]_{x=x_2} = 0. \tag{2.19}$$

This is the transversality condition in the problem of extremum of (2.17). Along with the equations $y_2 = \phi(x_2)$, $z_2 = \Psi(x_2)$, the condition (2.19) gives the equations necessary for determining the two arbitrary constants in the general solution of Euler's equations.

If, on the other hand, the boundary point $B(x_2, y_2, z_2)$ moves along a given surface $z_2 = \phi(x_2, y_2)$, then $\delta z_2 = \phi_{x_2} \delta x_2 + \phi_{y_2} \delta y_2$ such that the variations δx_2 and δy_2 are arbitrary. In this case (2.19) reduces to

$$[F - y'F_{y'} + (\phi_x - z')F_{z'}]_{x=x_2} \cdot \delta x_2 + [F_{y'} + \phi_y F_z]_{x=x_2} \cdot \delta y_2 = 0.$$

Since δx_2 and δy_2 are independent, we find

$$[F - y'F_{y'} + (\phi_x - z')F_{z'}]_{x=x_2} = 0$$

$$[F_{y'} + \phi_y F_z]_{x=x_2} = 0. \tag{2.20}$$

These two conditions, together with $z_2 = \phi(x_2, y_2)$, enable us to determine two arbitrary constants in the general solution of Euler's equation.

It may be easily seen that for the functional

$$I = \int_{x_1}^{x_2} A(x, y, z) \cdot (1 + y'^2 + z'^2)^{1/2} \, dx$$

with the end point (x_2, y_2, z_2) lying on the surface $z = \phi(x, y)$, the transversality condition reduces to the orthogonality condition of the extremal to the surface $z = \phi(x, y)$. From this, it immediately follows that the shortest distance between two surfaces $z = L(x, y)$, and $z = M(x, y)$, can only be attained on the straight lines, which are orthogonal to both these surfaces.

The above arguments can be readily extended to a functional of the form

$$I = \int_{x_1}^{x_2} F(x, y_1(x), y_2(x), ..., y_n(x), y_1'(x), y_2'(x), ..., y_n'(x)) \, dx$$

such that at the moving point x_2, we have

$$\left(F - \sum_{i=1}^{n} y_i' F_{y_i'}\right)_{x = x_2} \cdot \delta x_2 + \sum_{i=1}^{n} (F_{y_i'})_{x = x_2} \cdot \delta y_{i2} = 0. \tag{2.21}$$

Example 3.   Find the extremum of the functional

$$I = \int_{x_1}^{x_2} (y'^2 + z'^2 + 2yz) \, dx \text{ with } y(0) = 0,$$

$z(0) = 0$ and the point (x_2, y_2, z_2) moves over the fixed plane $x = x_2$.

Solution.   The Euler equation in this case gives $z'' - y = 0$ and $y'' - z = 0$ leading to $y^{iv} - y = 0$. The solutions are

$$y = C_1 \cosh x + C_2 \sinh x + C_3 \cos x + C_4 \sin x \tag{2.22}$$

$$z = C_1 \cosh x + C_2 \sinh x - C_3 \cos x - C_4 \sin x \tag{2.23}$$

The conditions $y(0) = z(0) = 0$ give $C_1 = C_3 = 0$. Further, the condition at the moving boundary point (x_2, y_2, z_2) can be derived from (2.18) with $\delta x_2 = 0$ (since x_2 is fixed) as

$$(F_{y'})_{x=x_2} = 0, \quad (F_{z'})_{x=x_2} = 0$$

giving

$$y'(x_2) = 0, \quad z'(x_2) = 0.$$

Thus (2.22) and (2.23) lead to

$$C_2 \cosh x_2 + C_4 \cos x_2 = 0, \quad C_2 \cosh x_2 - C_4 \cos x_2 = 0.$$

If $\cos x_2 \neq 0$, then $C_2 = C_4 = 0$ and, therefore, an extremum is attained on $y = 0$, $z = 0$. But if $\cos x_2 = 0$, then $C_2 = 0$ and C_4 remains arbitrary. In this case the extremal is $y = C_4 \sin x$, $z = -C_4 \sin x$.

2.3   One-Sided Variations

Let us consider again the functional (2.1) and suppose that a restriction is imposed on the class of permissible curves in such a way that the curves cannot pass through points of a certain region R bounded by the curve $\Psi(x, y) = 0$, as shown in Fig. 2.4.

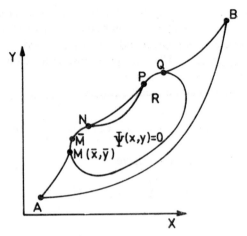

Fig. 2.4   An extremal not allowed to pass through a given region.

In such a problem the extremizing curve C either passes through a region which is completely outside R or C consists of arcs lying outside R and also consists of parts of the boundary of the region R. In the former case, the presence of R does not at all influence the properties of the functional, and its variation in the neighbourhood of C and hence, the extremizing curve must be an extremal. In the latter case only one-sided variations of the curve C are possible on parts of the boundary of the region R since the permissible curves are prohibited from entering R. Parts of the curve C outside the boundary of R are clearly extremals since on these parts two-sided variations (unaffected by the region R) are possible. We now derive conditions at the points of transition M, N, P and Q.

While computing the variation of the functional δI of the functional

$$I = \int_{x_1}^{x_2} F(x, y, y')\, dx = \int_{x_1}^{\bar{x}} F(x, y, y')\, dx + \int_{\bar{x}}^{x_2} F(x, y, y')\, dx$$

$$= I_1 + I_2 \tag{2.24}$$

we suppose that the variation is caused solely by the displacement of the point $M(\bar{x},\ \bar{y})$ on the curve $\Psi(x,\ y) = 0$. Thus for any position M on the curve, we may consider that AM is an extremal and the segment $MNPQB$ does not vary. For the extremal in (2.24) the upper boundary point $\bar{x}$ moves along the boundary of the region R and if $y = \phi(x)$ be the equation of the boundary (as deduced from $\Psi(x,\ y) = 0$), then it follows from (2.9) that

$$\delta I_1 = [F + (\phi' - y')F_{y'}]_{x=\bar{x}} \cdot \delta \bar{x}. \tag{2.25}$$

The functional $I_2 = \int_{\bar{x}}^{x_2} F(x, y, y')\, dx$ also has a moving boundary point $(\bar{x},\ \bar{y})$.

But in the neighbourhood of this point, the curve $y = \phi(x)$ on which an extremum can be achieved does not vary. Thus,

$$\Delta I_2 = \int_{\bar{x}+\Delta\bar{x}}^{x_2} F(x, y, y')\, dx - \int_{\bar{x}}^{x_2} F(x, y, y')\, dx$$

$$= - \int_{\bar{x}}^{\bar{x}+\Delta\bar{x}} F(x, y, y')\, dx = - \int_{\bar{x}}^{\bar{x}+\Delta\bar{x}} F(x, \phi(x), \phi'(x))\, dx,$$

since $y = \phi(x)$ on the interval $(\bar{x}, \bar{x} + \Delta\bar{x})$. Using the mean value theorem and the continuity of F, we get

$$\Delta I_2 = - [F(x, \phi, \phi')]_{x=\bar{x}} \cdot \Delta\bar{x} + \alpha\Delta\bar{x},$$

where $\alpha \to 0$ as $\Delta\bar{x} \to 0$. This gives

$$\delta I_2 = - [F(x, \phi, \phi')]_{x=\bar{x}} \cdot \Delta\bar{x}. \tag{2.26}$$

Combining (2.25) and (2.26), we find that

$$\delta I = [F(x, y, y') - F(x, y, \phi') - (y' - \phi')F_{y'}(x, y, y')]_{x=\bar{x}} \cdot \delta\bar{x}$$

with $y(\bar{x}) = \phi(\bar{x})$.

Since $\delta\bar{x}$ is arbitrary, it follows that the necessary condition $\delta I = 0$ for an extremum reduces to

$$[F(x, y, y') - F(x, y, \phi') - (y' - \phi')F_{y'}(x, y, y')]_{x=\bar{x}} = 0.$$

Applying the mean value theorem to this equation, we get

$$[(y' - \phi')\{F_{y'}(x, y, q) - F_{y'}(x, y, y')\}]_{x=\bar{x}} = 0. \tag{2.27}$$

where q lies between $y'(\bar{x})$ and $\phi'(\bar{x})$.

Applying the mean value theorem once more to (2.27), we finally obtain

$$[(y' - \phi')(q - y')F_{y'y'}(x, y, \bar{q})]_{x=\bar{x}} = 0$$

where $\bar{q}$ lies between q and $y'(\bar{x})$.

Assume $F_{y'y'}(x, y, \bar{q}) \neq 0$ (which is a valid assumption for many variational problems). In this case $y'(\bar{x}) = \phi'(\bar{x})$ because $q = y'$ only when $y'(\bar{x}) = \phi'(\bar{x})$.

Hence we conclude that at the point M, the extremal AM meets the boundary curve MN tangentially.

Example 4. Find the shortest path from the point $A(-2, 3)$ to the point $B(2, 3)$ located in the region $y \leq x^2$.

Solution. The problem is to find the extremum of the functional

$$I[y] = \int_{-2}^{2} [1 + y'^2(x)]^{1/2}\, dx$$

subject to the conditions

$$y \leq x^2, \quad y(-2) = 3, \quad y(2) = 3.$$

Clearly, the extremals of $I[y]$ are the straight lines $y = C_1 + C_2 x$.

If F is the integrand in $I[y]$, then $F_{y'y'}$ $(= [1 + y'^2(x)]^{3/2}) \neq 0$. Hence by the result of Section 2.3, the desired extremal will consist of portions of the straight lines AP and QB both tangent to the paraboa $y = x^2$ and of the portion POQ of the parabola (Fig. 2.5).

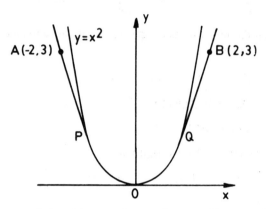

Fig. 2.5   Extremal through two given points outside a parabolic region.

Let the abscissae of P and Q be $-\bar{x}$ and $\bar{x}$, respectively. Then the condition of tangency of AP and BQ at P and Q demands

$$C_1 + C_2\bar{x} = \bar{x}^2, \qquad C_2 = 2\bar{x} \tag{2.28}$$

Since the tangent QB passes through $(2, 3)$,

$$C_1 + 2C_2 = 3. \tag{2.29}$$

Solution of (2.28) and (2.29) gives two values for $\bar{x}$ viz., $\bar{x}_1 = 1$ and $\bar{x}_2 = 3$. The second value is clearly inadmissible and so $\bar{x}_1 = 1$. This gives from (2.28) $C_1 = -1$, $C_2 = 2$. Thus the required extremal is

$$y = -2x - 1 \quad \text{if} - 2 \le x \le -1,$$
$$x^2 \qquad \text{if} - 1 \le x \le 1,$$
$$2x - 1 \quad \text{if } 1 \le x \le 2.$$

This obviously minimizes the functional.

2.4   Reflection and Refraction of Extremals

So far we have considered variational problems in which the desired function $y = y(x)$ is continuous with continuous derivatives. However, there do arise problems, where an extremum is achieved on curves (extremals), having corner points. Take for instance the problems involving reflection and refraction of extremals, which might be regarded as the generalization of the problems of reflection and refraction of light.

Let us begin by stating the problem of reflection of extremals: find the curve that extremizes the functional

$$I[y(x)] = \int_{x_1}^{x_2} F(x, y, y') \, dx$$

and passes through $A(x_1, y_1)$ and $B(x_2, y_2)$, the curve must arrive at B only after reflection from a given curve $y = f(x)$ (Fig. 2.6).

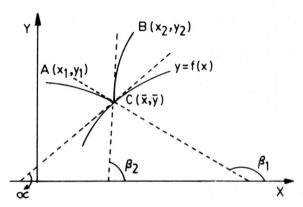

Fig. 2.6 Extremal through two given points after reflection from a given curve.

It is conceivable that at the point of reflection, $C(\bar{x}, \bar{y})$, the desired extremal may have a corner point so that $y'(\bar{x} - 0)$ and $y'(\bar{x} + 0)$ are, in general, distinct. Thus the functional I can be written as

$$I[y(x)] = \int_{x_1}^{\bar{x}} F(x, y, y') \, dx + \int_{\bar{x}}^{x_2} F(x, y, y') \, dx$$

so that the necessary condition for an extremum given by $\delta I = 0$ reduces to

$$\delta \int_{x_1}^{\bar{x}} F(x, y, y') \, dx + \delta \int_{\bar{x}}^{x_2} F(x, y, y') \, dx = 0. \qquad (2.30)$$

Evidently the curves AC and CB are both extremals because, if we assume that one of the curves is already found, and we vary the other one alone, then the problem reduces to finding the extremal of $\int_{x_1}^{\bar{x}} F \, dx \left(\text{or} \int_{\bar{x}}^{x_2} F \, dx \right)$ with fixed boundary points. Thus for calculating the variation of the functionals in (2.30), we will assume that the functionals are considered only on extremals with corner point C. Thus

$$\delta \int_{x_1}^{\bar{x}} F(x, y, y') \, dx = [F + (f' - y')F_{y'}]_{x=\bar{x} - 0} \cdot \delta x_1$$

$$\delta \int_{\bar{x}}^{x_2} F(x, y, y') \, dx = -[F + (f' - y')F_{y'}]_{x=\bar{x} + 0} \cdot \delta x_1.$$

Substituting the above expressions in (2.30) and remembering that δx_1 is arbitrary, we find that

$$[F + (f' - y')F_{y'}]_{x=x_1-0} = [F + (f' - y')F_{y'}]_{x=x_1+0}. \tag{2.31}$$

This relation assumes a particularly simple form for a functional of the form

$$I[y(x)] = \int_{x_1}^{x_2} A(x, y) \cdot (1 + y'^2)^{1/2} \, dx$$

In this case (2.31) becomes

$$A(x_1, y_1) \cdot \left[\sqrt{1 + y'^2} + \frac{(f' - y')y'}{\sqrt{1 + y'^2}} \right]_{x=x_1-0}$$

$$= A(x_1, y_1) \left[\sqrt{1 + y'^2} + \frac{(f' - y')y'}{\sqrt{1 + y'^2}} \right]_{x=x_1+0}$$

Assuming $A(x_1, y_1) \neq 0$, the above relation gives

$$[(1 + f'y')/\sqrt{1 + y'^2}]_{x=x_1-0} = [(1 + f'y')/\sqrt{1 + y'^2}]_{x=x_1+0}.$$

Referring to Fig. 2.6, we find that $y'(\bar{x} - 0) = \tan \beta_1$, $y'(\bar{x} + 0) = \tan \beta_2$, $f'(\bar{x}) = \tan \alpha$.

Thus the above reflection condition becomes

$$- (1 + \tan \alpha \cdot \tan \beta_1)/\sec \beta_1 = (1 + \tan \alpha \cdot \tan \beta_2)/\sec \beta_2$$

where the negative sign on the left arises because $\sec \beta_1 < 0$. On simplification the above equation gives

$$- \cos (\alpha - \beta_1) = \cos (\alpha - \beta_2)$$

which expresses the equality of the angle of incidence, and the angle of reflection.

As for the refraction of extremals, we consider the specific problem of refraction of light as follows. The velocity of light in medium 1 is v_1 (constant) while in medium 2, it is v_2 (constant). Medium 1 is separated from medium 2 by the curve $y = \phi(x)$. We wish to derive the law of refraction of a light ray traversing from a point A in medium 1 to a point B in medium 2 subject to the condition that the light ray traverses this path in the shortest time interval in accordance with Fermat's principle.

Clearly, the problem reduces to finding the minimum of the functional

$$I[y] = \int_a^c \frac{\sqrt{1 + y'^2}}{v_1} \, dx + \int_c^b \frac{\sqrt{1 + y'^2}}{v_2} \, dx$$

$$= \int_a^c F_1(y') \, dx + \int_c^b F_2(y') \, dx \tag{2.32}$$

where a and b are the abscissae of A and B and c is the abscissa of the point C, where the extremal from A to B meets the curve $y = \phi(x)$. It is conceivable that the extremum suffers a jump in slope at the point C. The necessary condition $\delta I = 0$ for an extremum, then becomes as in the case of reflection of extremals

$$[F_1 + (\phi' - y')F_{1y'}]_{x=c-0} = [F_2 + (\phi' - y')F_{2y'}]_{x=c+0} \qquad (2.33)$$

Since in the present problem F_1 and F_2 given by (2.32) are functions of y' only, the extremals are straight lines such that $y = y_1(x) = lx + m$ is the extremal in medium 1 and $y = y_2(x) = px + q$ is the extremal in medium 2, (l, m, p and q being constants). Substituting for F_1 and F_2 from (2.32) in (2.33), we get

$$(1 + \phi' y_1')/v_1 \cdot \sqrt{1 + y_1'^2} = (1 + \phi' y_2')/v_2 \cdot \sqrt{1 + y_2'^2} \qquad (2.34)$$

Let γ be the angle formed with the x-axis by the tangent to the boundary curve $y = \phi(x)$ at the point C, α, the angle of the left hand ray with the x-axis, and β, the angle of the right hand ray with the x-axis. Then $\phi' = \tan \gamma$, $y_1' = \tan \alpha$, $y_2' = \tan \beta$ so that the condition (2.34) reduces to

$$\frac{\cos (\gamma - \alpha)}{v_1} = \frac{\cos (\gamma - \beta)}{v_2}$$

where $\gamma - \alpha$ and $\gamma - \beta$ are the angles between the rays and the tangent to the boundary curve. Introducing in their place the angles θ and ϕ between the normal to the boundary curve, and the incident and refracted rays, we obtain the well known law of refraction of light (Snell's law) as

$$\frac{\sin \theta}{\sin \phi} = \frac{v_1}{v_2} = \text{constant.}$$

From the foregoing discussion it should not, however, be thought that a corner point (where there is a discontinuity in the slope) on an extremal occurs only in problems involving reflection and refraction of extremals. Such a point can, in fact, exist on an extremal of the functional

$$\int_{x_1}^{x_2} F(x, y, y') \, dx$$

where F is three times differentiable and the admissible curves pass through the given points $A(x_1, y_1)$ and $B(x_2, y_2)$.

Let us now determine the conditions that must be satisfied by the solutions of the extremum problems of the above functional. For simplicity, we assume that the extremal for this problem has just one corner point at $C(\bar{x}, \bar{y})$ as shown in Fig. 2.7. Now AC and CB are integral curves of Euler equation for the functional. If C moves in any fashion, we get from

$$I[y] = \int_{x_1}^{\bar{x}} F(x, y, y') \, dx + \int_{\bar{x}}^{x_2} F(x, y, y') \, dx,$$

the necessary condition $\delta I = 0$ for an extremum of I as

$$(F - y'F_{y'})_{x=\bar{x}-0} \cdot \delta \bar{x} + (F_{y'})_{x=\bar{x}-0} \cdot \delta \bar{y}$$

$$- (F - y'F_{y'})_{x=\bar{x}+0} \cdot \delta \bar{x} - (F_{y'})_{x=\bar{x}+0} \cdot \delta \bar{y} = 0$$

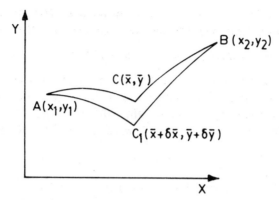

Fig. 2.7   Extremal having one corner point.

Since $\delta\bar{x}$ and $\delta\bar{y}$ are independent, we find from above that

$$(F - y'F_{y'})_{x=\bar{x}-0} = (F - y'F_{y'})_{x=\bar{x}+0} \qquad (2.35a)$$

and

$$(F_{y'})_{x=\bar{x}-0} = (F_{y'})_{x=\bar{x}+0} \qquad (2.35b)$$

These conditions (known as Weirstrass-Erdmann corner conditions) along with the continuity conditions of the desired extremal determine the coordinates of the corner point.

2.5   Diffraction of Light Rays

In Section 2.4, we have seen that the laws of geometrical optics involving reflection or refraction of light are characterized by variational principles. These are based on the assumption, that light travels along certain curves, (called rays) determined by Fermat's principle (see Example 8 of Chapter 1). But experience shows that while this theory is essentially correct, there are still many cases in which light appears in regions where there are no rays. This discrepancy between geometrical optics and experience accounts for the phenomenon of diffraction. However, geometrical optics can be suitably modified to include this new phenomenon. Such modification consists in introducing new rays, called diffracted rays, and can be formulated in terms of an extension of Fermat's principle (Keller, [9]).

Diffracted rays are generally produced, when a ray hits an edge or a vertex of a cone, or when a ray grazes an interface (between two media). Geometrical optics does not indicate what happens in these cases. At this stage we introduce diffracted rays. Once these rays are introduced, one can define diffracted wave fronts and the phase, or eiconal function by means of them. Let us cite an example in which the diffracted rays cover the shadows of ordinary geometrical optics. Consider an incident ray hitting the edge of a thin screen (Fig. 2.8). The incident ray produces many diffracted rays, travelling in the directions determined by laws of diffraction. This law states that each diffracted ray, which lies in the same medium as the incident ray, makes the same angle with the edge as does the

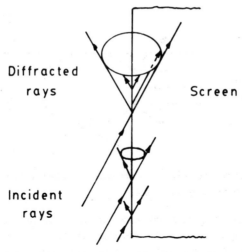

Fig. 2.8 The cone of diffracted rays produced by an incident ray which strikes the edge of a thin screen.

incident ray. Further, the incident and diffracted rays lie on opposite sides of the plane, normal to the edge at the point of diffraction. But the diffracted ray need not lie in the same plane, as the incident ray, and the edge. Hence the diffracted rays form the surface of a cone with its vertex at the point of diffraction (as in Fig. 2.8). If a diffracted ray and the incident ray lie in different media, the angle between the diffracted ray and the edge is connected with the angle between the incident ray and the edge by the Snell's law described in Section 2.4. Here also the diffracted ray is not restricted to lie in the same plane as the incident ray and the edge. Thus these diffracted rays also form a conical surface.

When an incident ray hits the vertex of an opaque cone, the diffracted rays emerge from the vertex in all directions as shown in Fig. 2.9.

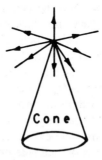

Fig. 2.9 Diffracted rays propagating in all directions from the tip of a cone.

Finally, Fig. 2.10 illustrates some of the diffracted rays produced when a plane wave hits an opaque convex cylinder. One of the grazing (tangent to the surface) rays is shown. This ray splits, part of it continuing unaffected, and the other part running along the surface. At each point of its path this surface ray sheds a diffracted ray tangent to the path.

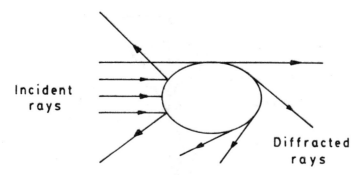

Fig. 2.10   Diffracted and reflected rays when a plane strikes an opaque convex
body at grazing incidence.

We now discuss the generalization of Fermat's variational principle mentioned
before. This principle can also be formulated in terms of the index of refraction
$n(x)$, which is a positive real function, characterizing the optical behaviour of the
medium. The optical length L of any curve connecting two points P and Q is defined
as

$$L = \int_P^Q n[x(s)] \, ds,$$

where the parameter s denotes the arc length. The link between this integral and
the one stated in the Example 7 of Chapter 1 is that $n = C_0/C$, where C_0 and C
are the velocities of light in a vacuum and the given medium, respectively. Thus
we may restate Fermat's principle as follows: the optical rays connecting P and
Q are those curves, joining P and Q, which make L stationary (or minimum) in
the class C^0 of all smooth curves joining P and Q. This principle does not apply
to a bounded medium or a medium where $n(x)$ is discontinuous. We have, however,
seen in Section 2.4, that in the case of reflection or refraction of light at the
interface between two media, we have to enlarge the class of curves, so as to
include class C^1. We can similarly introduce curves belonging to class C^r to
account for r-tuple reflected or refracted rays. However, this extended class of
curves still fails to take account of diffracted rays.

Hence we modify Fermat's principle by introducing additional classes of
curves. Let us define a class of curves D_{rst}, for each triplet of non-negative integers,
r, s and t. This consists of curves with r smooth arcs on the boundary or discontinuity
surfaces, s points on edges of the boundary or discontinuity surfaces, and t points
on vertices of these surfaces. Any number of r arcs may be degenerate arcs, i.e.,
points. To each arc the value of n on one side of the surface is assigned. In the
modified Fermat's principle, we define the rays as those curves in each class D_{rst},
which make the optical length defined above stationary in D_{rst}. Clearly, the class
D_{000} is the previously considered class C^0 and D_{r00} contains the class C^1 and
represents singly reflected/refracted rays. With this modified Fermat's principle,
we can show by the usual considerations of calculus of variations that it takes care
of reflection, refraction and diffraction of light rays.

Example 5. Find the extremals with corner points of the functional

$$I[y(x)] = \int_{x_1}^{x_2} y'^2 (1 - y')^2 \, dx$$

Solution. Since the integrand depends on y' only, the extremals are straight lines $y = C_1 x + C_2$. Now at a corner point, the conditions (2.35a) and (2.35b) become

$$[y'^2(1 - y') (1 - 3y')]_{x=\bar{x}-0} = [y'^2(1 - y') (1 - 3y')]_{x=\bar{x}+0}$$

$$[y'(1 - y') (1 - 2y')]_{x=\bar{x}-0} = [y'(1 - y') (1 - 2y')]_{x=\bar{x}+0}$$

If we ignore the trivial possibility, $y'(\bar{x} - 0) = y'(\bar{x} + 0)$, we find that the above equations are satisfied for either

$$y'(\bar{x} - 0) = 0, \quad y'(\bar{x} + 0) = 1$$

or

$$y'(\bar{x} - 0) = 1, \quad y'(\bar{x} + 0) = 0$$

Thus the broken line extremals consist of segments of straight lines belonging to the families $y = A_1$ and $y = x + A_2$ as shown in Fig. 2.11.

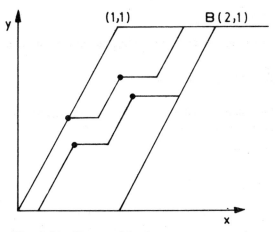

Fig. 2.11 Extremal having two corner points.

If the integrand in $I[y(x)]$ is denoted by F, then

$$F_{y'y'} = 2y'(1 - y') (1 - 2y')$$

which may vanish. This is a possible indication of the existence of a corner point. In fact by du Bois Reymond's theorem (see Section 1.9), the extremal is twice continuously differentiable if $F_{y'y'} \neq 0$.

PROBLEMS

1. Find the function on which the following functional can be extremized

$$I[y(x)] = \int_0^1 (y''^2 - 2xy)\, dx,\ y(0) = y'(0) = 0,$$

y(1) = 1/120 and y'(1) is not given.

Ans. $y = \dfrac{x^5}{120} + \dfrac{1}{24}(x^2 - x^3).$

2. Are there any solutions with corner points in the extremum of the functional

$$I[y(x)] = \int_0^{x_1} (y'^4 - 6y'^2)\, dx,\ y(0) = 0,\ y(x_1) = y_1\,?$$

Ans.   The polygonal lines passing through the given boundary points consist of rectilinear segments with slopes $\sqrt{3}$ and $-\sqrt{3}$.

3. Determine the stationary function y(x) for the problem

$$\delta\left\{ \int_0^1 y'^2\, dx + [y(1)]^2 \right\} = 0 \text{ with } y(0) = 1.$$

Ans. $y = 1 - \dfrac{x}{2}.$

4. Find the curves on which the following functional can attain an extremum

$$I[y] = \int_0^{10} y'^3\, dx,\quad y(0) = 0,\quad y(10) = 0$$

subject to the condition that the admissible curves cannot pass inside the area bounded by the circle

$(x - 5)^2 + y^2 = 9$

Ans. $y(x) = \pm \dfrac{3}{4} x \ \text{ for } 0 \le x \le \dfrac{16}{5}$

$y(x) = \pm \sqrt{9 - (x - 5)^2} \ \text{ for } \dfrac{16}{5} < x \le \dfrac{34}{5}$

$y(x) = \pm \dfrac{3}{4}(x - 10) \qquad \text{for } \dfrac{34}{5} < x \le 10.$

5. If l is not pre-assigned, show that the stationary functions corresponding to the problem

$$\delta \int_0^l y'^2\, dx = 0,\quad y(0) = 2,\quad y(l) = \sin l$$

are of the form $y = 2 + 2x \cos l$, where l satisfies

$2 + 2l \cos l - \sin l = 0.$

CHAPTER 3

SUFFICIENT CONDITIONS FOR AN EXTREMUM

3.1 Field of Extremals

A family of curves $y = y(x, C)$ is said to form a proper field in a given domain D of the xy-plane if through any point of D there passes one and only one curve of the family. For example inside the circle $x^2 + y^2 = 1$, the family of curves $y = Ce^x$ (C is an arbitrary constant) forms a proper field since through any point of the above circle there passes one and only one curve of the family (see Fig. 3.1).

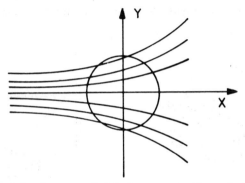

Fig. 3.1 A proper field of curves inside a circle.

The curves of the family of parabolas $y = (x + C)^2$ inside $x^2 + y^2 = 1$, however, do not constitute a proper field because different curves of the family intersect inside the circle (see Fig. 3.2).

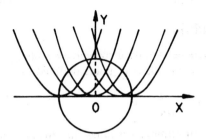

Fig. 3.2 A family of parabolas not forming a field inside a circle.

If, on the other hand, all the curves of the family $y = y(x, C)$ pass through a single point (x_0, y_0), then they are said to constitute a central field over a domain D if these curves cover D without self intersection and the point (x_0, y_0) lies outside

D. The point (x_0, y_0) is called the centre of the pencil of curves. For instance, the family of curves $y = Cx$ forms a central field in the domain $x > 0$.

If a field (proper or central) is formed by a family of extremals, then this is called a field of extremals.

Let $y = y(x)$ be an extremal of the variational problem concerning the extremum of

$$I[y(x)] = \int_{x_1}^{x_2} F(x, y, y') \, dx \tag{3.1}$$

and let the boundary points $A(x_1, y_1)$ and $B(x_2, y_2)$ be fixed. We say that the extremal $y = y(x)$ is embedded in an extremal field if a family of extremals $y = y(x, C)$ can be found such that this family forms a field with the curve $y = y(x)$ as a member of this field for some value of $C = C_0$, say, and the extremal does not lie on the boundary of the domain D in which $y = y(x, C)$ forms a field (Fig. 3.3).

Similarly, if a pencil of extremals emanating from the point $A(x_1, y_1)$ forms a central field including the extremal $y = y(x)$, then this curve AB is said to be embedded in a central field of extremals (Fig. 3.4). In this case the parameter of the family of curves forming the field can be taken as the slope of the tangent line to the curves at A.

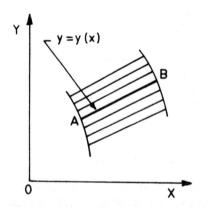

Fig. 3.3   An extremal embedded in   Fig. 3.4   An extremal embedded in a
an extremal field.   central field.

3.2   Jacobi Condition

Consider the one-parameter family of plane curves $\phi(x, y, C) = 0$. The C-discriminant of this family is the locus of points defined by

$$\phi(x, y, C) = 0, \qquad \frac{\partial \phi}{\partial C} = 0$$

In general, the C-discriminant includes the envelope of the above family of curves, the locus of nodal points and the locus of cusps. If we have a pencil of curves with centre at $A(x_1, y_1)$, then A belongs to the C-discriminant.

Consider a pencil of extremals $y = y(x, C)$ passing through $A(x_1, y_1)$ such that its C-discriminant is the curve $\Phi(x, y) = 0$. Clearly, the envelope Γ of this pencil of curves belongs to $\Phi(x, y) = 0$. The point A_1 where the extremal (given by $y = y(x)$) touches Γ is called the conjugate point of A. It is clear (see Fig. 3.5) that if the point $B(x_2, y_2)$ lies between A and A_1, then the extremals of the pencil close to AB do not intersect. Thus the extremals close to AB form a central field which includes the arc AB.

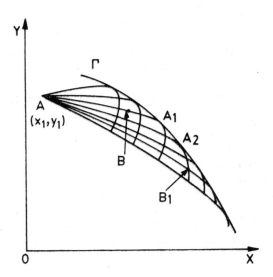

Fig. 3.5   A pencil of extremals with their envelope.

On the other hand, for the extremal AB_1 (for which the conjugate point A_2 of A lies between A and B_1), the curves of the pencil close to AB_1 intersect. Thus in this case the extremal AB_1 cannot be embedded in a central field.

We may sum up the above discussion as follows: In order to be able to embed an arc AB of the extremal in a central field of extremals, it is sufficient that the conjugate point of A does not lie on the arc. This is known as the Jacobi condition. This condition can be mathematically stated as follows: Let $y = y(x, C)$ be the equation of a pencil of extremals with centre at A such that the parameter C, for definiteness, can be regarded as the slope y' of the extremals of the pencil at A. The C-discriminant of the pencil is given by

$$y = y(x, C), \qquad \partial y/\partial C = 0$$

Along every fixed curve of the family, $\partial y(x, C)/\partial C$ is a function of x only. Denote $\partial y(x, C)/\partial C$ by u, where C is fixed. Since $y = y(x, C)$ is a solution of Euler equation for the extremum of $I[y(x)]$ in (3.1), we have

$$F_y(x, y(x, C), y_x'(x, C)) - \frac{d}{dx} F_{y'}(x, y(x, C), y_x'(x, C)) \equiv 0$$

Differentiating this identity with respect to C, we get

$$\left(F_{yy} - \frac{d}{dx} F_{yy'} \right) u - \frac{d}{dx}(F_{y'y'} u') = 0 \tag{3.2}$$

This second-order equation in u is known as the Jacobi equation.

Here, $F_{yy}(x,y,y')$, $F_{yy'}$ and $F_{y'y'}$ are known functions of x since the second argument y is a solution of Euler equation with $C = C_0$ (given) for the extremal AB.

If the solution $u = \partial y / \partial C$, which vanishes at $A(x_1, y_1)$—since the centre of the pencil belongs to the C-discriminant curve—also vanishes at some point of the interval $x_1 < x < x_2$, then the point conjugate to A defined by $y = y(x, C_0)$ and $(\partial y / \partial C)_{C=C_0} = 0$ lies on the arc AB of the extremal with B at the point (x_2, y_2). But if there exists a solution of (3.2) which vanishes for $x = x_1$ and does not further vanish at any point in $x_1 \le x \le x_2$, then clearly there are no points conjugate to A lying on the arc AB. Hence the Jacobi condition is satisfied and the arc AB of the extremal can be embedded in a central field of extremals with centre at A.

Example 1.   Is the Jacobi condition fulfilled for the extremal of the functional

$$I[y(x)] = \int_0^a (y'^2 + y^2 + x^2)\, dx$$

passing through $A\ (0, 0)$ and $B(a, 0)$?

Solution.   Clearly in this case the Jacobi equation (3.2) reduces to $u'' - u = 0$, whose solution is $u = C_1 \sinh x + C_2 \cosh x$. Using $u(0) = 0$, we find $C_2 = 0$ so that $u = C_1 \sinh x$. Evidently the curves of the pencil $u = C_1 \sinh x$ intersect the x-axis only at $x = 0$. Thus we conclude that the Jacobi condition is satisfied for any value of a.

3.3   Weirstrass Function

Consider the extremum of the functional

$$I[y(x)] = \int_{x_1}^{x_2} F(x,\, y,\, y')\, dx, \qquad y(x_1) = y_1, \qquad y(x_2) = y_2 \qquad (3.3)$$

Further, suppose that the extremal C through $A(x_1, y_1)$ and $B(x_2, y_2)$ satisfies the Jacobi condition so that C can be embedded in a central field whose slope is $p(x, y)$. Of course, an extremal can be considered as embedded in a proper field as well. We determine the sign of the increment ΔI of the functional I while passing from the extremal C of a neighbouring admissible curve $\bar{C}$ (Fig. 3.6).

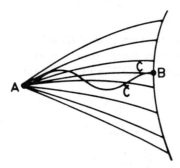

Fig. 3.6   An extremal embedded in a central field and a neighbouring curve.

Consider the functional

$$\int_{\bar{C}} \left[F(x, y, p) + \left(\frac{dy}{dx} - p \right) F_p(x, y, p) \right] dx \tag{3.4}$$

This obviously reduces to $\int_C F(x, y, y')\, dx$ on the extremal C, where $dy/dx = p$. Further, the functional (3.4) can be written as

$$\int_{\bar{C}} \{[F(x, y, p) - pF_p(x, y, p)]\, dx + F_p(x, y, p)\, dy\}, \tag{3.5}$$

which is the integral of an exact differential. In fact, the differential of the function $\bar{I}(x, y)$ into which the functional $I[y(x)]$ is transformed on the extremals of the field has the form (see (2.6))

$$d\bar{I} = [F(x, y, y') - y'F_{y'}(x, y, y')]\, dx + F_{y'}\, dy,$$

which differs from the integrand in (3.5) with y' replaced by p, the slope of the tangent line to the extremals. Now since the integrand in (3.5) is an exact differential, the integral is independent of the path of integration and is known as Hilbert's independence integral. Thus we have

$$\int_{\bar{C}} [F(x, y, p) + (y' - p)F_p(x, y, p)]\, dx = \int_C F(x, y, y')\, dx \tag{3.6}$$

for any choice of the curve $\bar{C}$. Hence by using (3.5), the increment

$$\Delta I = \int_{\bar{C}} F(x, y, y')\, dx - \int_C F(x, y, y')\, dx$$

can be written as

$$\Delta I = \int_{\bar{C}} [F(x, y, y') - F(x, y, p) - (y' - p)F_p(x, y, p)]\, dx$$

$$= \int_{x_1}^{x_2} E(x, y, p, y')\, dx, \tag{3.7}$$

where

$$E(x, y, p, y') = F(x, y, y') - F(x, y, p) - (y' - p)F_p(x, y, p) \tag{3.8}$$

and $E(x, y, p, y')$ is known as the Weirstrass function.

It is now clear from (3.7) that a sufficient condition for I to attain a minimum on the extremal C is $E \geq 0$ since it implies $\Delta I \geq 0$. Similarly, a sufficient condition for a maximum is $E \leq 0$ since then $\Delta I \leq 0$. Further, a sufficient condition for a weak minimum is that $E \geq 0$ is satisfied for values of x, y close to the values of x, y on the extremal and for values of y' close to $p(x, y)$ on the same extremal. But the sufficient condition for a strong minimum is that $E \geq 0$ is satisfied for all values of x, y close to the corresponding values on the extremal with values of y' arbitrary (so that y' need not be close to $p(x, y)$ on the extremal).

We may thus summarize our results on sufficient conditions for an extremum of a functional given by (3.3) as follows:

(a) *Weak extremum*   1. The curve C is an extremal satisfying the boundary conditions in (3.3).

2. The extremal C must be embeddable in a field of extremals. Alternatively, the Jacobi condition must be satisfied.

3. The Weirstrass function E does not change sign at a point (x, y) close to the curve C and for values of y' close to $p(x, y)$ on the extremal. Clearly, $E \geq 0$ for a minimum and $E \leq 0$ for a maximum.

(b) *Strong extremum*   1. The curve C is an extremal satisfying the boundary conditions in (3.3).

2. It should be possible to embed the extremal in a field of extremals (or Jacobi condition is fulfilled).

3. The function E does not change sign at any point (x, y) close to the curve C and for arbitrary values of y'. For a minimum, $E \geq 0$ and for a maximum $E \leq 0$.

A Link with Elementary Convexity

It is interesting to note that the significance of the Weirstrass condition $E \geq 0$ (or $E \leq 0$) described above can be understood in geometrical terms. If we regard $F(x, y, y')$ for fixed (x, y) as a function $f(\xi)$ with $y' = \xi$, then the condition $E \geq 0$ with E given by (3.8) implies that $f(\xi) \geq l(\xi)$, where $l(\xi)$ is the linear function that agrees with f at $\xi = p$ and whose graph touches that of f at this point. This statement merely corresponds to one of the several definitions of convexity, the so called 'arc above tangent' (see [6]) definition. We say that the $f(\xi)$ is convex at $\xi = p$ if a linear function $l(\xi)$ exists such that $l(\xi) \leq f(\xi)$ for all ξ with equality at $\xi = p$. If f is differentiable, then l is necessarily tangent at this point (see Fig. 3.7).

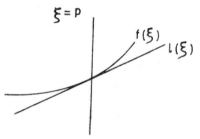

Fig. 3.7   Convexity of the function $F(x, y, \xi)$ for fixed (x, y) at $\xi = p$.

What is interesting here is that this definition of convexity is directly linked with the Weirstrass condition $E \geq 0$. We can simply say that $E \geq 0$ implies that F is convex in dy/dx at $dy/dx = p$. As a matter of fact, convexity and concavity of certain functionals are closely linked to the existence of maxima and minima of functionals.

Example 2. Investigate for an extremum the functional

$$I[Y(x)] = \int_0^1 \left(x + 2y + \frac{1}{2} y'^2 \right) dx, \quad y(0) = 0, \quad y(1) = 0.$$

Solution. The Euler equation for this functional is $y'' = 2$ whose solution satisfying the boundary conditions is $y = x^2 - x$. Now in this case the Jacobi equation (3.2) is $u'' = 0$. Its solution satisfying $u(0) = 0$ is $u(x) = Cx$. Since $u(x) = Cx$ does not vanish (for $C \neq 0$) anywhere in $[0, 1]$ except $x = 0$, it follows that the Jacobi condition is fulfilled and the extremal $y = x^2 - x$ can be embedded in the central field of extremals given by $y = x^2 + C_1 x$ with centre at the origin $(0, 0)$ (see Fig. 3.8).

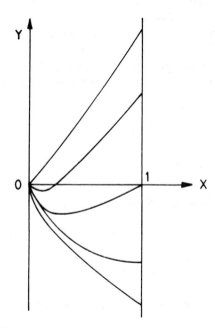

Fig. 3.8 The minimizing curve embedded in a central field.

Now the Weirstrass function is $E(x, y, p, y') = \frac{1}{2} (y' - p)^2$. Clearly, $E \geq 0$ for arbitrary y'. Thus a strong minimum (equal to $I[x^2 - x] = 1/3$) is attained on the extremal $y = x^2 - x$.

3.4 Legendre Condition

In some variational problems, testing the sign of E may pose some difficulties, That is why an alternative condition which is readily verifiable is desirable. We assume that the function $F(x, y, y')$ is thrice differentiable with respect to y'. Then by Taylor's formula, we have

$$F(x, y, y') = F(x, y, p) + (y' - p) F_p(x, y, p) + \frac{1}{2} (y' - p)^2 F_{y'y'}(x, y, q),$$

$$(3.9)$$

where q lies between y' and p. Thus from (3.8),

$$E(x, y, p, y') = \frac{1}{2} (y' - p)^2 F_{y'y'}(x, y, q). \tag{3.10}$$

Hence the sign of E is the same as that of $F_{y'y'}(x, y, q)$. For a weak extremum, therefore, $F_{y'y'}(x, y, q)$ must retain its sign for values of x and y close to the points of extremal under consideration and for values of q close to $p(x, y)$. Now if $F_{y'y'}(x, y, y') \neq 0$ at all points of the extremal C, then by virtue of continuity, $F_{y'y'}(x, y, y')$ maintains its sign at points close to the curve C and for values of y' close to values of y' on C. Thus for testing for a weak minimum, the condition $E \geq 0$ may be replaced by $F_{y'y'} > 0$ on the extremal C and for testing for a weak maximum, the condition $E \leq 0$ may be replaced by $F_{y'y'} < 0$ on C. This is known as the Legendre condition.

On the other hand, if $F_{y'y'}(x, y, q) \geq 0$ at points (x, y) close to points of C and for arbitrary values of q, then (3.10) implies that a strong minimum is attained on C. Of course, here it is assumed that the formula (3.9) holds good for any y'.

The above results can be readily extended to functionals of the form

$$I[y_1(x), y_2(x), \ldots, y_n(x)] = \int_{x_1}^{x_2} F(x, y_1, y_2, \ldots, y_n, y_1', \ldots, y_n') \, dx$$

subject to

$$y_i(x_1) = y_{i1}, \qquad y_i(x_2) = y_{i2}.$$

In this case the Weirstrass function is

$$E = F(x, y_1, y_2, \ldots, y_n, y_1', y_2', \ldots, y_n') - F(x, y_1, y_2, \ldots, y_n, p_1, p_2, \ldots, p_n)$$

$$- \sum_{i=1}^{n} (y_i' - p_i) F_{p_i}(x, y_1, y_2, \ldots, y_n, p_1, p_2, \ldots, p_n),$$

where p_i are the slope functions of the field. The Legendre condition in this case becomes

$$F_{y_1'y_1'} \geq 0, \qquad \begin{vmatrix} F_{y_1'y_1'} & F_{y_1'y_2'} \\ F_{y_2'y_1'} & F_{y_2'y_2'} \end{vmatrix} \geq 0, \ldots,$$

$$\begin{vmatrix} F_{y_1'y_1'} & F_{y_1'y_2'} & \cdots & F_{y_1'y_n'} \\ F_{y_2'y_1'} & F_{y_2'y_2'} & \cdots & F_{y_2'y_n'} \\ \vdots & \vdots & & \vdots \\ F_{y_n'y_1'} & F_{y_n'y_2'} & \cdots & F_{y_n'y_n'} \end{vmatrix} \geq 0.$$

Example 3.   Test for an extremum the functional

$$I[y] = \int_0^2 (e^{y'} + 3) \, dx, \qquad y(0) = 0, \qquad y(2) = 1.$$

Solution. The extremals are clearly the straight lines $y = C_1 x + C_2$. The extremal satisfying the boundary conditions is $y = x/2$. It can certainly be embedded in the central field of extremals $y = Cx$. Here, $F_{y'y'} = e^{y'} > 0$ for all y'. Thus a strong minimum is attained on $y = x/2$.

3.5 Second Variation

It is instructive to note that the sufficient conditions for a weak extremum may be derived by a technique based on the sign of the second variation of the functional (3.3).

$$\Delta I = \int_{x_1}^{x_2} [F(x, y + \delta y, y' + \delta y') - F(x, y, y')] \, dx$$

$$= \int_{x_1}^{x_2} [F_y \, \delta y + F_{y'} \, \delta y'] \, dx + \frac{1}{2} \int_{x_1}^{x_2} [F_{yy}(\delta y)^2$$

$$+ 2F_{yy'}\delta y \cdot \delta y' + F_{y'y'}(\delta y')^2] \, dx + R, \qquad (3.11a)$$

where R is of order higher than second in δy and $\delta y'$. On the extremal, the first variation represented by the first term on the right of (3.11a) vanishes. Hence for investigating weak extremum (for which both δy and $\delta y'$ are small), (3.11a) shows that the sign of ΔI coincides with that of $\delta^2 I$, the second variation being given by

$$\delta^2 I = \int_{x_1}^{x_2} [F_{yy}(\delta y)^2 + 2F_{yy'}\delta y \cdot \delta y' + F_{y'y'}(\delta y')^2] \, dx. \qquad (3.11b)$$

Consider the integral involving the differentiable function $G(x)$:

$$\int_{x_1}^{x_2} [G'(x) \cdot (\delta y)^2 + 2G(x) \cdot \delta y \cdot \delta y'] \, dx, \qquad (3.12)$$

which vanishes by virtue of the boundary conditions (3.3) because the integral is

$$\int_{x_1}^{x_2} d(G(x) \cdot (\delta y)^2) = [G(x) \cdot (\delta y)^2]_{x_1}^{x_2} = 0.$$

Adding (3.12) to the second variation above, we get

$$\delta^2 I = \int_{x_1}^{x_2} [(F_{yy} + G') \, (\delta y)^2 + 2 \, (F_{yy'} + G) \, \delta y \cdot \delta y' + F_{y'y'}(\delta y')^2] \, dx \qquad (3.13)$$

The integrand is a perfect square if

$$F_{y'y'}(F_{yy} + G') - (F_{yy'} + G)^2 = 0. \qquad (3.14)$$

For such a choice of G, (3.13) gives

$$\delta^2 I = \int_{x_1}^{x_2} F_{y'y'} \left[\delta y' + \frac{F_{yy'} + G}{F_{y'y'}} \cdot \delta y \right]^2 dx.$$

Thus the sign of $\delta^2 I$ is the same as that of $F_{y'y'}$. But such a transformation is possible provided (3.14) admits of a differentiable solution $G(x)$.

Substituting $G(x) = - F_{yy'} - (F_{y'y'} \cdot u'/u)$ in (3.14) leads to

$$\left(F_{yy} - \frac{d}{dx} F_{yy'} \right) u - \frac{d}{dx} (F_{y'y'} u') = 0,$$

which is the Jacobi equation derived earlier. If a solution u of this equation exists that does not vanish in $[x_1, x_2]$, i.e., if the Jacobi condition is satisfied, then clearly there exists a differential function $G(x)$ satisfying (3.14). Thus fulfilment of both Legendre and Jacobi conditions ensures that the sign of second variation $\delta^2 I$ does not change. Hence they constitute sufficient conditions for a weak minimum ($F_{y'y'} > 0$) or weak maximum ($F_{y'y'} < 0$).

Another sufficient condition for the minimum of functional specified on a normed space is as follows (see Gelfand and Fomin [10]): For a functional $I[Y(x)]$ defined on a normed space (with norm $\| \cdot \|$) to have a minimum at a stationary point $y = y_0(x)$, it is sufficient that the second variation $\delta^2 I[y_0, \delta y, \delta y']$ defined by (3.11b) satisfies the condition

$$\delta^2 I[y_0, \delta y, \delta y'] \geq k \parallel \delta y \parallel^2,$$

where k is a positive constant.

Example 4:   *Euler's problem on buckling*   If a rod simply supported at one end is compressed by a longitudinal force P acting at the other end, it is then in either stable or unstable equilibrium. This means that after a slight lateral bending, it will either return to its equilibrium position or buckle, depending on whether the magnitude of P is less than or greater than a certain critical value P_0. The problem is to determine the buckling force P_0 (see [3a]).

Solution.   In equilibrium the rod is of length l and if its lateral deflection is denoted by $u(x)$ ($0 \leq x \leq l$), then its potential energy V is

$$V = \frac{1}{2} \int_0^l [EI (u'')^2 - P(u')^2] \, dx, \tag{3.15}$$

where the first term on the right is the energy of bending and the second term represents the potential energy of elongation (as in the case of a string). Here, E is the modulus of elasticity and I is the moment of inertia of the cross-section of the rod.

For sufficiently small values of P, the minimum of V subject to $u(0) = u(l)$ $= 0$ is zero. This is in fact true for $P/EI < 1/l^2$ and can be seen as follows: Since

$$\int_0^l u' \, dx = 0, \text{ a point } x_0 \text{ exists for which } u'(x_0) = 0. \text{ Hence}$$

$$u'(x) = \int_{x_0}^x u''(x) \, dx$$

and then by the Schwarz inequality

$$(u')^2 = \left(\int_{x_0}^x u'' \, dx \right)^2 \le \int_{x_0}^x dx \int_{x_0}^x (u'')^2 \, dx \le l \int_0^l (u'')^2 \, dx$$

leading to

$$\int_0^l (u')^2 \, dx \le l^2 \int_0^l (u'')^2 \, dx$$

Hence from (3.15) and the inequality $P/EI < 1/l^2$, it follows that $V \ge 0$. But for large P, V can be negative by choosing, for example, a P satisfying

$$P \int_0^l (u')^2 \, dx > EI \int_0^l (u'')^2 \, dx$$

for an admissible function u. The buckling force P_0 is the largest value of P for which the minimum of V is zero.

Putting $u' = \phi$, the minimum of V reduces to that of

$$V[\phi] = \frac{1}{2} \int_0^l [EI(\phi')^2 - P\phi^2] \, dx$$

$$= \frac{1}{2} \int_0^l F(\phi, \phi') \, dx, \quad \text{say} \tag{3.16}$$

Its Euler equation

$$\phi'' + \alpha^2 \phi = 0 \text{ with } \alpha^2 = P/EI$$

has the solution

$$\phi = C_1 \sin \alpha x + C_2 \cos \alpha x,$$

which gives from $\phi = u'$,

$$u = -\frac{C_1}{\alpha} \cos \alpha x + \frac{C_2}{\alpha} \sin \alpha x + C_3. \tag{3.17}$$

Since the lower end $x = 0$ of the rod is simply supported, $u''(0) = 0$ so that (3.17) gives, along with $u(0) = 0$, the relation

$$y(x) = (C_2/\alpha) \sin \alpha x,$$

which is the desired extremal. Let us verify whether the Legendre and Jacobi conditions are satisfied or not. From (3.16), we get $\partial^2 F / \partial \phi'^2 = EI > 0$ and hence the Legendre condition is fulfilled. Now using (3.2), the Jacobi equation is

$$EI\Psi'' + P\Psi = 0$$

whose solution satisfying $\Psi(0) = 0$ is

$$\Psi(x) = A \sin \alpha x.$$

This vanishes at $x = k\pi/\alpha$ ($k = 1, 2, \ldots$). Hence the Jacobi condition is fulfilled if $\pi/\alpha \geq l$. Thus, using $\alpha^2 = P/EI$, we find that the critical force P_0 for buckling is

$$P_0 = \frac{\pi^2}{l^2} \cdot EI.$$

3.6 Canonical Equations and Variational Principles

In several problems of physics and mechanics it is convenient to recast Euler's equations in canonical form, which makes possible a general approach to variational problems. Further, the new variables introduced in the process admit of a simple physical interpretation.

Consider the extremum of the functional

$$I[y_1, y_2, \ldots, y_n] = \int_{x_1}^{x_2} F(x, y_1, y_2, \ldots, y_n, y_1', y_2', \ldots, y_n') \, dx, \qquad (3.18)$$

where $y_1(x), \ldots, y_n(x)$ satisfy certain boundary conditions at x_1 and x_2. The Euler equations are

$$F_{y_i} - \frac{d}{dx} F_{y_i'} = 0 \qquad (i = 1, 2, \ldots, n), \qquad (3.19)$$

which constitute a system of n ordinary differential equations in $y_1, y_2, \ldots, y_n$. We introduce

$$p_i = F_{y_i'}(x, y_1, \ldots, y_n, y_1', \ldots, y_n'), \qquad i = 1, 2, \ldots, n, \qquad (3.20)$$

which together with y_i ($i = 1, 2, \ldots, n$) are called canonical variables for the above functional. The variables y_i and p_i are known as canonically conjugate variables. Then (3.19) gives

$$\frac{dp_i}{dx} = \frac{\partial F}{\partial y_i} \qquad (i = 1, 2, \ldots, n). \qquad (3.21)$$

Now, if the Jacobian

$$\frac{D(F_{y_1'}, F_{y_2'}, \ldots, F_{y_n'})}{D(y_1', y_2', \ldots, y_n')} \neq 0,$$

then the system of equations (3.20) can be solved as

$$y_i' = \omega_i(x, y_1, \ldots, y_n, p_1, \ldots, p_n).$$

When these are substituted into (3.21), we get a system of first-order equations as

$$\frac{dy_i}{dx} = \omega_i(x, y_1, ..., y_n, p_1, ..., p_n), \qquad \frac{dp_i}{dx} = \left\{\frac{\partial F}{\partial y_i}\right\} \tag{3.22}$$

with $i = 1, 2, ..., n$. Henceforward, the parentheses in the second equation of (3.22) signify that y_i' in F are replaced by ω_i.

We now introduce the Hamiltonian function

$$H(x, y_1, ..., y_n, p_1, ..., p_n) = \sum_{i=1}^{n} \omega_i p_i - \{F\} \tag{3.23}$$

Then the system (3.22) can be written as

$$\frac{dy_i}{dx} = \frac{\partial H}{\partial p_i}, \qquad \frac{dp_i}{dx} = -\frac{\partial H}{\partial y_i} \qquad (i = 1, 2, ..., n). \tag{3.24}$$

This system is referred to as the Hamiltonian (canonical) system of Euler's equations and consists of $2n$ ordinary differential equations in $2n$ unknown functions $y_i(x)$ and $p_i(x)$ ($i = 1, 2, ..., n$).

It is interesting to note that according to Weirstrass-Erdmann corner conditions (discussed in Section 2.4), p_i ($i = 1, 2, ..., n$) and H are the quantities which vary continuously together with x and y_i ($i = 1, 2, ..., n$) when the variable point passes through a corner point of a piecewise smooth extremal. In fact, we can write an arbitrary variation of the functional $I[y_1, ..., y_n]$ in the vector form

$$\delta \int_{x_1}^{x_2} F(x, \mathbf{y}, \mathbf{y}') \, dx = \int_{x_1}^{x_2} \left(F_{\mathbf{y}} - \frac{d}{dx} F_{\mathbf{y}'}\right) \cdot \delta\mathbf{y} \, dx$$

$$+ (\mathbf{p} \cdot \delta\mathbf{y}(x) - H \, \delta x)_{x=x_1}^{x_2} \tag{3.25}$$

and take into account the method of deriving the corner conditions discussed in Section 2.4.

3.7 Complementary Variational Principles

An interesting application of Hamilton's canonical equations (3.24) can be found in the formulation of complementary variational principles first introduced by B. Noble in 1964 (see Arthurs [11]). These principles provide a systematic approach to several linear and nonlinear boundary-value problems involving differential or integral equations.

In this section we give an introduction to the basic concepts of complementary variational principles and illustrate these ideas by considering a simple boundary value problem.

Consider the functional

$$E(U(x), \Phi(x)) = \int_a^b L(x, U, \Phi, U', \Phi') \, dx. \tag{3.26}$$

Suppose $U = u$ and $\Phi = \phi$ render the above functional stationary so that u and ϕ satisfy

$$\frac{\partial L}{\partial U} - \frac{d}{dx}\left(\frac{\partial L}{\partial U'}\right) = 0, \qquad \frac{\partial L}{\partial \Phi} - \frac{d}{dx}\left(\frac{\partial L}{\partial \Phi'}\right) = 0. \tag{3.27}$$

The trial functions U and Φ in (3.26) satisfy certain boundary conditions. Let us now introduce the Hamiltonian $H(x, U, \Phi)$ such that

$$L = U\frac{d\Phi}{dx} - H(x, U, \Phi). \tag{3.28}$$

With this choice, equations (3.27) become

$$\frac{d\Phi}{dx} = \frac{\partial H}{\partial U}, \qquad -\frac{dU}{dx} = \frac{\partial H}{\partial \Phi} \tag{3.29}$$

These are Hamilton's canonical equations which we have considered in Section 3.6.

We now introduce the differentiable functional

$$I(U, \Phi) = \int_a^b \left[U\frac{d\Phi}{dx} - H(x, U, \Phi)\right] dx + [\Gamma(U, \Phi) - U\Phi]_a^b, \tag{3.30}$$

where Γ is a boundary function to be specified later on. Taking small variations about u and ϕ by putting

$$U = u + \varepsilon\eta, \qquad \Phi = \phi + \varepsilon\xi \tag{3.31}$$

in (3.30), we get

$$I(U, \Phi) = I(u, \phi) + \delta I + \delta^2 I + 0(\varepsilon^3) \tag{3.32}$$

where

$$\delta I = \varepsilon \int_a^b \left[u\xi' + \eta\phi' - \xi\left(\frac{\partial H}{\partial \Phi}\right)_{u,\phi} - \eta\left(\frac{\partial H}{\partial U}\right)_{u,\phi}\right] dx$$

$$+ \varepsilon\left[\eta\left(\frac{\partial \Gamma}{\partial U}\right)_{u,\phi} + \xi\left(\frac{\partial \Gamma}{\partial \Phi}\right)_{u,\phi} - u\xi - \eta\phi\right]_a^b \tag{3.33}$$

$$\delta^2 I = \frac{\varepsilon^2}{2}\int_a^b\left[-2\eta'\xi - \eta^2\left(\frac{\partial^2 H}{\partial U^2}\right)_{u,\phi} - 2\eta\xi\left(\frac{\partial^2 H}{\partial U\partial\Phi}\right)_{u,\phi}\right.$$

$$\left. - \xi^2\left(\frac{\partial^2 H}{\partial\Phi^2}\right)_{u,\phi}\right] dx + \frac{\varepsilon^2}{2}\left[\eta^2\left(\frac{\partial^2 \Gamma}{\partial U^2}\right)_{u,\phi}\right.$$

$$\left. + 2\eta\xi\left(\frac{\partial^2 \Gamma}{\partial U\partial\Phi}\right)_{u,\phi} + \xi^2\left(\frac{\partial^2 \Gamma}{\partial\Phi^2}\right)_{u,\phi}\right]_a^b \tag{3.34}$$

For the functional I in (3.30) to be stationary at $U = u$, $\Phi = \phi$, it is necessary that $\delta I = 0$. After integrating $u\zeta'$ by parts, this gives from the equation (3.33)

$$\int_a^b \left[\eta \left(\frac{d\Phi}{dx} - \frac{\partial H}{\partial U} \right)_{u, \phi} + \xi \left(- \frac{\partial H}{\partial \Phi} - \frac{dU}{dx} \right)_{u, \phi} \right] dx$$

$$+ \left[\eta \left(\frac{\partial \Gamma}{\partial U} - \Phi \right)_{u, \phi} + \xi \left(\frac{\partial \Gamma}{\partial \Phi} \right)_{u, \phi} \right]_a^b = 0. \tag{3.35}$$

Let us now select Γ as

$$\Gamma = \begin{cases} \alpha U & \text{at } x = a, \\ \beta U & \text{at } x = b. \end{cases} \tag{3.36}$$

Then (3.30) becomes

$$I = \int_a^b \left[U \frac{d\Phi}{dx} - H \right] dx + U(b) \{\beta - \Phi(b)\} - U(a) \{\alpha - \Phi(a)\} \tag{3.37a}$$

$$= \int_a^b \left[- \frac{dU}{dx} \Phi - H \right] dx + \beta U(b) - \alpha U(a). \tag{3.37b}$$

Thus we have the following theorem.

Theorem 1. The functional I in (3.37a) and (3.37b) is stationary at u, ϕ, where u, ϕ satisfy

$$\frac{d\Phi}{dx} = \frac{\partial H}{\partial U}, \quad - \frac{dU}{dx} = \frac{\partial H}{\partial \Phi} \quad \text{for } a \le x \le b \tag{3.38}$$

with

$$\Phi(a) = \alpha, \qquad \Phi(b) = \beta \tag{3.39}$$

Other boundary conditions can also be considered by choosing appropriate forms of Γ.

Next we turn to the derivation of extremum principles such that under certain circumstances $I(u, \phi > \text{or} < I(U, 0))$. In the theory developed so far, such results cannot be obtained since the trial functions U and Φ are taken as arbitrary and independent. Some restrictions on the trial functions are to be imposed so as to make one trial function dependent on the other.

Let us first select a trial function Φ and then determine U as a function $Y(\Phi)$ of Φ by satisfying (3.38) identically. When this $U(= Y)$ is substituted in (3.37a), we get

$$I[Y(\Phi), \Phi] = J(\Phi), \text{ say.} \tag{3.40}$$

It is clear from the above theorem that $J(0)$ is stationary at ϕ and we write

$$J(\Phi) = I(u, \phi) + \delta^2 J + 0(\varepsilon^3), \tag{3.41}$$

where from (3.34) and (3.36), we have

$$\delta^2 J = \frac{\varepsilon^2}{2} \int_a^b \left[2\eta\xi' - \eta^2 \left(\frac{\partial^2 H}{\partial U^2} \right)_{u, \phi} - 2\eta\xi \left(\frac{\partial^2 H}{\partial U \partial \Phi} \right)_{u, \phi} - \xi^2 \left(\frac{\partial^2 H}{\partial \Phi^2} \right) \right] dx$$

$$- \varepsilon^2 (\eta\xi)_a^b \tag{3.42}$$

In deriving the above equation, we have used (3.31) by replacing U with $Y(\Phi)$. From (3.38), we have

$$\frac{d\xi}{dx} = \left(\frac{\partial^2 H}{\partial U^2} \right)_{u, \phi} \cdot \eta + \left(\frac{\partial^2 H}{\partial U \partial \Phi} \right)_{u, \phi} \cdot \xi + 0(\varepsilon) \tag{3.43}$$

Further, we choose Φ so that

$$\Phi(a) = \alpha, \qquad \Phi(b) = \beta \tag{3.44}$$

leading to

$$\xi(a) = 0, \qquad \xi(b) = 0. \tag{3.45}$$

Then (3.42) becomes

$$\delta^2 J = \frac{1}{2} \int_a^b \left[\{Y(\Phi) - u\}^2 \left(\frac{\partial^2 H}{\partial U^2} \right)_{u, \phi} - (\Phi - \phi)^2 \left(\frac{\partial^2 H}{\partial \Phi^2} \right)_{u, \phi} \right] dx. \tag{3.46}$$

Considering all the above results together, we have the following theorem.

Theorem 2.   The functional $J(\Phi)$ defined by (3.40) is stationary when Φ is varied about ϕ, which is the exact solution of (3.38) and (3.39). Further, if Φ satisfies the boundary conditions (3.39), then

$$J(\phi) = I[u, \phi] + \delta^2 J + 0(\varepsilon^3),$$

where $\delta^2 J$ is given by (3.46). If the $0(\varepsilon^3)$ terms are neglected, it follows that

$$J(\Phi) \leq I(u, \phi) \quad \text{if } \delta^2 J \leq 0 \tag{3.47a}$$

or

$$J(\Phi) \geq I(u, \phi) \quad \text{if } \delta^2 J \geq 0 \tag{3.47b}$$

The complementary variational principle is derived by considering (3.37b). Now we first choose U and then assume that Φ is determined as $\theta(U)$ such that (3.38b) is identically satisfied. This $\Phi(= \theta(U))$ is then substituted in (3.37b) and we write

$$I(U, \theta(U)) = G(U) \tag{3.48}$$

From Theorem 1, it is clear that $G(U)$ is stationary at $U = u$ and we write

$$G(U) = I(u, \phi) + \delta^2 G + 0(\varepsilon^3). \tag{3.49}$$

From (3.42) and (3.44), we have

$$\delta^2 G = \frac{\varepsilon^2}{2} \int_a^b \left[-2\xi\eta' - \eta^2 \left(\frac{\partial^2 H}{\partial U^2} \right)_{u,\phi} \right.$$

$$\left. - 2\eta\xi \left(\frac{\partial^2 H}{\partial U \partial \Phi} \right)_{u,\phi} - \xi^2 \left(\frac{\partial^2 H}{\partial \Phi^2} \right)_{u,\phi} \right] \tag{3.50}$$

Now from (3.38b), we get

$$-\frac{d\eta}{dx} = \left(\frac{\partial^2 H}{\partial \Phi \partial U} \right)_{u,\phi} \cdot \eta + \left(\frac{\partial^2 H}{\partial \Phi^2} \right)_{u,\phi} \cdot \xi + 0(\varepsilon)$$

and when this is used in (3.50), we finally get

$$\delta^2 G = -\frac{1}{2} \int_a^b \left[(U-u)^2 \left(\frac{\partial^2 H}{\partial U^2} \right)_{u,\phi} - (\theta(U) - \phi)^2 \left(\frac{\partial^2 H}{\partial \Phi^2} \right)_{u,\phi} \right] dx. \tag{3.51}$$

All the above results are combined together in the following theorem.

Theorem 3. The functional $G(U)$ defined by (3.48) is stationary as U is varied round u, the exact solution appearing in Theorem 1. Further.

$$G(U) = I(u, \phi) + \delta^2 G + 0(\varepsilon^3), \tag{3.52}$$

where $\delta^2 G$ is given by (3.50). When $0(\varepsilon^3)$ terms are neglected in (3.52), it follows that

$$G(U) \leq I(u, \phi) \quad \text{if } \delta^2 G \leq 0 \tag{3.53a}$$

or

$$G(U) \geq I(u, \phi) \quad \text{if } \delta^2 G \geq 0 \tag{3.53b}$$

Combining Theorems 2 and 3, we state the complementary variational principle in the following theorem.

Theorem 4. With the assumptions of Theorems 2 and 3, we get

$$G(U) \leq I(u, \phi) \leq J(\Phi) \quad \text{if } \delta^2 G \leq 0, \quad \delta^2 J \geq 0, \tag{3.54}$$

where the equality sign holds when U and Φ are exact solutions. This result is also valid when all the inequality signs are reversed.

These maximum and minimum principles give upper and lower bounds for $I(u, \phi)$, provided that $\delta^2 G$ and $\delta^2 J$ do not have the same sign and provided that

U and Φ are close to u and ϕ. If $\delta^2 G$ and $\delta^2 J$ are of same sign then $G(U)$ and $J(\Phi)$ become different one-sided bounds for $I(u, \phi)$.

We now illustrate the above principle by an example. Let ϕ be the exact solution of

$$-\frac{d}{dx}\left[v(x)\frac{d\Phi}{dx}\right] + w(x)\Phi = q(x), \quad a \le x \le b \tag{3.55}$$

satisfying

$$\Phi(a) = \alpha, \quad \Phi(b) = \beta \tag{3.56}$$

We assume that $v > 0$ and $w > 0$ in $a \le x \le b$. Here, the Euler equations (3.24) give

$$\frac{d\Phi}{dx} = \frac{U}{v} = \frac{\partial H}{\partial U}, \tag{3.57a}$$

$$-\frac{dU}{dx} = -w\Phi + q \tag{3.57b}$$

leading to

$$H = \frac{U^2}{2v} - \frac{1}{2}w\Phi^2 + q\Phi \tag{3.58}$$

Now, $I(U, \Phi)$ in (3.37a) and (3.37b) can be easily constructed. Let us choose a trial function Φ satisfying (3.56) and then determine $U = Y(\Phi)$ so that (3.57a) holds identically. Then $Y(\Phi) = v\ d\Phi/dx$ and substituting in (3.37a), we get

$$J(\Phi) = I(v\Phi', \Phi) = \frac{1}{2}\int_a^b [v\Phi'^2 + w\Phi^2 - 2q\Phi]\,dx \tag{3.59}$$

Now from Theorem 2, we have

$$J(\Phi) = I(u, \phi) + \delta^2 J$$

where

$$\delta^2 J = \frac{1}{2}\int_a^b \left[\{Y(\Phi) - u\}^2\frac{1}{v} + \{\Phi - \phi\}^2 w\right]dx \tag{3.60}$$

Since $v > 0$ and $w > 0$, we find the minimum principle

$$J(\Phi) \ge I(u, \phi) \tag{3.61}$$

Proceeding in exactly the same manner for the complementary variational principle, we find that

$$G(U) = I(u, \phi) + \delta^2 G, \tag{3.62}$$

where

$$\delta^2 G = -\frac{1}{2}\int_a^b \left[(U - u)^2 \cdot \frac{1}{v} + (\theta - \phi)^2 w\right]dx \tag{3.63}$$

Since $v > 0$ and $w > 0$, it follows from above that

$$G(U) \leq I(u, \phi). \tag{3.64}$$

Combining (3.61) and (3.62), we obtain the upper and lower bounds for $I(u, \phi)$ as

$$G(U) \leq I(u, \phi) \leq J(\Phi). \tag{3.65}$$

3.8 Poisson Bracket

Let us consider a function $\Phi(x, y_1, \ldots, y_n; p_1, \ldots, p_n)$ and take its values along a solution of the system (3.24). That is to say, we substitute into Φ the solution of the system (3.24) for y_i, p_i ($i = 1, \ldots, n$).

We may then write

$$\frac{d\Phi}{dx} = \frac{\partial\Phi}{\partial x} + \sum_{i=1}^{n} \left(\frac{\partial\Phi}{\partial y_i} \cdot \frac{dy_i}{dx} + \frac{\partial\Phi}{\partial p_i} \cdot \frac{dp_i}{dx} \right)$$

$$= \frac{\partial\Phi}{\partial x} + \sum_{i=1}^{n} \left(\frac{\partial\Phi}{\partial y_i} \cdot \frac{\partial H}{\partial p_i} - \frac{\partial\Phi}{\partial p_i} \cdot \frac{\partial H}{\partial y_i} \right)$$

$$= \frac{\partial\Phi}{\partial x} + [\Phi, H] \tag{3.66}$$

The expression $[\Phi, H]$ defined above is known as the Poisson bracket of the functions Φ and H. It may be readily verified that

$$[\Phi, \Psi] = - [\Psi, \Phi], \qquad [\Phi, \Phi] = 0,$$

$$[c(\Phi_1 + \Phi_2), \Psi] = c[\Phi_1, \Psi] + c[\Phi_2, \Psi], \qquad (c = \text{constant})$$

$$[\Phi_1\Phi_2, \Psi] = \Phi_1[\Phi_2, \Psi] + \Phi_2[\Phi_1, \Psi]$$

Further, it follows from (3.24) that the relation $\Phi = $ constant holds along any solution of the system (3.21) if the identity

$$\frac{\partial\Phi}{\partial x} + [\Phi, H] \equiv 0 \tag{3.67}$$

holds. A relation of the form $\Phi(x, y_1, \ldots, y_n; p_1, \ldots, p_n) = $ constant is called a first integral of the system (3.24). Now if H does not contain x explicitly, then it follows from (3.67) on putting $\Phi = H$ and the relation $[H, H] = 0$ that (3.67) is satisfied identically. This means that H is constant along any integral curve of the system (3.24) if it does not contain x explicitly.

By using the above result we can readily establish the law of conservation of energy for a conservative dynamical system with n degrees of freedom by appealing to Hamilton's principle of least action for a system of n particles of masses m_i ($i = 1, 2, \ldots, n$) located at (x_i, y_i, z_i) ($i = 1, 2, \ldots, n$). According to this principle,

$\int_{t_1}^{t_2} (T - U) \, dt$ is an extremum for the system for fixed terminal times where the kinetic energy T is given by

$$T = \frac{1}{2} \sum_{i=1}^{n} m_i(\dot{x}_i^2 + \dot{y}_i^2 + \dot{z}_i^2)$$

and the potential energy U is independent of time t. The Hamiltonian H for this system is

$$H = \sum_{i=1}^{n} m_i(\dot{x}_i^2 + \dot{y}_i^2 + \dot{z}_i^2) - (T - U) = T + U,$$

which does not involve t explicitly. Therefore, H remains constant throughout the motion.

Thus we find that for a conservative dynamical system, $T + U$ remains constant during the motion. In this case, Hamilton's principle takes the simple form

$$\delta \int_{t_1}^{t_2} (T - U)\, dt = \delta \int_{t_1}^{t_2} [2T - (T + U)]\, dt = 0$$

leading to

$$\delta \int_{t_1}^{t_2} 2T\, dt = 0,$$

which is sometimes referred to as the Maupertuis principle of least action. For a conservative dynamical system with generalized coordinates $q_1(t), q_2(t), \ldots, q_n(t)$, the above principle can be put in the form

$$\delta \int_{\sigma_1}^{\sigma_2} T^{1/2}\, ds = 0,$$

where the kinematic metric ds is defined by

$$ds = \sum_{i,j} (g_{ij}\dot{q}_i\dot{q}_j)^{1/2}\, dt = (2T)^{1/2}\, dt.$$

In the topology defined by a new metric $\overline{ds} = T^{1/2}\, ds$, one can say from the foregoing equations that the motion of the system (which is determined by the kinetic energy function only) corresponds to a curve of the shortest distance, i.e., a geodesic curve. Henri Poincare and later George Birkhoff gave a topological interpretation of the above principle.

Let us now give an interesting application of Hamilton's canonical equations to a problem of fluid mechanics (Gardner [12]).

We consider the well known Korteweg-de Vries (K-dV) equation

$$\frac{\partial u}{\partial t} = u\frac{\partial u}{\partial x} + \frac{\partial^3 u}{\partial x^3} \tag{3.68}$$

which represents the time evolution of finite amplitude gravity waves in shallow water. This equation admits of a wave propagating without change in form and is known as a solitary wave in the literature. This is an example of a nonlinear dispersive wave where the first and second terms on the right-hand side of (3.68) represent the nonlinear and dispersive term, respectively.

Let us assume that the solution of (3.68) has period 2π. Then (3.68) can be derived from the functional

$$F(u) = \int_0^{2\pi} \left[\frac{1}{6} u^3 - \frac{1}{2} \left(\frac{\partial u}{\partial x} \right)^2 \right] dx \qquad (3.69)$$

by

$$\frac{\partial u}{\partial t} = \frac{\partial}{\partial x} \frac{\delta F}{\delta u}, \qquad (3.70)$$

where $\delta F/\delta u$ is the functional derivative given by $u^2/2 + \partial^2 u/\partial x^2$ such that $\delta F/\delta u = 0$ gives the Euler equation for the functional (3.69).

We expand $u(x, t)$ in a Fourier series

$$u(x, t) = \sum_{n=-\infty}^{\infty} u_n(t) \, e^{inx} \qquad (3.71)$$

Then

$$\frac{\partial F}{\partial u_k} = \int_0^{2\pi} \frac{\delta F}{\delta u} \frac{\partial u}{\partial u_k} dx = \int_0^{2\pi} \frac{\delta F}{\delta u} e^{ikx} dx,$$

which gives on inversion the relation

$$\frac{\delta F}{\delta u} = \frac{1}{2\pi} \sum_{n=-\infty}^{\infty} \frac{\partial F}{\partial u_{-n}} e^{inx}. \qquad (3.72)$$

Hence by (3.70) and (3.71), we get the equation of motion as

$$\frac{du_n}{dt} = \frac{i}{2\pi} n \frac{\partial F}{\partial u_{-n}}. \qquad (3.73)$$

Introducing the canonical variables q_n and p_n, where q_n and p_n stand for coordinate and momentum, respectively, such that

$$q_n = \frac{2\pi}{i} \frac{u_n}{n}, \qquad p_n = u_{-n}, \qquad H = F, \qquad (3.74)$$

the K-dV equation (3.73) can be written in terms of the Hamiltonian H as

$$\frac{dq_n}{dt} = \frac{\partial H}{\partial p_n}, \qquad \frac{dp_n}{dt} = -\frac{\partial H}{\partial q_n}, \qquad (3.75)$$

which are Hamilton's canonical equations. Introducing the Poisson bracket

$$[F, G] = \sum_{n=1}^{\infty} \left(\frac{\partial F}{\partial q_n} \frac{\partial G}{\partial p_n} - \frac{\partial F}{\partial p_n} \frac{\partial G}{\partial q_n} \right),$$

we have, from (3.74), the relation

$$[F, G] = \frac{i}{2\pi} \sum_{n=-\infty}^{\infty} n \frac{\partial F}{\partial u_n} \frac{\partial G}{\partial u_{-n}} \qquad (3.76)$$

This can also be written as

$$[F, G] = \int_0^{2\pi} \frac{\delta F}{\delta u} \frac{\partial}{\partial x} \frac{\delta G}{\delta u} \, dx \tag{3.77}$$

by using (3.72). We now put

$$u = \frac{\partial \phi}{\partial x} \tag{3.78}$$

and define the Lagrangian L by

$$L = \int \phi_t \frac{\delta L}{\delta \phi_t} \, dx - H = \int \left(\frac{1}{2} \phi_x \phi_t - \frac{1}{6} \phi_x^3 + \frac{1}{2} \phi_{xx}^2 \right) dx$$

Then the *K-dV* equation (3.68) can be expressed in terms of Hamilton's variational principle as

$$\delta \int L \, dt = 0.$$

3.9   Contact Transformations

The canonical equations (3.24) can be considered regardless of the original variational problem for which the quantities p_i have been introduced. We can regard these equations in the $(2n + 1)$-dimensional space x, y_i, p_i $(i = 1, 2, \ldots, n)$. Further, if the Hamiltonian H is independent of x, we can also regard these equations as giving rise to trajectories in the $2n$-dimensional space of y_i and p_i $(i = 1, 2, \ldots, n)$ with x as a parameter. In other words, we simply deal with differential equations (3.24) in which H is a given function of $2n + 1$ variables x, y_i and p_i, which determines the right-hand side terms of (3.24).

It is clear, however, that every system of ordinary differential equations in the space of x, y and p does not form a canonical system. It may be easily proved that an arbitrary system of differential equations

$$\frac{dy_i}{dx} = \Phi_i(x, y_1, \ldots, y_n; p_1, \ldots, p_n),$$

$$\frac{dp_i}{dx} = \Psi_i(x, y_1, \ldots, y_n; p_1, \ldots, p_n)$$

where $(i = 1, 2, \ldots, n)$, is canonical if and only if

$$\frac{\partial \Phi_i}{\partial p_j} = \frac{\partial \Phi_j}{\partial p_i}, \quad \frac{\partial \Psi_i}{\partial y_j} = \frac{\partial \Psi_j}{\partial y_i}, \quad \frac{\partial \Phi_i}{\partial y_j} + \frac{\partial \Psi_j}{\partial p_i} = 0, \tag{3.79}$$

where $i = 1, 2, \ldots, n$.

Hence if we make a change of variables

$$Y_i = G_i(x, y_1, \ldots, y_n; p_1, \ldots, p_n),$$

$$P_i = H_i(x, y_1, \ldots, y_n; p_1, \ldots, p_n), \qquad i = 1, 2, \ldots, n \tag{3.80}$$

in (3.24), then the system of equations in the new variables x, Y_i, P_i ($i = 1$, 2, ..., n) thus obtained is not necessarily canonical. But if the transformed system retains its canonical form, the transformation (3.80) is then referred to as a canonical transformation.

Canonical transformations are related to a family of transformations known as contact transformations, which transform line elements (i.e., both position and direction) rather than points. Since our object is to transform both position (q's) and momentum (p's, connected with the direction of motion of the system), the connection is obvious. Consider, for example, a two-dimensional situation shown in Fig. 3.9, where S is a function of (x, y) and of (x', y'). Corresponding to each

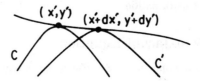

Fig. 3.9 The curve $S = $ constant in the $x' - y'$ plane for fixed (x, y) and a neighbouring curve.

point P in (x, y)-plane (i.e., for fixed values of x and y), the relation $S(x, y, x', y')$ = constant defines a curve C in the (x', y')-plane, and vice versa. If the point (x, y) traces out a curve K, the corresponding sequence of curves in the (x', y')-plane may have an envelope curve E, which may be called the related curve in the (x', y')-plane. To each point in the (x, y)-plane, there is a corresponding curve in the (x', y')-plane and to each curve in the (x, y)-plane, there is a corresponding envelope curve in the (x', y')-plane. Thus to each line element (i.e., position and direction) in the (x, y)-plane, there is a corresponding line element in the (x', y')-plane. Consider the correspondence between a line element connecting two points (x, y) and $(x + dx, y + dy)$ and its image in the (x', y')-plane. The curves in the (x', y')-plane are given by

$$S(x, y; x', y') = C$$

$$S(x + dx, y + dy; x', y') = S(x, y; x', y') + \frac{\partial S}{\partial x} dx + \frac{\partial S}{\partial y} dy = C$$

to first order in dx and dy.

Setting $dx = \dot{x}\, ds$, $dy = \dot{y}\, ds$, we get from the above two relations, the equations

$$S(x, y, x', y') = C, \tag{3.81a}$$

$$\dot{x}\frac{\partial S}{\partial x} + \dot{y}\frac{\partial S}{\partial y} = 0, \tag{3.81b}$$

which can be solved to obtain the point (x', y') corresponding to the point (x, y). The direction of the envelope curve in the (x', y')-plane is obtained by differentiating (3.81a) with respect to the primed coordinates:

$$\dot{x}'\frac{\partial S}{\partial x'} + \dot{y}'\frac{\partial S}{\partial y'} = 0.$$

The symmetry of the equation in the derivatives implies that the transformation is symmetrical with respect to the two planes.

For a dynamical system with Hamiltonian H, which does not depend on time explicitly, it turns out that the quantity $\Sigma\, p\, dq - \Sigma\, P\, dQ$, when expressed as a function of the p's and q's (or of the q's and Q's etc.), is an exact differential whenever the transformation from the p's and q's to the P's and Q's is a canonical transformation. In this case the transformation function S can be found by integrating

$$\Sigma\, p_r dq_r - \Sigma\, P_r dQ_r = dS$$

The function S can be expressed in terms of q's and Q's and is then the function defining the contact transformation.

3.10   The Hamilton-Jacobi Equation

Let us consider the functional in (3.18). The Euler equations for this functional admit of solutions involving $2n$ arbitrary constants. Here specification of two points A and B in the space of variables $x, y_1, ..., y_n$ through which an extremal must pass gives precisely $2n$ equations for determining these constants. Hence in the general case there appears a discrete set of extremals (which may contain one or many extremals or none) joining these points. Let I_{AB} be the value of the functional on each of these extremals, A being regarded as the initial and B as the terminal point. Let A be fixed while $B(x, y_1, y_2, ..., y_n)$ is regarded as a movable point. Then I_{AB} is a function of $x, y_1, y_2, ..., y_n$ and we write

$$I_{AB} = S(x, y_1, y_2, ..., y_n) \tag{3.82}$$

If B changes its position, (3.23) gives

$$dS = -H\, dx + \sum_{i=1}^{n} p_i dy_i,$$

which in turn leads to

$$\frac{\partial S}{\partial x} = -H, \qquad \frac{\partial S}{\partial y_i} = p_i \qquad (i = 1, 2, ..., n)$$

It then follows that S satisfies the following partial differential equation of first order

$$\frac{\partial S}{\partial x} + H\left(x, y_1, y_2, ..., y_n, \frac{\partial S}{\partial y_1}, ..., \frac{\partial S}{\partial y_n}\right) = 0, \tag{3.83}$$

which is known as the Hamilton-Jacobi equation.

If a one-parameter family $S(x, y_1, ..., y_n, \alpha)$ of solutions of (3.83) is known, then the first integral $\partial S/\partial \alpha = \beta$ of the canonical system (3.24) can be found, β being a constant. In fact,

$$\frac{d}{dx}\left(\frac{\partial S}{\partial \alpha}\right) = \frac{\partial^2 S}{\partial x\, \partial \alpha} + \sum_{i=1}^{n} \frac{\partial^2 S}{\partial y_i\, \partial \alpha} \frac{\partial y_i}{\partial x}$$

$$= \frac{\partial^2 S}{\partial x\, \partial \alpha} + \sum_{i=1}^{n} \frac{\partial^2 S}{\partial y_i\, \partial \alpha} \frac{\partial H}{\partial p_i}. \tag{3.84}$$

Now, differentiating the identity

$$\frac{\partial S(x, y_1, \ldots, y_n, \alpha)}{\partial x}$$

$$\equiv - H\left(x, y_1, \ldots, y_n, \frac{\partial S(x, y_1, \ldots, y_n, \alpha)}{\partial y_1}, \ldots, \frac{\partial S(x, y_1, \ldots, y_n, \alpha)}{\partial y_n}\right)$$

with respect to α, we get

$$\frac{\partial^2 S}{\partial x \partial \alpha} \equiv - \sum_{i=1}^{n} \frac{\partial H}{\partial p_i} \frac{\partial^2 S}{\partial y_i \partial \alpha}.$$

This gives, from (3.84), the relation

$$\frac{d}{dx}\left(\frac{\partial S}{\partial \alpha}\right) = 0$$

leading to $\partial S / \partial \alpha = \beta$, β being a constant.

Hence if the complete integral of the Hamilton-Jacobi equation (3.83) is known and has the form

$$S = S(x, y_1, y_2, \ldots, y_n, \alpha_1, \alpha_2, \ldots, \alpha_n),$$

then we can find n first integrals of the canonical system (3.24) as

$$\frac{\partial S}{\partial \alpha_i} = \beta_i \quad (i = 1, 2, \ldots, n). \tag{3.85}$$

If the Jacobian of the system (3.85) does not vanish, i.e.,

$$\det \left| \frac{\partial^2 S}{\partial y_i \partial \alpha_i} \right| \neq 0,$$

then the system (3.85) gives y_i as

$$y_i = y_i(x, \alpha_1, \alpha_2, \ldots, \alpha_n, \beta_1, \beta_2, \ldots, \beta_n), \quad i = 1, 2, \ldots, n \tag{3.86}$$

Thus we have obtained a $2n$-parameter family of extremals, and (3.86) is the general solution of the system of Euler equations.

Let us next consider the question of separability of the Hamilton-Jacobi equation, which has an important bearing on certain physical problems.

Equation (3.83) with x replaced by t and y_i $(i = 1, 2, \ldots, n)$ replaced by $q_i (i = 1, 2, \ldots, n)$ involves a particular coordinate q_1 in the combination $\phi(q_1, \partial S / \partial q_1)$ (see Landau and Lifshitz [13]) and is given by

$$\Phi\left\{q_i, t, \frac{\partial S}{\partial q_i}, \frac{\partial S}{\partial t}, \phi\left(q_1, \frac{\partial S}{\partial q_1}\right)\right\} = 0,$$

where q_i denotes all the coordinates except q_1. Its solution is sought in the form

$$S = S'(q_i, t) + S_1(q_1),$$

which, when substituted in the above equation, gives

$$\Phi\left\{q_i, t, \frac{\partial S'}{\partial q_i}, \frac{\partial S'}{\partial t}, \phi\left(q_1, \frac{dS_1}{dq_1}\right)\right\} = 0.$$

When the solution in the above separated form is substituted in this equation, we get an identity valid for any particular coordinate q_1. When q_1 changes, only ϕ is affected and hence the identity gives

$$\phi\left(q_1, \frac{dS_1}{dq_1}\right) = \alpha_1, \quad \Phi\left\{q_i, t, \frac{\partial S'}{\partial q_i}, \frac{\partial S'}{\partial t}, \alpha_1\right\} = 0.$$

If we successively separate in this way all the n coordinates and the time t, determination of a complete integral of (3.83) is reduced to quadratures. For a conservative system in which the Lagrangian and hence the Hamiltonian do not involve time explicitly, the aforementioned separation of variables gives

$$S = \sum_k S_k(q_k; \alpha_1, \alpha_2, \ldots, \alpha_n) - E(\alpha_1, \alpha_2, \ldots, \alpha_n)t$$

$$= S_0 - E(\alpha_1, \alpha_2, \ldots, \alpha_n) \cdot t,$$

where S_k depends on the coordinate q_k only and E is a constant depending on the parameters $\alpha_1, \ldots, \alpha_n$.

In spherical polar coordinates r, θ, ϕ, the Hamiltonian is

$$H = \frac{1}{2m}\left(p_r^2 + \frac{p_\theta^2}{r^2} + \frac{p_\phi^2}{r^2 \sin^2 \theta}\right) + U(r, \theta, \phi)$$

and the variables can be separated if

$$U = a(r) + \frac{b(\theta)}{r^2} + \frac{c(\phi)}{r^2 \sin^2 \theta},$$

where $a(r)$, $b(\theta)$ and $c(\phi)$ are arbitrary functions. Since the last term in U is not of much physical interest, we take

$$U = a(r) + \frac{b(\theta)}{r^2}$$

In this case the Hamilton-Jacobi equation is

$$\frac{1}{2m}\left(\frac{\partial S_0}{\partial r}\right)^2 + a(r) + \frac{1}{2mr^2}\left[\left(\frac{\partial S_0}{\partial \theta}\right)^2 + 2mb(\theta)\right] + \frac{1}{2mr^2 \sin^2 \theta}\left(\frac{\partial S_0}{\partial \phi}\right)^2$$

$$= E$$

Since the coordinate ϕ is cyclic, we seek a solution in the form $S_0 = p_\phi\phi + S_1(r) + S_2(\theta)$. This gives

$$\left(\frac{dS_2}{d\theta}\right)^2 + 2mb(\theta) + \frac{p_\phi^2}{\sin^2\theta} = \beta,$$

$$\frac{1}{2m}\left(\frac{dS_1}{dr}\right)^2 + a(r) + \frac{\beta}{2mr^2} = E$$

Integration gives

$$S = -Et + p_\phi\,\phi + \int \left[\beta - 2mb(\theta) - \frac{p_\phi^2}{\sin^2\theta}\right]^{1/2} d\theta$$

$$+ \int \left[2m\{E - a(r)\} - \frac{\beta}{r^2}\right]^{1/2} dr$$

Here the arbitrary constants are p_ϕ, β and E. On differentiating the above expression with respect to these and equating the results to other constants, we get the general solution of the Hamilton-Jacobi equation.

It is important to point out that the separability of Hamilton-Jacobi equation is closely related to some sort of symmetry of the system, which in turn implies, in general, the existence of an integral of motion. One knows, for instance, that if there is rotational symmetry, then one has an angular momentum integral, and there is a corresponding separation of variables.

Example 5. Find the geodesic curves on a surface on which a line element *ds* is of the form

$$(ds)^2 = [\phi(x) + \Psi(y)][(dx)^2 + (dy)^2].$$

Solution. Here the problem reduces to determination of the extremals of

$$S = \int \sqrt{[\phi(x) + \Psi(y)](1 + y'^2)}\, dx.$$

Further, the Hamiltonian *H* defined by (3.23) in this case is given by

$$H(x, y, p) = -\sqrt{\phi(x) + \Psi(y) - p^2},$$

where

$$p = y'\sqrt{\frac{\phi(x) + \Psi(y)}{1 + y'^2}}$$

Hence the Hamilton-Jacobi equation (3.83) becomes

$$\left(\frac{\partial S}{\partial x}\right)^2 + \left(\frac{\partial S}{\partial y}\right)^2 = \phi(x) + \Psi(y)$$

A first integral of this equation is easily found by setting

$$\left(\frac{\partial S}{\partial x}\right)^2 - \phi(x) = \alpha, \qquad \Psi(y) - \left(\frac{\partial S}{\partial y}\right)^2 = \alpha,$$

α being a constant. This gives

$$S = \int \sqrt{\phi(x) + \alpha}\; dx + \int \sqrt{\Psi(y) - \alpha}\; dy$$

Hence the equation of geodesic curves given by $\partial S/\partial \alpha = \beta$ has the form

$$\int \frac{dx}{\sqrt{\phi(x) + \alpha}} - \int \frac{dy}{\sqrt{\Psi(y) - \alpha}} = \beta,$$

β being a constant.

3.11   Clairaut's Theorem

An important result in the theory of geodesic curves on a surface (a geodesic is a curve of shortest length on a given surface joining two given points on the surface) given by $\mathbf{r} = \mathbf{r}(u, v)$, is embodied in Clairaut's theorem [14]. This theorem states that at every point of any geodesic on a surface of revolution, the product of the radius of a parallel and the sine of the angle between a geodesic and a meridian is constant. This can be shown as follows. Any curve on the surface $r = r(u, v)$ may be specified parametrically by $u = u(t)$, $v = v(t)$. Hence the determination of geodesic between the points corresponding to the values t_0 and t_1 reduces to determination of the extremals of the functional

$$J[u, v] = \int_{t_0}^{t_1} \sqrt{Eu'^2 + 2Fu'v' + Gv'^2}\; dt \tag{3.87}$$

Here E, F and G are the coefficients of the first quadratic form of the surface given by

$$E = \left(\frac{\partial \mathbf{r}}{\partial u} \cdot \frac{\partial \mathbf{r}}{\partial u}\right), \qquad F = \left(\frac{\partial \mathbf{r}}{\partial u} \cdot \frac{\partial \mathbf{r}}{\partial v}\right), \qquad G = \left(\frac{\partial \mathbf{r}}{\partial v} \cdot \frac{\partial \mathbf{r}}{\partial v}\right).$$

A surface of revolution with the z-axis as the axis of revolution has its equation

$$x = \rho \cos \phi, \qquad y = \rho \sin \phi, \qquad z = f(\rho)$$

in cylindrical polar coordinates. Thus

$$E = 1 + f'^2(\rho), \qquad F = 0, \qquad G = \rho^2.$$

The differential dS of an arc length on the surface of revolution is, therefore, given by

$$dS = \sqrt{\rho^2 + (1 + f'^2(\rho))\rho'^2(\phi)}\; d\phi.$$

Thus by (3.87), the geodesics are given by the extremals of

$$\int_{\phi_0}^{\phi_1} \sqrt{\rho^2 + (1 + f_\rho'^2)\rho'^2(\phi)} \, d\phi,$$

where the parameter t is identified with ϕ and ϕ_0 and ϕ_1 correspond to t_0 and t_1, respectively. Since the integrand in the above expression does not contain ϕ explicitly, the Euler equation leads to

$$\rho^2[\rho^2 + (1 + f_\rho'^2)\rho'^2(\phi)]^{-1/2} = \text{constant}$$

giving $\rho^2(d\phi/ds) = \text{constant}$. Since $\rho(d\phi/ds) = \sin\omega$, where ω is the angle between a geodesic and a meridian curve, it follows immediately that $\rho \sin\omega = \text{constant}$, which is what we wanted to prove.

3.12 Noether's Theorem

We now discuss a theorem which enables us to obtain first integrals of systems of Euler equations for functionals admitting of some invariance properties.

Let us begin by introducing the concept of a continuous group of transformations of the space E_n (or of a region lying in the space). We regard a point $(x_1, x_2, ..., x_n)$ of the space as being represented by its radius vector $\mathbf{x}$. Then the transformation formulae

$$\bar{x}_i = \Phi_i(x_1, x_2, ..., x_n), \qquad i = 1, 2, ..., n$$

representing the mapping of E_n into itself can be written in a vector form as

$$\bar{\mathbf{x}} = \Phi(\mathbf{x}).$$

Consider a one-parameter family of one-to-one transformations

$$\bar{\mathbf{x}} = \Phi(\mathbf{x}, t), \tag{3.88}$$

where t is a scalar parameter. This family constitutes a continuous group of transformations if it possesses the following group properties:

(i) The result of two consecutively applied mappings corresponding to values t_1 and t_2 of the parameter is equivalent to the mapping with parameter $t_1 + t_2$ belonging to the same family.

(ii) The identity mapping corresponds to $t = 0$ so that $\Phi(\mathbf{x}, 0) \equiv \mathbf{x}$.

(iii) The inverse of the mapping (3.88) is given by $\Phi(\mathbf{x}, -t)$.

It is convenient to regard the parameter t as time and the family (3.88) of mappings as a flux in the space E_n. Then the group property means that the flux is stationary. We introduce the vector field $\Phi_0(\mathbf{x})$ defined by

$$\Phi_0(\mathbf{x}) = \Phi_t'(\mathbf{x}, 0), \tag{3.89}$$

(where the subscript t denotes derivatives with respect to t) as repesenting the velocity field of the flux. Then for small Δt, by using group property we have

$$\Delta \mathbf{x} = \boldsymbol{\Phi}(\mathbf{x}, t + \Delta t) - \boldsymbol{\Phi}(\mathbf{x}, t)$$

$$= \boldsymbol{\Phi}(\overline{\mathbf{x}}, \Delta t) - \boldsymbol{\Phi}(\overline{\mathbf{x}}, 0)$$

$$= \boldsymbol{\Phi}_0(\overline{\mathbf{x}})\Delta t + 0(\Delta t) \tag{3.90}$$

This leads to the notion of the infinitesimal generator of the group (3.88) applied to the auxiliary mapping $\overline{\mathbf{x}} = \boldsymbol{\Phi}_0(\mathbf{x})$, which is independent of t. Conversely, (3.90) implies that the family (3.88) is derived from its infinitesimal generator by means of solving the system of differential equations in vector form

$$\frac{d\overline{\mathbf{x}}}{dt} = \boldsymbol{\Phi}_0(\overline{\mathbf{x}}) \text{ with } (\overline{\mathbf{x}})_{t=0} = \mathbf{x}.$$

Now let us consider the functional (3.18) and suppose that under the one-parameter group of transformations of the form

$$\overline{x} = \phi(x, \mathbf{y}, t), \quad \overline{\mathbf{y}} = \boldsymbol{\Phi}(x, \mathbf{y}, t) \tag{3.91}$$

defined in the $(n + 1)$-dimensional space x, $\mathbf{y}$ (where $\mathbf{y} = (y_1, y_2, ..., y_n)$), the functional remains invariant. In fact, for this $(n + 1)$-dimensional space, the family (3.91) is equivalent to the family (3.88) if we write $x = x_1$ and $y_i = x_{i+1}(i = 1, ..., n)$. However, it proves more expedient to use (3.91) since the role of the independent variable x is different from that of the dependent variables y_i. The condition of invariance implies that if we interpret (3.18) as a functional dependent on the curve $y = y(x)$, $(x_1 \leq x \leq x_2)$, then the integral (3.18) must take equal values on all the curves going into one another under the mapping (3.91). In keeping with (3.89), we write

$$\phi_0(x, \mathbf{y}) = \phi_t'(x, \mathbf{y}, 0), \quad \boldsymbol{\Phi}_0(x, \mathbf{y}) = \boldsymbol{\Phi}_t'(x, \mathbf{y}, 0) \tag{3.92}$$

and compare the value of the functional assumed on an arc of an extremal with its value attained on the curve into which this arc is transformed under the mapping (3.91) corresponding to an infinitesimal value of t. By virtue of the invariance of the functional, the left member of (3.25) then equals zero and the integral on the right side vanishes by the Euler equation. Hence using (3.91) in (3.25) gives

$$[\mathbf{p} \cdot \boldsymbol{\Phi}_0 t - H\phi_0 t]_{x_1}^{x_2} = 0$$

leading to

$$(\mathbf{p} \cdot \boldsymbol{\Phi}_0 - H\phi_0)_{x_2} = (\mathbf{p} \cdot \boldsymbol{\Phi} - H\phi_0)_{x_1} \tag{3.93}$$

Since (3.93) holds for any two points of the extremal under consideration, the relation

$$\mathbf{p} \cdot \boldsymbol{\Phi}_0(x, \mathbf{y}) - H(x, \mathbf{y}, \mathbf{p})\phi_0(x, \mathbf{y}) = \text{constant} \tag{3.94}$$

holds along every extremal. Thus we have obtained a first integral of Euler's equations corresponding to the functional (3.18). The relation (3.94) expresses the well known Noether's theorem first derived by Amalie Emmy Noether (1882–1935), a German mathematician [15].

As an example, let us assume that F in (3.18) is independent of x. Thus this functional is invariant under the group $\bar{x} = x + t$, $\bar{y} = y$. Then by (3.92) we have $\phi_0 \equiv 1$ and $\boldsymbol{\Phi}_0 \equiv 0$. On using Noether's theorem (3.94), this leads to the first integral $H = $ constant derived earlier in Section 1.2.

As another example, consider the orbits of the particles of a system of mass points given by Hamilton's principle (discussed earlier)

$$\delta \int_{t_1}^{t_2} (T - U)\, dt = 0,$$

(where the kinetic energy $T = \frac{1}{2} \Sigma m (\dot{x}^2 + \dot{y}^2 + \dot{z}^2)$ and the potential energy U depend on the relative positions of the mass points), i.e. does not suffer any change under a translation or rotation of the system as a whole. The above integral is clearly invariant under a translation

$$t^* = t, \qquad x^* = x + \alpha, \qquad y^* = y, \qquad z^* = z$$

or under a rotation

$$t^* = t, \qquad x^* = x \cos \alpha + y \sin \alpha, \qquad y^* = - x \sin \alpha + y \cos \alpha$$

Hence using Noether's theorem (3.94), we obtain two independent integrals

$$\Sigma\, m\dot{x} = \text{constant}, \qquad \Sigma\, m(y\dot{x} - x\dot{y}) = \text{constant}$$

expressing the conservation of linear and angular momentum, respectively.

A group of transformations under which a functional remains invariant may contain more than one parameter. For example, in the case $n = 3$, we may consider a two-parameter group of motions along the coaxial helices or the noncommutative three-parameter rotation group about a point. We write the transformation of the family involving k parameters in the form

$$\bar{\mathbf{x}} = \boldsymbol{\Phi}(\mathbf{x}, t_1, t_2, \ldots, t_k)$$

This family must include the identity mapping, the inverse mapping as well as the result of consecutive applications of two mappings. If a functional remains invariant with respect to this group, we can deduce by means of differentiation with respect to each of the parameters, k independent integrals of the type (3.94) for the corresponding system of Euler's equations.

The theory of continuous groups of transformations known as Lie groups after the Norwegian mathematician M.S. Lie (1842–1899) is a well-developed branch of modern mathematics with useful applications.

PROBLEMS

1. Find the minimum of the functional

$$I[y] = \int_0^1 \left(\frac{1}{2}\, y'^2 + yy' + y' + y \right) dx$$

if the values at the ends of the interval are not given.

Ans.   A strong minimum is attained when

$$y = \frac{1}{2}(x^2 - x - 1).$$

2.   Find the extremum of

$$I[y] = \int_1^2 \frac{x^3}{y'^2}\, dx, \qquad y(1) = 1, \qquad y(2) = 4.$$

Ans.   A weak minimum is attained on $y = x^2$.

3.   Investigate the motion of a material point under the action of an attractive central force proportional to the distance from the centre O by proceeding from the principle of least action and by applying the Hamilton-Jacobi method.

Ans.   The trajectories are conics.

CHAPTER 4

VARIATIONAL PROBLEMS WITH SUBSIDIARY CONDITIONS

So far we have considered the extremum of a functional in which the argument functions could be chosen arbitrarily subject only to boundary conditions, and the solution of the variational problem could be obtained from Euler equations with given or natural boundary conditions. We now investigate variational problems in which subsidiary conditions (or constraints) are imposed on the argument functions. This consideration leads to essential modifications of Euler equations.

4.1 Constraints of the Form

$$\phi(x, y_1(x), y_2(x), \ldots, y_n(x), y_1'(x), y_2'(x), \ldots, y_n'(x)) = 0$$

We examine the extremum of the functional

$$I[y_1(x), \ldots, y_n(x)] = \int_{x_1}^{x_2} F(x, y_1, \ldots, y_n, y_1', \ldots, y_n') \, dx \tag{4.1}$$

subject to the boundary conditions

$$y_j(x_1) = y_{j1}, \qquad y_j(x_2) = y_{j2} \qquad (j = 1, 2, \ldots, n) \tag{4.2}$$

and the following finite constraints

$$\phi_i(x, y_1, y_2, \ldots, y_n, y_1', y_2', \ldots, y_n') = 0, \qquad i = 1, 2, \ldots, m. \tag{4.3}$$

Note that the constraints are in the form of differential equations and in mechanics such relations are known as non-holonomic constraints as against holonomic constraints which are of the form

$$\phi_i(x, y_1, y_2, \ldots, y_n) = 0$$

Suppose that one of the following functional determinants of order m is distinct from zero:

$$\frac{D(\phi_1, \phi_2, \ldots, \phi_m)}{D(y_1', y_2', \ldots, y_m')} \neq 0 \tag{4.4}$$

This condition ensures the independence of the constraints. Solving (4.3) for $y_1', y_2', \ldots, y_m'$ (which is possible by virtue of (4.4)), we get

$$y_i' = \Psi_i(x, y_1, y_2, \ldots, y_n, y_{m+1}', y_{m+2}', \ldots, y_n'), \qquad i = 1, 2, \ldots, m.$$

If y_{m+1}, y_{m+2}, ..., y_n are arbitrarily specified functions, then y_1, y_2, ..., y_m are determined from this system of differential equations. Hence y_{m+1}, y_{m+2}, ..., y_n are arbitrary differentiable functions with fixed boundary values and to that extent their variations are arbitrary.

We suppose that y_1, y_2, ..., y_n are arbitrary admissible system of functions satisfying the constraints $\phi_i = 0$ ($i = 1, 2, ..., m$). Let us vary the constraints (4.3) such that

$$\sum_{j=1}^{n} \frac{\partial \phi_i}{\partial y_j} \delta y_j + \sum_{j=1}^{n} \frac{\partial \phi_i}{\partial y_j'} \delta y_j' = 0 \quad (i = 1, 2, ..., m).$$

Multiply by the undetermined function $\lambda_i(x)$ and integrate from x_1 to x_2. This gives

$$\int_{x_1}^{x_2} \lambda_i(x) \sum_{j=1}^{n} \frac{\partial \phi_i}{\partial y_j} \delta y_j \, dx + \int_{x_1}^{x_2} \lambda_i(x) \sum_{j=1}^{n} \frac{\partial \phi_i}{\partial y_j'} \delta y_j' \, dx = 0.$$

Integrating each of the second integrals by parts and taking into account $\delta y_j' = (\delta y_j)'$, and $(\delta y_j)_{x=x_1} = (\delta y_j)_{x=x_2} = 0$, we get

$$\int_{x_1}^{x_2} \sum_{j=1}^{n} \left[\lambda_i(x) \frac{\partial \phi_i}{\partial y_j} - \frac{d}{dx} \left(\lambda_i(x) \frac{\partial \phi_i}{\partial y_j'} \right) \right] \delta y_j \, dx = 0. \tag{4.5}$$

From the necessary condition for an extremum given by $\delta I = 0$, we find

$$\int_{x_1}^{x_2} \sum_{j=1}^{n} \left(F_{y_j} - \frac{d}{dx} F_{y_j}' \right) \delta y_j \, dx = 0 \tag{4.6}$$

since

$$\delta I = \int_{x_1}^{x_2} \sum_{j=1}^{n} (F_{y_j} \delta y_j + F_{y_j'} \delta y_j') \, dx$$

$$= \int_{x_1}^{x_2} \sum_{j=1}^{n} \left(F_{y_j} - \frac{d}{dx} F_{y_j'} \right) \delta y_j \, dx$$

Introducing

$$F^* = F + \sum_{i=1}^{m} \lambda_i(x) \phi_i$$

and adding term-wise all the equations in (4.5) and (4.6), we get

$$\int_{x_1}^{x_2} \sum_{j=1}^{n} \left(F_{y_j}^* - \frac{d}{dx} F_{y_j}^* \right) \delta y_j \, dx = 0 \tag{4.7}$$

Here the variations $\delta y_j (j = 1, 2, ..., n)$ are not arbitrary due to constraints (4.3). Select m functions $\lambda_1(x)$, ..., $\lambda_m(x)$ so that they satisfy

$$F_{y_j}^* - \frac{d}{dx} F_{y_j}^* = 0 \quad (j = 1, 2, ..., m). \tag{4.8}$$

Written in full, these equations constitute a system of linear differential equations in $\lambda_i(x)$ and $d\lambda_i/dx$ ($i = 1, 2, \ldots, m$), and admit of solution $\lambda_1(x), \lambda_2(x), \ldots, \lambda_m(x)$, involving m arbitrary constants. With this choice of $\lambda_1(x), \ldots, \lambda_m(x)$, (4.7) becomes

$$\int_{x_1}^{x_2} \sum_{j=m+1}^{n} \left(F_{y_j}^* - \frac{d}{dx} F_{y_j'}^* \right) \delta y_j \, dx = 0,$$

where the variations δy_j ($j = m + 1, m + 2, \ldots, n$) are now arbitrary. Thus, invoking the fundamental lemma and using (4.8), we obtain

$$F_{y_j}^* - \frac{d}{dx} F_{y_j'}^* = 0 \quad (j = 1, 2, \ldots, n)$$

and

$$\phi_i = 0 \quad (i = 1, 2, \ldots, m).$$

Clearly, these are Euler equations for the functional

$$I^*[y_1, y_2, \ldots, y_n, \lambda_1, \lambda_2, \ldots, \lambda_n] = \int_{x_1}^{x_2} F^* \, dx. \tag{4.9}$$

A variational problem with finite holonomic constraints is generally referred to as Lagrange's problem.

It may be noted that for constraints of the holonomic type

$$\phi_i(x, y_1(x), y_2(x), \ldots, y_n(x)) = 0 \quad (i = 1, 2, \ldots, m, \ m < n)$$

the functions $y_1, y_2, \ldots, y_n$ which extremize the functional (4.1) can also be found by the method described above. Thus in this case $y_1, y_2, \ldots, y_n$ satisfy the following Euler equations for the functional (4.9) for appropriate choice of the functions $\lambda_i(x)$, ($i = 1, 2, \ldots, m$):

$$F_{y_j}^* - \frac{d}{dx} F_{y_j'}^* = 0 \quad (j = 1, 2, \ldots, n)$$

and

$$\phi_i = 0 \quad (i = 1, 2, \ldots, m).$$

However, the distinction between this problem and the foregoing problem involving non-holonomic constraints lies in the fact that Euler's equations for holonomic constraints involve only $\lambda_i(x)$ while those for non-holonomic constraints involve both $\lambda_i(x)$ and $d\lambda_i/dx$.

Example 1. Determine the shape of the closed path along which an airplane must fly in a given time T on condition that the wind velocity v is constant in magnitude and direction and that the area bounded by the path is maximum (the problem of Chaplygin [15]).

Solution. Take a Cartesian coordinate system x, y in which the y-axis is along the direction of the wind and let V be the relative velocity of the airplane. If $x = x(t)$ and $y = y(t)$ represent the parametric equations of the closed trajectory, then it follows that

$$\dot{x}^2(t) + (\dot{y} - v)^2 = V^2, \tag{4.10}$$

where the dot over the letters denotes derivative with respect to time t. The area A enclosed by the above trajectory is given by

$$A = \frac{1}{2} \int_0^T (x\dot{y} - y\dot{x}) \, dt \tag{4.11}$$

subject to the obvious boundary conditions

$$x(0) = x(T) = x_0, \qquad y(0) = y(T) = y_0. \tag{4.12}$$

Our problem then is to maximize the functional (4.11) subject to the non-holonomic constraint (4.10). Using the theory described above, we form Euler's equations for the functional F^* given by

$$F^* = \frac{1}{2}(x\dot{y} - y\dot{x}) - \lambda(t)[\dot{x}^2 + (\dot{y} - v)^2].$$

Euler's equations are

$$\frac{1}{2}\dot{y} - \frac{d}{dt}\left[-\frac{1}{2}y - \lambda(t) \cdot 2\dot{x}\right] = 0,$$

$$-\frac{1}{2}\dot{x} - \frac{d}{dt}\left[\frac{1}{2}x - \lambda(t) \cdot 2(\dot{y} - v)\right] = 0,$$

which give, on integration with respect to t, the relations

$$y(t) + 2\lambda(t)\dot{x} = C_1, \qquad -x + 2\lambda(t)(\dot{y} - v) = C_2. \tag{4.13}$$

By suitable translation of coordinate axes, we may make $C_1 = C_2 = 0$. Then eliminating $\lambda(t)$ from (4.13), we find

$$dt = (x \, dx + y \, dy)/vy$$

Substituting this in (4.10) leads to

$$v^2(x^2 + y^2)(dx)^2 = V^2(x \, dx + y \, dy)^2. \tag{4.14}$$

This is a homogeneous differential equation which can be easily solved by introducing the polar coordinates (ρ, ϕ) such that $x = \rho \cos \phi$, $y = \rho \sin \phi$. Substituting these in (4.14), we get

$$\frac{d\rho}{\rho} = \left[\frac{\pm \varepsilon \sin \phi}{1 \pm \varepsilon \cos \phi}\right] d\phi, \qquad \varepsilon = v/V,$$

which gives, on integration, the relation

$$\rho = C/(1 \pm \varepsilon \cos \phi), \; C \text{ being a constant.}$$

These represent a family of ellipses with the same eccentricity $\varepsilon \, (< 1)$, their major axes being perpendicular to the direction of the wind.

4.2 Isoperimetric Problems

As already mentioned in Chapter 1, these problems in the strict sense of the word involve the determination of the shape of a closed curve of the given perimeter enclosing maximum area (the so-called Dido's problem). The solution to this problem has already been given in the last example of Section 1.6 where the area of the closed curve in the parametric form is given by

$$\frac{1}{2} \int_{t_0}^{t_1} (x\dot{y} - y\dot{x}) \, dt$$

and the perimeter is

$$\frac{1}{2} \int_{t_0}^{t_1} (\dot{x}^2 + \dot{y}^2) \, dt.$$

However, these problems embrace a much wider class of problems, e.g., the determination of extremum of the functional

$$I[y_1, \ldots, y_n] = \int_{x_1}^{x_2} F(x, y_1, y_2, \ldots, y_n, y_1', y_2', \ldots, y_n') \, dx$$

subject to the isoperimetric constraints

$$\int_{x_1}^{x_2} G_i(x, y_1, y_2, \ldots, y_n, y_1', y_2', \ldots, y_n') \, dx = l_i,$$

where $i = 1, 2, \ldots, m$, l_i being constants. It may be noted that here m may be greater than, equal to, or less than n.

These problems can be reduced to the conditional extremum problem studied in the previous section by introducing

$$\int_{x_1}^{x} G_i \, dx = z_i(x), \qquad i = 1, 2, \ldots, m \tag{4.15}$$

such that $z_i(x_1) = 0$. From the above isoperimetric constraints we have $z_i(x_2) = l_i$. Differentiating, (4.15) gives

$$z_i'(x) = G_i(x, y_1, \ldots, y_n, y_1', y_2', \ldots, y_n'), \qquad i = 1, 2, \ldots, m \tag{4.16}$$

Thus the integral constraints are reduced to the differential constraints (4.16) and hence the present problem is reduced to the problem considered in the previous section. The problem, therefore, reduces to the study of the unconditional extremum of

$$I^* = \int_{x_1}^{x_2} \left[F + \sum_{i=1}^{m} \lambda_i(x)(G_i - z_i') \right] dx$$

$$= \int_{x_1}^{x_2} F^* \, dx. \tag{4.17}$$

The Euler equations are then given by

$$F_{y_j} + \sum_{i=1}^{m} \lambda_i G_{iy_j} - \frac{d}{dx}\left(F_{y_j'} + \sum_{i=1}^{m} \lambda_i G_{iy_j'}\right) = 0 \quad (j = 1, 2, ..., n), \tag{4.18}$$

$$\frac{d}{dx}\lambda_i(x) = 0 \quad (i = 1, 2, ..., m). \tag{4.19}$$

From (4.18), we find that $\lambda_i(x)$ are constant. The arbitrary constants $C_1, C_2, ..., C_n$ in the general solution of the system (4.18) and the constants λ_i $(i = 1, 2, ..., m)$ are determined from the boundary conditions

$$y_j(x_1) = y_{j1}, \qquad y_j(x_2) = y_{j2} \qquad (j = 1, 2, ..., n),$$

$$\int_{x_1}^{x_2} G_i \, dx = l_i \quad (i = 1, 2, ..., m). \tag{4.20}$$

It is interesting to note that the extremals of the functional

$$I[y(x)] = \int_{x_1}^{x_2} F(x, y, y') \, dx \tag{4.21}$$

subject to the constraint

$$J[y(x)] = \int_{x_1}^{x_2} G(x, y, y') \, dx = \text{constant} \tag{4.22}$$

coincide with the extremals of $J[y(x)]$ under the constraint $I[y(x)] = $ constant. This can be easily seen from the fact that Euler's equations for the two variational problems are the same. This property is known as the reciprocity principle. Thus the problem of finding the curve enclosing the maximum area bounded by a closed curve of given perimeter and the problem of the minimum length of a closed curve enclosing a given area are reciprocal and the two problems admit of common extremals (which are known to be circles (as shown in Section 1.6)).

It should be noted that these results are valid for curves on a plane surface. A similar isoperimetric problem can also be considered on any surface provided we replace the radius of curvature R of a curve on a plane by the geodesic curvature $\Gamma = \sin \phi / R$, where R is the radius of curvature at any point P of the curve on the given curved surface and ϕ is the angle between the principal normal at P of the curve and the normal at P to the given surface (see [2]). The solution of the isoperimetric problem is now as follows: Of all closed curves on a curved surface bounding a given area, the curve with a constant geodesic curvature has the minimum length.

It may be noted that variational problems with isoperimetric constraints are quite often encountered in practical problems. For instance, we often deal with a situation in which certain resources have to be allocated so as to yield maximum profit. If the various possible ways in which the decision maker can specify the allocation are described by a function or a set of functions, we usually arrive at a variational problem in which the conditions determining the amounts of resources available are expressed in the form of integral constraints.

Further, some problems of geometry can also be easily solved by using the reciprocity principle enunciated above. This is illustrated in Example 2. Example 3 discusses an isoperimetric problem of mechanics. Finally, Example 4 shows that the fundamental equation of quantum mechanics can be derived from a variational principle.

Example 2. Show that an isosceles triangle has the smallest perimeter for a given area and a given base.

Solution. Consider an ellipse whose foci are the ends of the base of the triangles ACB, APB and AQB. From the property of an ellipse, all these triangles have the same perimeter. But the isosceles triangle ABC has the maximum area since it has the greatest height. Thus, according to the reciprocity law, an isosceles triangle has the shortest perimeter for a given area and a given base.

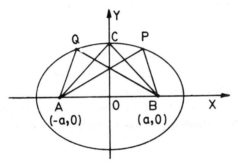

Fig. 4.1 Isosceles triangle of largest area for a given perimeter and base.

Example 3. Find the shape of an absolutely flexible, inextensible homogeneous and heavy rope of given length l suspended at the points A and B.

Solution. The rope in equilibrium takes a shape such that its centre of

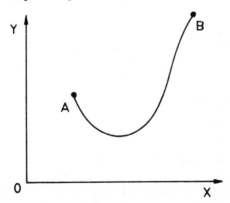

Fig. 4.2 Equilibrium shape of a heavy rope suspended from two fixed points.

gravity occupies the lowest position. Thus we have to find the minimum of the y-coordinate of the centre of gravity of the string given by

$$I[y(x)] = \frac{\displaystyle\int_{x_1}^{x_2} y\sqrt{1 + y'^2}\, dx}{\displaystyle\int_{x_1}^{x_2} \sqrt{1 + y'^2}\, dx} \tag{4.23}$$

subject to the constraint

$$\int_{x_1}^{x_2} \sqrt{1 + y'^2}\, dx = l. \tag{4.24}$$

This implies that we have to minimize the numerator of the right side of (4.23) subject to (4.24). We, therefore, form the functional

$$I^* = \int_{x_1}^{x_2} (y + \lambda) \sqrt{1 + y'^2}\, dx,$$

λ being a constant.

The first integral of the Euler equation for this functional is $y + \lambda = C_1 \sqrt{1 + y'^2}$, C_1 being a constant. Introducing $y' = \sinh t$, we find $y + \lambda = C_1 \cosh t$, giving $dx = dy/y' = C_1\, dt$. Thus, $x = C_1 t + C_2$ so that $y + \lambda = C_1 \cosh [(x - C_2)/C_1]$ is the desired curve representing a Catenary. The three constants λ, C_1 and C_2 are determined from (4.24) and the boundary conditions that the rope passes through A and B.

Example 4.　Derive the fundamental equation of quantum mechanics from a variational principle (The Schrödinger equation [7]).

Solution.　First we define an operator known as the Hamiltonian operator as follows:

$$H \equiv - kV^2 + V(x, y, z). \tag{4.25}$$

Here $k = h^2/(8\pi^2 m)$, where h and m stand for the Planck's constant and the mass of the particle whose motion is considered in a field of potential energy V. We now seek a wave function Ψ (possibly complex) which extremizes the functional

$$\iiint \Psi^*(H\Psi)\, dx\, dy\, dz \tag{4.26}$$

subject to the constraint

$$\iiint \Psi^* \Psi\, dx\, dy\, dz = 1, \tag{4.27}$$

where Ψ^* is the complex conjugate of Ψ.

The integration is over a fixed domain of x, y and z. We further assume that the admissible functions Ψ and Ψ^* either vanish at the boundaries of the domain or take on same values and derivatives at corresponding points on opposite boundaries. As a consequence

$$\iiint \Psi^* \, \nabla^2 \Psi \, dx \, dy \, dz = - \iiint \nabla \Psi^* \cdot \nabla \Psi \, dx \, dy \, dz.$$

Introducing the Lagrange multiplier λ, we then find the extremum of the functional

$$\iiint K \, dx \, dy \, dz = \iiint [k(\Psi_x^* \Psi_x + \Psi_y^* \Psi_y + \Psi_z^* \Psi_z$$

$$+ V\Psi^* \Psi - \lambda \Psi^* \Psi] \, dx \, dy \, dz$$

The Euler equations are

$$\frac{\partial K}{\partial \Psi} - \frac{\partial}{\partial x}\left(\frac{\partial K}{\partial \Psi_x}\right) - \frac{\partial}{\partial y}\left(\frac{\partial K}{\partial \Psi_y}\right) - \frac{\partial}{\partial z}\left(\frac{\partial K}{\partial \Psi_z}\right) = 0,$$

$$\frac{\partial K}{\partial \Psi^*} - \frac{\partial}{\partial x}\left(\frac{\partial K}{\partial \Psi_x^*}\right) - \frac{\partial}{\partial y}\left(\frac{\partial K}{\partial \Psi_y^*}\right) - \frac{\partial}{\partial z}\left(\frac{\partial K}{\partial \Psi_z^*}\right) = 0,$$

which reduce to

$$- k\nabla^2 \Psi + V\Psi = \lambda \Psi. \tag{4.28}$$

This may be written as

$$H\Psi = \lambda \Psi.$$

If we multiply this by Ψ^* and integrate over the domain of x, y, z, the left side becomes the stationary integral (4.26), which is denoted by E. Hence by (4.27), we have $\lambda = E$.

With $\lambda = E$, (4.28) reduces to the Schrödinger equation. It is worth pointing out here that there is an interesting and important connection between Hamilton-Jacobi equation (Section 3.10) for a classical system and the Schrödinger equation for a quantum mechanical system. In fact, if we put the wave function $\Psi = e^{(i/h)S}$, where S is the action function of the classical system (see (3.82)), then the Schrödinger equation reduces to the Hamilton-Jacobi equation (3.83) provided S is much larger than Planck's constant h. Thus in the limit of large values of action and energy, the surfaces of constant phase for the wave function Ψ reduce to surfaces of constant action S for the corresponding classical system. In this case, wave mechanics reduces to classical mechanics just as wave optics reduces to geometrical optics in the limit of very small wavelengths.

It may be noted that the Klein-Gordon equation

$$\nabla^2 \Psi - \frac{1}{c^2}\frac{\partial^2 \Psi}{\partial t^2} - \left(\frac{mc}{h}\right)^2 \Psi = 0,$$

(c = velocity of light) representing a possible wave equation for a relativistic particle (though it is not correct for an electron or proton) can be constructed in the same manner from the Lagrange functions

$$L = - \frac{h^2}{2m}\left[\nabla \Psi^* \cdot \nabla \Psi - \frac{1}{c^2}\left(\frac{\partial \Psi}{\partial t}\right)^2 + \left(\frac{mc}{h}\right)^2 \Psi^* \Psi\right].$$

4.3   Problems of Mayer and Bolza

These are two important classes of variational problems with conditional extrema (see [15]) which are reducible to Lagrange's problem mentioned in Section 4.1.

Mayer's Problem

It is necessary to find two functions $y_1(x)$ and $y_2(x)$ satisfying the relation

$$f(x, y_1(x), y_1'(x), y_2(x), y_2'(x)) = 0 \qquad (4.29)$$

and the boundary conditions

$$y_1(a) = y_{1a}, \qquad y_2(a) = y_{2a}, \qquad y_2(b) = y_{2b} \qquad (4.30)$$

such that the quantity $y_1(b)$ assumes an extremum in comparison with the other functions satisfying (4.29). This is a particular case of the general problem known as Mayer's problem. Introducing an unknown function

$$y_3(x) = y_1'(x), \qquad (4.31)$$

we reduce the above problem to Lagrange's problem of the extremum of

$$\int_a^b y_3(x)\, dx$$

subject to the non-holonomic constraints (4.29) and (4.31).

The general Mayer's problem with an arbitrary number n of unknown functions connected by a system of m differential equations ($m < n$) is treated in a similar fashion.

Bolza's Problem

The problem is to extremize a functional

$$\int_a^b F(x, y(x), y'(x), \lambda)\, dx + \phi(y(a), y(b), \lambda) \qquad (4.32)$$

containing a parameter λ.

It can be readily shown that this problem is reduced to Lagrange's problem for extremum of the functional

$$\int_a^b [F(x, y_1(x), y_1'(x), y_2(x)) + y_3(x)]\, dx$$

under the differential constraints

$$y_2'(x) = 0, \qquad y_3'(x) = 0$$

and the additional boundary condition

$$(b - a)y_3(a) - \phi(y_1(a), y_1(b), y_2(a)) = 0 \qquad (4.33)$$

Equation (4.33) shows that a boundary condition may connect the values of the unknown functions at both end points of the interval on which they are defined.

4.4 Equilibrium Problem for Elastic Bodies— Castigliano's Principle

We consider first a problem involving equilibrium of a rod. Let a rod of length l be fixed at the end points (x_1, y_1) and (x_2, y_2). From the theory of elasticity we know that the potential energy of the rod in the deformed state is proportional to the integral of the square of curvature taken along the rod. We take the length s of the rod reckoned from the point (x_1, y_1). Let $\theta(s)$ be the angle between the tangent to the rod and the x-axis. The equilibrium of the rod is determined from the extremum of the functional

$$I[\theta(s)] = \int_0^l [\theta'(s)]^2 \, ds \tag{4.34}$$

Since $dx = \cos \theta \cdot ds$ and $dy = \sin \theta \cdot ds$, we have the following equations of constraint:

$$\int_0^l \cos \theta \, ds = x_2 - x_1, \qquad \int_0^l \sin \theta \, ds = y_2 - y_1 \tag{4.35}$$

Since the rod is fixed at the end points, we take

$$\theta(0) = a, \qquad \theta(l) = b \tag{4.36}$$

Thus the Lagrangian function for this problem is

$$\Phi(\theta, \theta') = [\theta'(s)]^2 + \lambda_1 \cos \theta + \lambda_2 \sin \theta$$

This function is independent of s, and hence we can write down the first integral of Euler's equation as

$$\theta'^2 = C + \lambda_1 \cos \theta + \lambda_2 \sin \theta \tag{4.37}$$

Introducing the new constants

$$h = C + \sqrt{\lambda_1^2 + \lambda_2^2}, \qquad k^2 = \frac{2\sqrt{\lambda_1^2 + \lambda_2^2}}{C + \sqrt{\lambda_1^2 + \lambda_2^2}}$$

and the variable $\phi = (\theta - \theta_0)/2$ with $\theta_0 = \tan^{-1}(\lambda_2/\lambda_1)$, we can write (4.37) as

$$\frac{d\phi}{ds} = \frac{\sqrt{h}}{2} \cdot \sqrt{1 - k^2 \sin^2 \phi}$$

giving

$$s = \frac{2}{\sqrt{h}} \int \frac{d\phi}{\sqrt{1 - k^2 \sin^2 \phi}} + s_0.$$

The constants h, k^2, θ and s_0 are determined from (4.35) and (4.36). The cartesian coordinates of the points of the rod are found by quadrature from

$$dx = \cos\theta \cdot ds = [2\cos(2\phi + \theta_0)/\sqrt{h(1 - k^2 \sin^2\phi)}]\,d\phi,$$

$$dy = \sin\theta \cdot ds = [2\sin(2\phi + \theta_0)/\sqrt{h(1 - k^2 \sin^2\phi)}]\,d\phi.$$

This problem may be looked upon as an example of a general variational principle for equilibrium of an isotropic elastic body. Suppose such a body at rest occupies a region G in the xyz-space with piecewise smooth boundary Γ. Imagine that some forces deform this body from this state to a new equilibrium state such that a point (x, y, z) of the body suffers a displacement (u, v, w). The components of the strain tensor ε_{ij} (which is symmetric) satisfy

$$\varepsilon_{ij} = \frac{1}{2}(u_{i,j} + u_{j,i})$$

such that

$$\varepsilon_{11} = u_x, \quad \varepsilon_{12} = \varepsilon_{21} = \frac{1}{2}(u_y + v_x), \quad \varepsilon_{13} = \varepsilon_{31} = \frac{1}{2}(u_z + w_x), \quad (4.38)$$

$$\varepsilon_{22} = v_y, \quad \varepsilon_{33} = w_z, \quad \varepsilon_{23} = \varepsilon_{32} = \frac{1}{2}(v_z + w_y), \quad (4.39)$$

with the dilatation

$$\varepsilon = \varepsilon_{11} + \varepsilon_{22} + \varepsilon_{33}. \quad (4.40)$$

The components of the stress tensor (which is also symmetric) S_{ij} are linearly related to the strain components by Hooke's law

$$S_{11} = a\varepsilon_{11} + b\varepsilon, \quad S_{12} = S_{21} = a\varepsilon_{12}, \quad S_{13} = S_{31} = a\varepsilon_{13}, \quad (4.41a)$$

$$S_{22} = a\varepsilon_{22} + b\varepsilon, \quad S_{33} = a\varepsilon_{33} + b\varepsilon \quad S_{23} = S_{32} = a\varepsilon_{23}, \quad (4.41b)$$

where a and b are constants.

If a force $\mathbf{P}$ (P_1, P_2, P_3) acts at each point (x, y, z) of the body and a surface force $\mathbf{p}$ (p_1, p_2, p_3) acts at each point on the surface Γ of the body, then the equations of equilibrium are given by

$$S_{ij,j} + P_i = 0 \qquad (i = 1, 2, 3) \quad (4.42)$$

inside the body which is subject to the condition

$$S_{11}x_n + S_{21}y_n + S_{31}z_n - p_1 = 0, \quad (4.43a)$$

$$S_{12}x_n + S_{22}y_n + S_{32}z_n - p_2 = 0, \quad (4.43b)$$

$$S_{13}x_n + S_{23}y_n + S_{33}z_n - p_3 = 0, \quad (4.43c)$$

on the boundary Γ, where (x_n, y_n, z_n) are the direction cosines of the outer normal on Γ. We may consider a more general boundary condition such that the surface forces are given by $p_1 = \bar{p}_1, p_2 = \bar{p}_2, p_3 = \bar{p}_3$ on a portion Γ_1 of the boundary and the displacements are given by $u = \bar{u}, v = \bar{v}, w = \bar{w}$ on the remaining portion Γ_2 of the boundary. For determining the stresses and displacements at each point in equilibrium, we study the minimum of the potential energy $U[u, v, w]$ of the body given by

$$U[u, v, w] = \frac{1}{2} \iiint_G [\varepsilon_{11}S_{11} + \varepsilon_{22}S_{22} + \varepsilon_{33}S_{33} + 2\varepsilon_{12}S_{12} + 2\varepsilon_{13}S_{13}$$

$$+ 2\varepsilon_{23}S_{23}] \, dx \, dy \, dz - \iiint_G [P_1 u + P_2 v + P_3 w] \, dx \, dy \, dz$$

$$- \iiint_{\Gamma_1} [p_1 u + p_2 v + p_3 w] \, ds. \tag{4.44}$$

subject to the condition that (u, v, w) attain the above prescribed values on Γ_2. This is the well known principle of the minimum of potential energy. If we now apply the theory of reciprocal variational principle discussed earlier to the above problem, we are led to another important variational principle known as Castigliano's principle. This simply states that in equilibrium the work of deformation is minimum. It turns out that one can discuss some problems of elasticity more simply by applying Castigliano's principle than by the principle of minimum potential energy.

4.5   A Problem of Electrostatics

Let (u, v, w) be the components of the electric field **E** in a condenser, i.e., in the region G bounded by two closed surfaces S_1 and S_2 in space. If the field **E** is free from sources, then

$$u_x + v_y + w_z = 0. \tag{4.45}$$

Suppose that the charges on S_1 and S_2 are Q and $-Q$ respectively. Then

$$\iint_{S_1} (ux_n + vy_n + wz_n) \, ds = Q,$$

$$\iint_{S_2} (ux_n + vy_n + wz_n) \, ds = -Q, \tag{4.46}$$

where (x_n, y_n, z_n) are the direction cosines of the outward normal.

For electrostatic equilibrium, the energy of the field given by

$$\frac{1}{2} \iiint_G (u^2 + v^2 + w^2) \, dx \, dy \, dz$$

must be a minimum. For solving this variational principle by the method of Lagrange multipliers, we take $\lambda(x, y, z)$ as the multiplier for the constraint (4.45) and μ_1 and μ_2 as the constant multipliers for (4.46). We then obtain the Euler equations

$$u = \lambda_x, \qquad v = \lambda_y, \qquad w = \lambda_z$$

with the natural boundary conditions $\lambda = \mu_1 = $ constant on S_1, $\lambda = \mu_2 = $ constant on S_2. Thus the field is the gradient of the potential λ satisfying $\nabla^2 \lambda = 0$.

PROBLEMS

1. Find the extremal in the isoperimetric problem of the extremum of

$$I[y(x), z(x)] = \int_0^1 (y'^2 + z'^2 - 4xz' - 4z) \, dx$$

   subject to

$$\int_0^1 (y'^2 - xy' - z'^2) \, dx = 2, \quad y(0) = 0, \quad z(0) = 0, \quad y(1) = 1, \quad z(1) = 1.$$

   Ans. $y = -\dfrac{5}{2} x^2 + \dfrac{7}{2} x; z = x.$

2. Derive the differential equation for the extremals of the isoperimetric problem

$$I[y(x)] = \int_0^{x_1} [p(x) y'^2 + q(x)y^2] \, dx$$

   subject to

$$\int_0^{x_1} r(x)y^2 \, dx = 1, \quad y(0) = 0, \quad y(x_1) = 0.$$

   Ans. $[p(x)y']' + [\lambda r(x) - q(x)] y = 0$, λ being an eigenvalue.

3. Find the surface with the smallest area which encloses a given volume.

   Ans.   A sphere.

4. Consider the surface of least area bounded by a given curve which, together with a given surface bounded by the same curve, encloses a prescribed volume. Find the extremals.

   Ans.   Extremals are the surfaces of constant mean curvature.

APPENDIX

THEORY OF OPTIMAL CONTROL

It is interesting to point out that the methods for solving isoperimetric problems described above can be extended to more complex functionals.

We shall discuss at some length the problem of optimal control. The basic problem can be stated as follows: Find the control (vector) function $\mathbf{u}(t) = (u_1, u_2, ..., u_m)^T$, which minimizes the functional, called the performance index

$$I = \int_0^{T_0} f_0(\mathbf{x}, \mathbf{u}, t)\, dt, \tag{A4.1}$$

where $\mathbf{x}(t)$ ($= (x_1, x_2, ..., x_n)^T$) is called the state vector, t is the time parameter, T_0 is the terminal time and f_0 is a given function of $\mathbf{x}$, $\mathbf{u}$ and t. Here the superscript T stands for transpose. The relations between $\mathbf{x}(t)$ and $\mathbf{u}(t)$ are given by

$$\frac{dx_i}{dt} = f_i(x_1, x_2, ..., x_n; u_1, u_2, ..., u_m, t), \quad i = 1, 2, ..., n \tag{A4.2}$$

As in an isoperimetric problem, we introduce Lagrange multipliers $\lambda_i(t)$ and form the augmented functional I^* from (A4.1) and (A4.2) as follows:

$$I^* = \int_0^{T_0} \left[f_0 + \sum_{i=1}^{n} \lambda_i(f_i - \dot{x}_i) \right] dt, \tag{A4.3}$$

where the dot over x denotes derivative with respect to time. Introducing the Hamiltonian functional H as

$$H = f_0 + \sum_{i=1}^{n} \lambda_i f_i, \tag{A4.4}$$

we find from (A4.3),

$$I^* = \int_0^{T_0} (H - \sum_{i=1}^{n} \lambda_i \dot{x}_i)\, dt \tag{A4.5}$$

The Euler equations are

$$\frac{\partial H}{\partial x_i} = -\lambda_i \quad (i = 1, 2, ..., n), \tag{A4.6}$$

$$\frac{\partial H}{\partial u_j} = 0 \quad (j = 1, 2, ..., m) \tag{A4.7}$$

The optimal solutions for $\mathbf{x}$, $\mathbf{u}$ and λ are obtained by solving (A4.2, A4.6 and A4.7). In fact, these are $2n + m$ equations for x_i's, u_i's and λ_i's. If the initial conditions $x_i(0) = 0$ ($i = 1, 2, ..., n$) and the terminal conditions $x_j(T_0)$, $j = 1, 2, ..., l$, $l < n$ are known, then the terminal values $x_j(T_0)$ for $j = l + 1$, $l + 2, ..., n$ are free. In this case we use the free end conditions

$$\lambda_j(T) = 0, \quad j = l + 1, \quad l + 2, ..., n. \tag{A4.8}$$

Equations (A4.8) are known as the transversality conditions.

Consider, for example, the problem of finding the optimal control u which makes the functional

$$I = \int_0^1 (x^2 + u^2)\, dt$$

stationary with $x(0) = 1$ and $dx/dt = u$. Here the Hamiltonian function is

$$H = x^2 + u^2 = \lambda u.$$

Hence (A4.6) and (A4.7) give

$$2x = -\dot{\lambda}, \qquad 2u + \lambda = 0$$

which along with $dx/dt = u$ leads to

$$\ddot{x} - x = 0.$$

Its solution satisfying $x(0) = 1$ is

$$x(t) = C_1 \sinh t + \cosh t.$$

Since x is not specified at the terminal point $T_0 = 1$, we take $\lambda = 0$ at $t = 1$. This at once gives $u(1) = 0$ from $2u + \lambda = 0$. Since $u = \dot{x}$, we immediately get $C_1 = -\sinh 1/(\cosh 1)$. Thus the optimal control is

$$u(t) = -\frac{\sinh (1 - t)}{\cosh 1}.$$

The corresponding state vector is given by

$$x(t) = \frac{\cosh (1 - t)}{\cosh 1}.$$

Remark.   In practical problems, the optimal functions quite often lie on the boundary of a set of admissible control functions. For instance, if the control function is the engine power to be switched on, then this power has an upper bound which is the maximum power output of the engines. In solutions of such problems, it becomes sometimes necessary to run the engines at maximum power output at least over a certain time interval.

However, if the optimal function lies on the boundary of a set of admissible control functions, then the theory we have developed so far for problems involving conditional extremum and including two-sided variations is not applicable. The study of these problems is, of course, outside the scope of this book. Interested readers should consult the pioneering studies by L.S. Pontryagin and R. Bellman for solving such problems of optimal control. A succinct account of the contributions made by these authors can be found in the monograph by Razumikhin [91].

CHAPTER 5

EIGENVALUE PROBLEMS

5.1 Variational Theory of Eigenvalues

In this chapter we shall discuss about the bounds on the eigenvalues of a Stürm-Liouville system by using variational methods.

Consider the functional

$$I[y(x)] = \int_a^b [P(x)y'^2 + Q(x)y^2]\, dx \tag{5.1}$$

subject to the boundary conditions

$$y(a) = 0, \qquad y(b) = 0. \tag{5.2}$$

We shall assume that $P(x)$ and $Q(x)$ are continuous in $a \le x \le b$ and $P(x) > 0$ in the same interval. Now Euler's equation giving the extremum of $I[y(x)]$ is

$$(P(x)y')' - Q(x)y = 0 \tag{5.3}$$

The quadratic functional (5.1) satisfying $P(x) > 0$ can be investigated by using an approach which is analogous to the method of studying quadratic forms. Based on this analogy, we shall consider the values of the functional (5.1) for the functions $y(x)$ satisfying the constraint

$$\int_a^b w(x)y^2\, dx = 1, \tag{5.4}$$

where $w(x)$ is a continuous function satisfying $w > 0$ in $[a, b]$. These values of $I[y]$ are clearly bounded below because by (5.4) we have

$$I[y] \ge \int_a^b Q(x)y^2\, dx \ge \min_{[a,\,b]} \frac{Q(x)}{w(x)} \int_a^b wy^2\, dx$$

$$= \min_{[a,\,b]} \frac{Q(x)}{w(x)}.$$

Let $y = y_1(x)$ be the function satisfying (5.2) and (5.4) for which $I[y]$ attains the minimum value given above. This, however, needs proof since a functional whose values are bounded below need not attain a minimum. By using the principle of Lagrange multipliers, it can be easily shown that $y_1(x)$ satisfies

$$[P(x)y_1'(x)]' - [Q(x) - \lambda_1 w(x)]y_1(x) = 0, \tag{5.5}$$

where λ_1 is the Lagrange multiplier. We write (5.5) in the form

$$L[y_1] = \lambda_1 w(x)y_1, \tag{5.6}$$

where the operator L given by

$$L[y] = - [P(x)y'(x)]' + Q(x)y \tag{5.7}$$

is a linear operator in the corresponding function space. Equation (5.6) shows that y_1 is an eigenfunction corresponding to the eigenvalue λ_1.

Let $u(x)$ and $v(x)$ be any two functions satisfying the boundary conditions (5.2). Then using (5.7) and integrating by parts, it can be readily shown that

$$\int_a^b uLv \, dx = \int_a^b vLu \, dx. \tag{5.8}$$

It is important to point out here that we should take the functions $u(x)$ and $v(x)$ such that their derivatives appearing in (5.8) are finite or such that the integrals involved are absolutely convergent. Instead of assuming these conditions, it is convenient to interpret these functions as elements of the Hilbert space $L_2[a, b]$ such that the operator L defined on the subspace of functions satisfying (5.2) is self-adjoint.

After the function $y_1(x)$ is constructed, we proceed to determine the function $y_2(x)$ which minimizes the functional (5.1) satisfying (5.2) and the constraints

$$\int_a^b wy^2 \, dx = 1, \tag{5.9a}$$

$$\int_a^b wyy_1 \, dx = 0. \tag{5.9b}$$

This function can again be found by the method of Lagrange multipliers to satisfy the equation $Ly_2 = \mu_1 wy_1 + \lambda_2 wy_2$. Multiplying both sides of this equation by y_1 and integrating with respect to x from a to b and using (5.6), (5.8) and (5.9), we find that $\mu_1 = 0$. Thus $y_2(x)$ is an eigenfunction of the operator L with eigenvalue λ_2. Similarly, we find the eigenfunction $y_3(x)$ associated with the eigenvalue λ_3 such that the functional (5.1) attains a minimum on $y = y_3(x)$ satisfying

$$\int_a^b wy^2 \, dx = 1, \tag{5.10a}$$

$$\int_a^b wyy_1 \, dx = 0, \tag{5.10b}$$

$$\int_a^b wyy_2 \, dx = 0. \tag{5.10c}$$

In this way we obtain an infinite sequence

$$y_1(x), y_2(x), y_3(x), \ldots, \tag{5.11}$$

of eigenfunctions of L which satisfy (5.2). Due to the constraints (5.9b), (5.10b) and (5.10c) imposed on these functions, they are all mutually orthogonal with respect to the weight function $w(x)$ and satisfy the normalizing condition (5.4). Thus we get a normalized sequence of mutually orthogonal functions.

Using integration by parts, it can be easily shown that

$$I[y] = \int_a^b (L[y])y \, dx + [P(x)yy']_a^b.$$

This gives, from (5.2) and $L[y_n] = \lambda_n y_n w$, the relation

$$I[y_n] = \int_a^b w\lambda_n y_n^2 \, dx = \lambda_n \quad (n = 1, 2, \ldots,). \tag{5.12}$$

It can be easily seen that

$$I[y_1] \leq I[y_2] \leq I[y_3] \leq \ldots, \tag{5.13}$$

because if we impose an additional constraint, the class of functions under consideration becomes narrower so that the minimum attained on this restricted class can only increase. It can be shown that the sequence $I\{y_n\}$ is infinitely large.

The sequence (5.11) possesses another important property: it is complete in the sense that any arbitrary function (belonging to a wide class of functions) can be expanded in a series of the functions in (5.11).

Take, for instance, the functional

$$I[y] = \int_0^l y'^2 \, dx \tag{5.14}$$

subject to

$$y(0) = y(l) = 0 \tag{5.15}$$

and the constraint (5.4) with $w(x) \equiv 1$. In this case, (5.6) becomes $y'' + \lambda y = 0$. It can be easily seen that the eigenvalues and the normalized eigenfunctions are

$$y_k(x) = \sqrt{\frac{2}{l}} \sin \frac{k\pi x}{l}, \quad \lambda_k = \left(\frac{k\pi}{l}\right)^2, \quad k = 1, 2, \ldots,$$

The factor $\sqrt{2/l}$ is the normalization constant introduced to make the norms of the functions equal to unity.

Let us now consider the functional (5.1) subject to (5.2). We have seen that under these conditions, the corresponding operator (5.7) admits of a sequence of eigenfunctions (5.11) with associated eigenvalues (5.12). If the coefficients $P(x)$ and $Q(x)$ or the limits a and b change, then the eigenvalues also undergo change. In certain cases it is possible to get certain definite results as follows:

(i) If the coefficients $P(x)$ and $Q(x)$ are replaced by new coefficients $\bar{P}(x)$ and $\bar{Q}(x)$ satisfying the inequalities

$$\bar{P}(x) \geq P(x), \quad \bar{Q}(x) \geq Q(x), \quad a \leq x \leq b, \tag{5.16}$$

then every new eigenvalue $\bar{\lambda}_n$ exceeds the corresponding eigenvalue λ_n provided that the relations (5.16) do not simultaneously become equalities. That this assertion is true for the first eigenvalue λ_1 follows from the fact

$$\bar{\lambda}_1 = I\{\bar{y}_1\} > I\{\bar{y}_1\} \geq I\{y_1\} = \lambda_1.$$

To establish the truth of the above assertion for the nth eigenvalue, we apply Courant's theorem (see [15]) for functionals: let $\rho_1(x)$, $\rho_2(x)$, ..., $\rho_{n-1}(x)$ be an arbitrary set of $n-1$ functions and $\lambda(\rho_1, \rho_2, ..., \rho_{n-1})$ be the least value of (5.1) attained on the class of functions satisfying (5.2) and (5.4) and orthogonal to each function $\rho_i(x)$, $(i = 1, 2, ..., n-1)$, then the greatest of the members $\lambda(\rho_1, \rho_2, ..., \rho_{n-1})$ considered for all possible combinations of $\rho_1(x)$, $\rho_2(x)$, ..., $\rho_{n-1}(x)$ is equal to the eigenvalue λ_n. This is the minimax property of the eigenvalues.

(ii) Another simple result is as follows. If a constant C is added to $Q(x)$ in (5.1), all the resulting eigenvalues receive the increment C provided the weight function $w(x) \equiv 1$. In fact, by virtue of (5.4),

$$\int_a^b [P(x)y'^2 + (Q(x) + C)y^2]\, dx = \int_a^b [P(x)y'^2 + Q(x)y^2]\, dx + C$$

and hence the constant C is added to all the values of the functional (5.1). This proves the result.

From the above properties we can obtain an estimate of the bounds of the eigenvalues λ_n $(n = 1, 2, ...)$ of the operator L in (5.7) with $w(x) \equiv 1$ as follows:

$$\left[\min_{[a,\, b]} P(x) \right]\left(\frac{n\pi}{b - a} \right)^2 + \min_{[a,\, b]} Q(x) \leq \lambda_n$$

$$\leq \left[\max_{[a,\, b]} P(x) \right]\left(\frac{n\pi}{b - a} \right)^2 + \max_{[a,\, b]} Q(x). \tag{5.17}$$

This estimate, albeit somewhat crude, can be deduced from (5.12) and the properties (i) and (ii) mentioned above.

To obtain a more refined estimate, we introduce a change of variables

$$y = \phi(x) \cdot z, \quad dx = \Psi(x)\, dt \tag{5.18}$$

such that the constraint (5.4) (with $w(x) \equiv 1$) and the orthogonality conditions of the form (5.9b) retain their form. However, the functional (5.1) reduces to

$$\int_0^l [z'^2 + r(t)zz' + s(t)z^2]\, dt = \int_0^l \left[z'^2 + \left(s(t) - \frac{1}{2}r'(t) \right)z^2 \right] dt, \tag{5.19}$$

where the prime denotes derivative with respect to t. The above condition on (5.4) gives $\phi^2\Psi = 1$ while the integral form (5.19) demands $P\phi^2/\Psi = 1$. It then follows that

$$\phi(x) = [P(x)]^{-1/4}, \qquad \Psi(x) = [P(x)]^{1/2}, \tag{5.20a}$$

$$t = \int_a^x [P(x)]^{-1/2}\, dx, \quad l = \int_a^b [P(x)]^{-1/2}\, dx \tag{5.20b}$$

Further, we have

$$s - \frac{1}{2}r' = \frac{1}{4}P''(x) - \frac{1}{16P} \cdot P'^2(x) + Q. \tag{5.21}$$

Now using the fact that eigenvalues remain invariant under the above change of variables, we can apply (5.17), (5.20) and (5.21) to derive from (5.19) the following bounds on λ_n:

$$\left(\frac{n\pi}{\int_a^b P^{-1/2} \, dx} \right)^2 + \min\left(\frac{1}{4}P''(x) - \frac{P'^2(x)}{16P} + Q \right) \le \lambda_n$$

$$\le \left(\frac{n\pi}{\int_a^b P^{-1/2} \, dx} \right)^2 + \max\left(\frac{1}{4}P''(x) - \frac{P'^2(x)}{16P} + Q \right). \tag{5.22}$$

These bounds are clearly sharper than those in (5.17) since, unlike (5.17), the difference in the rightmost and leftmost members of (5.22) is bounded for $n \to \infty$.

We may also show that if a is increased or b is decreased in (5.1), then all the eigenvalues become greater. To prove this we suppose that $\bar{a} = a$ and $\bar{b} > b$. Let us extend the function $y_1(x)$ to the interval $\bar{a} \le x \le \bar{b}$ by putting $y_1(x) \equiv 0$ in $b \le x \le \bar{b}$. Then denoting the extended function by $z(x)$, we can write after using (5.12),

$$\lambda_1 = I(y_1) = \bar{I}(z) > \bar{I}(\bar{y}_1) = \bar{\lambda}_1.$$

Similarly, the corresponding estimates for the other eigenvalues can be obtained by using Courant's theorem.

Let us next suppose that we do not introduce a boundary condition on one or both end points of the closed interval $[a, b]$. Then the eigenfunctions satisfy the condition $y' = 0$ at that end point. It can be readily shown that all the above statements about the eigenvalues are valid for those boundary conditions as well. Further if at one of the end points a or b, the condition $y = 0$ is replaced by the condition $y' = 0$, all the eigenvalues are decreased. In fact this replacement is equivalent to discarding the boundary condition for the corresponding end point. This clearly implies that we pass to a wider class of functions for which the values of the functional (5.1) are compared. Hence the least value of the functional is diminished resulting in a decrease in the eigenvalue. We can apply similar considerations to the minimization of the functional

$$I(z) = \iint_G \left[\left(\frac{\partial z}{\partial x} \right)^2 + \left(\frac{\partial z}{\partial y} \right)^2 + Q(x, y)z^2 \right] dx \, dy \tag{5.23}$$

over a domain G in the xy-plane with the constraint

$$\iint\limits_G z^2 \, dx \, dy = 1 \tag{5.24}$$

and the boundary condition

$$z \mid_\Gamma = 0, \tag{5.25}$$

where Γ is the boundary of G. It can be shown that if the domain G is replaced by its subdomain, all the eigenvalues of the operator

$$L(z) = -\frac{\partial^2 z}{\partial x^2} - \frac{\partial^2 z}{\partial y^2} + Q(x, y)z \tag{5.26}$$

considered on the class of functions satisfying (5.25) are increased.

5.2   Asymptotic Behaviour of the Eigenvalues

The foregoing considerations do not indicate any uniform law according to which the eigenvalues of the system

$$L(y) = \lambda w(x)y, \qquad y(a) = y(b) = 0 \tag{5.27}$$

are arranged. Here the operator L is given by (5.7). But some regularity can be found for eigenvalues of very large magnitude. Let all the λ's be arranged in numerical order. Now (5.12) and (5.13) suggest that

$$\lambda_1 \leq \lambda_2 \leq \lambda_3 \leq \ldots \leq \lambda_n \leq \lambda_{n+1} \leq \ldots \, . \tag{5.28}$$

By substituting

$$z(t) = (wP)^{1/4} \, u, \qquad t = \int_a^x \left(\frac{w}{P}\right)^{1/2} dx \tag{5.29}$$

and by an analysis similar to that given in Section 5.1, the Stürm-Liouville equation (5.27) takes the form

$$\frac{d^2 z}{dt^2} - f(t)z + \lambda z = 0, \tag{5.30}$$

where $f(t)$ is a continuous function. Now consider, in place of (5.30), the equation

$$\frac{d^2 z}{dt^2} + \lambda' z = 0 \tag{5.31}$$

over the interval $[0, \tau]$, where τ corresponds to the value of t (given by (5.29)) at $x = b$. The boundary conditions for (5.31) are the same as those for (5.30), viz.,

$$z(0) = z(\tau) = 0, \tag{5.32}$$

which follow from (5.27).

Clearly, the eigenvalues of (5.31) are the minima of $\int_0^\tau (dz/dt)^2 \; dt$. But the eigenvalues of (5.30) are the minima of

$$\int_0^\tau \left[\left(\frac{dz}{dt} \right)^2 + fz^2 \right] dt.$$

Hence

$$\lambda = \text{minimum of } \int_0^\tau \left[\left(\frac{dz}{dt} \right)^2 + fz^2 \right] dt, \tag{5.33a}$$

$$\lambda' = \text{minimum of } \int_0^\tau \left(\frac{dz}{dt} \right)^2 dt. \tag{5.33b}$$

Let z' be the specific function which produces the minimum λ', whereas z produces the minimum λ. Clearly,

$$\lambda \le \int_0^\tau \left[\left(\frac{dz'}{dt} \right)^2 + fz'^2 \right] dt = \lambda' + \int_0^\tau fz'^2 \; dt.$$

Since f is bounded and z' is normalized, the integral $\int_0^\tau fz'^2 \; dt$ has, say, a finite value F'. Thus

$$\lambda \le \lambda' + F'. \tag{5.34}$$

Conversely,

$$\lambda' \le \int_0^\tau \left(\frac{dz}{dt} \right)^2 dt \le \lambda - \int_0^\tau fz^2 \; dt = \lambda - F, \tag{5.35}$$

where F is also a finite quantity. Combining (5.34) and (5.35), we get

$$\lambda' + F \le \lambda \le \lambda' + F',$$

which shows that λ differs from λ' by atmost a finite quantity. Hence if the values of λ' tend to ∞, so do λs. But the eigenvalues of system (5.31)–(5.32) are known and are given by

$$\lambda_n' = \frac{n^2 \pi^2}{\tau^2}, \tag{5.36}$$

n being an integer. If, instead of the boundary conditions (5.27) or (5.32), only periodicity of u or z is required, then the eigenvalues are, clearly,

$$\lambda_n' = \frac{4n^2 \pi^2}{\tau^2}.$$

In any case, it follows from (5.36) and the above equation that for large n,

$$\lambda_n' = \text{constant} \cdot n^2. \tag{5.37}$$

Since λ_n's and λ_n''s differ by a finite amount, it follows that

$$\lambda_n \sim \text{constant} \cdot n^2 \quad \text{as } n \to \infty, \tag{5.38}$$

which represents the asymptotic behaviour of the eigenvalues. It should be noted that the above behaviour of the eigenvalues is based on the assumption of a finite value of τ, which in turn implies a finite range of x. If the range of x is infinite, the above result may not hold. Take, for instance, the Hermite equation

$$\frac{d^2 u}{dx^2} - 2x \frac{du}{dx} + 2\lambda u = 0$$

with infinite range for x. Its eigenvalues λ_n are proportional to n rather than n^2 even asymptotically. But it is still true that $\lambda_n \to \infty$ as $n \to \infty$.

In fact, in the variational eigenvalue problems studied above, the eigenvalues λ_n (see (5.12)) become infinite for $n \to \infty$. This implies, in particular, that each eigenvalue can have a finite multiplicity and that only a finite number of eigenvalues can be negative. Another important consequence of the unboundedness of eigenvalues is the completeness of the system of eigenfunctions. This system, therefore, coincides with the system of eigenfunctions of the associated differential equation.

Before we consider these aspects, let us discuss the extremum properties of eigenvalues by variational methods.

5.3   Extremum Properties of Eigenvalues

Eigenvalue Problem with the Natural Boundary Condition

$$\frac{\partial u}{\partial n} + \sigma u = 0$$

Consider the eigenvalue problem associated with a self-adjoint second order partial differential equation

$$L[u] + \lambda \rho u = (pu_x)_x + (pu_y)_y - qu + \lambda \rho u = 0 \tag{5.39}$$

with $p(x, y) > 0$ and $\rho(x, y) > 0$. Here a subscript denotes a partial derivative and x and y are independent variables in the domain G bounded by one or several continuous curves Γ with piecewise continuous tangents. Let the function $u(x, y)$ in (5.39) be subject to the boundary condition $u = 0$ or $\partial u / \partial n + \sigma u = 0$, where σ is a piecewise continuous function of position on the boundary Γ and $\partial / \partial n$ denotes differentiation in the direction of the outward normal. The associated quadratic functional expressions for the variational eigenvalue problems are

$$\bar{D}[\phi] = D[\phi] + \int_\Gamma p\sigma\phi^2 \, ds \tag{5.40}$$

with

$$D[\phi] = \iint_G p(\phi_x^2 + \phi_y^2) \, dx \, dy + \iint_G q\phi^2 \, dx \, dy, \tag{5.41a}$$

$$D[\phi,\ \Psi] = \iint_G p(\phi_x \Psi_x + \phi_y \Psi_y)\ dx\ dy + \iint_G q\phi\Psi\ dx\ dy, \qquad (5.41\text{b})$$

$$H[\phi] = \iint_G \rho\phi^2\ dx\ dy. \qquad (5.42\text{a})$$

Further, we introduce the following functions $H[\phi,\ \Psi]$ and $\bar{D}[\phi,\ \Psi]$:

$$H[\phi,\ \Psi] = \iint_G \rho\phi\Psi\ dx\ dy, \qquad (5.42\text{b})$$

$$\bar{D}[\phi,\ \Psi] = D[\phi,\Psi] + \int_\Gamma p\sigma\phi\Psi\ ds. \qquad (5.42\text{c})$$

We require the argument ϕ to be continuous in $G + \Gamma$ and to possess piecewise continuous first derivatives in G.

Following the same procedure for finding the extremum of the functional (5.1) subject to (5.2), we can derive the following result for the extremum of the functional (5.41a) satisfying $H[\phi] = 1$: The admissible function which minimizes $\bar{D}[\phi]$ in (5.40) subject to $H[\phi] = 1$ is an eigenfunction u_1 for the differential equation (5.39) and satisfies the natural boundary condition $\partial\phi/\partial n + \sigma\phi = 0$, the minimum value of $\bar{D}$ in (5.40) being the corresponding eigenvalue. Further, if we impose the orthogonality condition $H[\phi, u_1] = 0$ in addition to $H[\phi] = 1$, then the solution is again an eigenfunction u_2 of (5.39) subject to the same boundary condition and the minimum value given by $\bar{D}[u_2] = \lambda_2$ is the associated eigenvalue. This process can be repeated so that the problem $\bar{D}[\phi] = $ minimum with $H[\phi] = 1$ and the orthogonality conditions

$$H[\phi,\ u_i] = 0 \qquad (i = 1,\ 2,\ ...,\ \nu - 1)$$

define the eigen functions u_ν of (5.39) satisfying $\partial\phi/\partial n + \sigma\phi = 0$. The associated eigenvaue λ_ν equals the minimum of $\bar{D}[u_\nu]$. It should be noted that by minimizing the quotient $\bar{D}[\phi]/H[\phi]$, we can omit $H[\phi] = 1$. In this case the solution is determined up to a factor of proportionality. This quotient, known in the literature as the Rayleigh quotient ([16]), is named after Rayleigh who first realized that the eigenvalue λ may be considered as the ratio of kinetic to potential energy of the dynamical system represented by (5.39).

It is thus clear that the Rayleigh quotient gives an upper bound to the eigenvalue of (5.39) with a self-adjoint operator L subject to the boundary condition $\partial u/\partial n + \sigma u = 0$. The question naturally arises: How to find a lower bound to this eigenvalue? To answer this question, we now address ourselves to the problem of finding the lower bounds of the eigenvalues of

$$Ly + \lambda f(\mathbf{x})y = 0 \quad \text{in a region } V \qquad (5.43\text{a})$$

subject to

$$B_i y = 0 \quad \text{on } S, \tag{5.43b}$$

where L is a self-adjoint operator in a Hilbert space.

We present the method due to Weinstein (see Gould [17]) in which comparison equations are constructed, which are easier to solve than (5.43). These equations are such that its eigenvalues are lower bounds to the eigenvalues of (5.43).

Let us rewrite (5.43a) as

$$Ly + \lambda \alpha y - \lambda(\alpha - f)y = 0, \tag{5.44}$$

where $\alpha \geq \max f(\mathbf{x})$. We introduce the intermediate problem

$$Ly = \mu \left\{ \alpha y - (y, y_n) \left(\int_V \frac{y_n^2}{\alpha - f} \, dV \right)^{-1} y_n \right\} = 0, \tag{5.45}$$

where y_n is any eigenfunction of the problem $Ly + \Lambda y = 0$, which is normalized such that $(y_n, y_k) = \delta_{nk}$. Here, (y, y_n) stands for the inner product of the Hilbert space defined by

$$(y, y_n) = \int_V y y_n \, dV$$

over the region V.

We first calculate the Rayleigh quotient for the above intermediate problem and then get

$$R(y) = (- Ly, y) \Big/ \left\{ \alpha(y, y) - (y, y_n)^2 \left(\int_V \frac{y_n^2}{\alpha - f} \, dV \right)^{-1} \right\}. \tag{5.46}$$

By Schwarz inequality, we find that

$$(y, y_n)^2 = \left(\int_V \frac{(\alpha - f)^{1/2} y y_n}{(\alpha - f)^{1/2}} \, dV \right)^2 \leq \left(\int_V (\alpha - f)y^2 \, dV \right) \left(\int_V \frac{y_n^2}{\alpha - f} \, dV \right). \tag{5.47}$$

Hence the denominator of (5.46) is greater than or equal to (fy, y) and is less than or equal to $\alpha(y, y)$. This leads to

$$\frac{(- Ly, y)}{\alpha(y, y)} \leq R(y) \leq \frac{(- Ly, y)}{(fy, y)}. \tag{5.48}$$

For $k \neq n$, the eigenfunction for (5.45) is y_k and the eigenvalue is $\mu_k = \Lambda_k / \alpha$. For the nth eigenvalue the eigenfunction is y_n with

$$\mu D(\alpha) y_n = \Lambda_n y_n,$$

$$D(\alpha) = \alpha - \left(\int \frac{y_n^2}{\alpha - f} \, dV \right)^{-1}. \tag{5.49}$$

The eigenvalues then satisfy

$$\frac{\Lambda_1}{\alpha} \le \frac{\Lambda_2}{\alpha} \dots \le \frac{\Lambda_{n-1}}{\alpha} \le \frac{\Lambda_{n+1}}{\alpha} \le \dots . \tag{5.50}$$

The value $\mu_q = \Lambda_n/D(\alpha)$ should be placed in its proper numerical position in (5.50). We wish to select α to obtain the best bound for λ_n. Now from (5.49) it is clear that $\Lambda_n/D(\alpha)$ is above Λ_n/α for $\alpha \ge f$. Again,

$$\frac{dD}{d\alpha} = 1 - \left(\int \frac{y_n^2}{\alpha - f} \, dV \right)^{-2} \cdot \left(\int \frac{y_n^2}{(\alpha - f)^2} \, dV \right). \tag{5.51}$$

By Schwarz inequality,

$$\left(\int \frac{y_n^2}{\alpha - f} \, dV \right)^2 \le \left(\int \frac{y_n^2}{(\alpha - f)^2} \, dV \right)(y_n, y_n) = \int \frac{y_n^2}{(\alpha - f)^2} \, dV$$

so that $dD/d\alpha < 0$ from (5.51). Hence D decreases with α. Thus $\Lambda_n/D(\alpha)$ increases with increasing α. The other eigenvalues in (5.50) clearly decrease with increase in α. Hence for small α, the eigenvalue $\Lambda_n/D(\alpha)$ lies between Λ_n/α and Λ_{n+1}/α. As α is increased, we get a point where $\Lambda_n/D(\alpha) = \Lambda_{n+1}/\alpha$. Any additional increase in α gives no improvement, since the lower bound for λ_n is then Λ_{n+1}/α and $\Lambda_n/D(\alpha)$ is a lower bound for λ_{n+1}, and so on. Thus the best value of α satisfies

$$\frac{\Lambda_n}{D(\alpha)} = \frac{\Lambda_{n+1}}{\alpha}. \tag{5.52}$$

There is one more complication. Let $\alpha = M$ = positive maximum of f. If

$$\Lambda_{n+1}/M \le \Lambda_n/D(M), \tag{5.53}$$

then the best lower bound for λ_n is Λ_{n+1}/M. The value of α cannot be taken any lower (the integrals are then undefined) and any larger α gives worse bounds, Λ_{n+1}/α. Thus the procedure is: check (5.53). If it is not satisfied, select α which satisfies (5.52), which gives the best lower bound for λ_n.

Eigenvalue Problem with the Boundary Condition $u = 0$

When the boundary condition is $u = 0$, the same variational problems define the eigenvalues and the eigenfunctions.

In this case the term $\int_\Gamma p\sigma\phi^2 \, ds$ in (5.40) drops out automatically because the boundary condition $\phi = 0$ is now added to the admissible functions. Detailed analysis shows that our minimum problem admits of a solution with continuous second derivatives.

Courant's Theorem

We now state Courant's theorem (see [3a]) which is a generalization of the minimax property of the eigenvalues stated in Section 5.1: Given $n - 1$ functions $v_1, v_2, \dots,$

v_{n-1} which are piecewise continuous in G, let $d(v_1, v_2, ..., v_{n-1})$ be the greatest lower bound of the set of values attained by the functional $\overline{D}[\phi]$, where ϕ is any function continuous in G with piecewise continuous derivatives such that $H[\phi] = 0$ with the orthogonality conditions

$$H[\phi, v_i] = 0 \quad (i = 1, 2, ..., n - 1). \tag{5.54}$$

Then λ_n is the largest value which this lower bound d attains when the functions $v_1, v_2, ..., v_{n-1}$ range over the set of all admissible functions. This minimax is attained for $u = u_n, v_1 = u_1, v_2 = u_2, ..., v_{n-1} = u_{n-1}$.

To establish this theorem, we begin by noting that by definition we have

$$d[v_1, v_2, ..., v_{n-1}] = \lambda_n \quad \text{for } v_i = u_i \ (1 \le i \le n - 1).$$

Then we say that for arbitrary $v_1, v_2, ..., v_{n-1}$, the result $d[v_1, v_2, ..., v_{n-1}] \le \lambda_n$ holds. To this end we need to determine a function ϕ satisfying $H[\phi, v_i] = 0$, $(i = 1, ..., n - 1)$ such that $D[\phi] \le \lambda_n$. We now express $\phi = \sum\limits_{i=1}^{n} C_i u_i$ as a linear combination of the n eigenfunctions u_i, C_i being constants. Then the relation (5.54) implies $n - 1$ relations among the n constants C_i $(i = 1, 2, ..., n)$ and hence can always be satisfied. The normalizing condition $H[\phi] = \sum\limits_{i=1}^{n} C_i^2 = 1$ determines a factor of proportionality. From (5.41a), (5.41b) and (5.42d), it can be easily shown that $\overline{D}[u_i, u_k] = 0$ for $i \ne k$ and $\overline{D}[u_i] = \lambda_i$. Hence it follows from

$$\overline{D}[\phi] = \sum\limits_{i,k=1}^{n} C_i C_k \overline{D}[u_i, u_k]$$

that

$$\overline{D}[\phi] = \sum\limits_{i=1}^{n} C_i^2 \lambda_i.$$

When this is combined with the relations

$$\sum\limits_{i=1}^{n} C_i^2 = 1, \ \lambda_n \ge \lambda_i \quad (i = 1, 2, ..., n),$$

we get

$$\overline{D}[\phi] \le \lambda_n.$$

Thus the minimum $d[v_1, v_2, ..., v_{n-1}]$ is certainly not greater than λ_n. Hence λ_n is the largest value which this minimum can assume, and this proves the theorem.

5.4   Some Important Consequences of the Extremum Properties of Eigenvalues

Several important conclusions can be drawn from the minimax property described above.

Consider, for example, a system capable of vibration such that its eigenvalues are determined by an eigenvalue problem of a type considered in Section 5.3. If some constraint is imposed on the vibrating system, then it can be expressed mathematically as an auxiliary condition imposed on the admissible functions ϕ in the corresponding variational problem. Now, whenever the conditions on ϕ in a minimax problem are strengthened, the lower bound $d[v_1, v_2, ..., v_{n-1}]$ increases or at any rate does not decrease. Consequently this is true for the maximum of these lower bounds, which is the nth eigenvalue by the minimax property explained in Section 5.3. Similarly, when the conditions on the admissible functions ϕ are weakened, the eigenvalue is diminished or at least not increased. In physical terms, this means that if a system capable of vibrating is subjected to certain constraints, the pitch of the fundamental tone and every overtone increases or at least does not decrease. But, if restraining conditions are removed, the fundamental tone and every overtone decrease (or at least does not increase) in pitch. For example, if a membrane is fixed not only along the boundary but also along some other curve on it, then the fundamental tone and the overtones increase. But if the membrane is slit, these tones decrease. In the latter case the continuity for the admissible functions ϕ or their derivatives is lost.

Using the minimax property, we may readily prove another important theorem.

Theorem 1. Suppose that G_1, G_2, G_3, ... are a finite number of non-overlapping subdomains of the domain G in the eigenvalue problem (5.39). Let $A(\lambda)$ be the number of eigenvalues less than λ of (5.39) with the boundary condition $u = 0$. Then the total number of eigenvalues less than λ for all the separate subdomains with the same boundary condition does not exceed $A(\lambda)$.

This theorem leads to an important property of monotonicity of the eigenvalues associated with the boundary condition $u = 0$.

Theorem 2. With the boundary condition $u = 0$, the nth eigenvalue for a domain G will never exceed the corresponding eigenvalue for any subdomain of G.

We now prove a theorem concerning the relative behaviour the spectra of the differential equation (5.39) for different types of boundary conditions.

Theorem 3. Let λ_n be the nth eigenvalue of (5.39) for the domain G with the boundary condition $u = 0$, and let μ_n be the nth eigenvalue for the same equation with the boundary condition $\partial u/\partial n + \sigma u = 0$ or more generally with the condition $\partial u/\partial n + \sigma u = 0$ on a part of the boundary, and $u = 0$ on the remaining part. Then $\mu_n \leq \lambda_n$.

This may be proved by considering the minimax problem which characterizes the nth eigenvalue μ_n of G without boundary conditions, as the maximum of the minimum of $\overline{D}[\phi]$ (see Section 5.3). If we now impose on ϕ the additional condition of vanishing of ϕ on the boundary Γ of G, then the individual minimum and hence also the maximum-minimum increases or at any rate, does not decrease. But this new maximum-minimum is λ_n since $\overline{D}[\phi] = D[\phi]$ when the boundary condition $\phi = 0$ is imposed. Thus $\mu_n \leq \lambda_n$.

Another important significance of this result can be seen in transient heat transfer problems. Here the eigenvalues determine the speed of response of a system to a change in the boundary conditions, with a higher value indicating a faster speed of response. Hence a system always responds quicker if the temperature remains fixed on the boundary rather than having the heat flux proportional to the temperature there.

We now state another simple principle (which is quite evident) of the calculus of variations. It states: Given two minimum problems with the same class of admissible functions ϕ such that for each ϕ, the functional to be minimized is no smaller in the first problem than in the second. Then the minimum for the first problem is no smaller than the minimum for the second.

Using this principle, the following theorem may be readily established.

Theorem 4.   If in the boundary condition $\partial u/\partial n + \sigma u = 0$ on Γ, the function σ is either increased or decreased at every point, then each eigenvalue can change only in the same sense.

This stems from the fact that if we change σ, the expression $\bar{D}[\phi]$ changes in the same sense as σ for each ϕ and, consequently, the same is true of its lower bound for given v_i (see Courant's theorem in Section 5.3) as also for the maximum of these lower bounds.

The above theorems admit of an interesting physical interpretation. The boundary condition $\partial u/\partial n + \sigma u = 0$ implies a boundary fixed by elastic forces such that the magnitude of the constraining forces depends on σ.

Theorems 3 and 4 suggest that as σ (which is a measure of the intensity of the force) increases, the eigen frequency increases. In the limit $\sigma \to \infty$, $\partial u/\partial n + \sigma u = 0$ reduces to $u = 0$, which represents the case of an infinite force or a completely fixed boundary.

Finally, the minimax property of eigenvalues enables us to examine the dependence of eigenvalues on the coefficients of the differential equation (5.39) and on the domain G. This is embodied in the following theorem.

Theorem 5.   If the coefficient p in (5.39) varies at every point in the same sense, then for boundary conditions $u = 0$ or $\partial u/\partial n + \sigma u = 0$ (with $\sigma \geq 0$), the nth eigenvalue changes in the opposite sense. Further, if p or q changes everywhere in the same sense, every eigenvalue also changes in the same sense.

To prove the second part of the theorem, we suppose that p is changed everywhere in the same sense. Then for any admissible function ϕ, the value of $\bar{D}[\phi]$, and hence the lower bounds of these values for fixed v_i and the maximum of these lower bounds, change monotonically in the same sense. This implies that the nth eigenvalue also changes in the same sense. The first part can be similarly proved by noting that the eigenvalues are obtained by minimizing the quotient $\bar{D}[\phi]/H[\phi]$ when the normalizing condition $H[\phi] = 1$ is not imposed (see Section 5.2) and the fact that when p is changed monotonically, resulting in a function $\rho' \geq \rho$ such that

$$\bar{D}[\phi] : \iint_G \rho\phi^2 \, dx \, dy \geq \bar{D}[\phi] : \iint_G \rho'\phi^2 \, dx \, dy$$

for any admissible function ϕ.

We now take up the question we have left unanswered in Section 5.2, viz., in the variational eigenvalue problems the eigenvalues $\lambda_n \to \infty$ as $n \to \infty$.

Referring to (5.39), we denote by p_M, q_M, ρ_M and p_m, q_m and ρ_m the largest and smallest values respectively of p, q, ρ in G and consider the boundary condition $u = 0$. If we replace the functions p, q, ρ in $\bar{D}$ and H by the constants p_m, q_m, ρ_M and p_M, q_M, ρ_m, we get new eigenvalue problems with the eigenvalues λ'_n and λ''_n respectively and by Theorem 5 we have $\lambda'_n \leq \lambda_n \leq \lambda''_n$. We show first the eigenvalues λ'_n are unbounded. Now in the case of one independent variable, the associated differential equation eigenvalue problem can be solved explicitly in terms of trigonometric functions. The eigenvalues are $(p_m v^2 + q_m)/\rho_M$, $v = 1, 2, \ldots$. Since the eigenvalues λ'_n arising out of the variational problem are certainly contained in this sequence, the assertion $\lambda_n \to \infty$ clearly holds.

We now say a few words about the continuity of eigenvalues. Let us assume that the function ρ is changed to a function ρ' such that $0 < (1 - \varepsilon)\rho \leq \rho' \leq (1 + \varepsilon)\rho$ for $\varepsilon > 0$. Then by Theorem 5, the nth eigenvalue of the differential equation lies between the nth eigenvalues derived by replacing ρ by $\rho(1 - \varepsilon)$ and by $\rho(1 + \varepsilon)$ respectively, in the differential equation. This is tantamount to multiplication of the nth eigenvalue by the factor $(1 - \varepsilon)^{-1}$ and $(1 + \varepsilon)^{-1}$, respectively. For sufficiently small ε, these two numbers are arbitrarily close to each other. Hence the nth eigenvalue depends continuously on ρ.

Further, the nth eigenvalue also depends continuously on the function q. To prove this, we first note that from the relation $\rho \geq \rho_m$, where ρ_m is a positive constant, we have

$$1 = \iint\limits_G \rho\phi^2 \, dx \, dy \geq \rho_m \iint\limits_G \phi^2 \, dx \, dy.$$

Hence the integral $\displaystyle\iint\limits_G \phi^2 \, dx \, dy$ is uniformly bounded for any admissible function ϕ. This leads to the fact that a small change in q results in a small change in $\bar{D}[\phi]$. Hence the same is true for the maximum-minimum of $\bar{D}[\phi]$, which establishes our assertion. Similarly, the eigenvalues can be shown to depend continuously on the function p as well as the function σ occurring in the boundary condition $\partial u/\partial n + \sigma u = 0$.

We may thus say that for all boundary conditions considered, any eigenvalue of $L[u] + \lambda\rho u = 0$ depends continuously on the coefficients of the equation.

Finally, we state without proof an important result which throws light on the continuity of the nth eigenvalue considered as a function of the domain G. This is embodied in the following theorem.

Theorem 6. Let the domain G be deformed to a domain G' such that the boundary of G' approximates that of G pointwise and in addition the normals to the boundary of G' approximate those of G. Then for any of the boundary conditions considered, the nth eigenvalue of $L[u] + \lambda\rho u = 0$ varies continuously when the domain G is deformed continuously in the sense defined above.

In Section 5.2, we made the remark that in view of the fact that the eigenvalues λ_n in a variational problem become infinite as $n \to \infty$, only a finite number of eigenvalues can be negative. In this context we consider the eigenvalue problem of the Stürm-Liouville equation

$$[p(x)\, u'(x)]' - q(x)u(x) + \lambda p(x)u(x) = 0 \tag{5.55}$$

over the interval $0 \le x \le \pi$ with the boundary conditions

$$u'(0) - h_1 u(0) = u'(\pi) + h_2 u(\pi) = 0 \tag{5.56}$$

such that $h_1 \ge 0$ and $h_2 \ge 0$. This corresponds to the variational problem of the minimum of

$$\bar{D}[\phi] = \int_0^\pi [p\phi'^2 + q\phi^2]\, dx + h_1 p(0)\, \phi^2(0) + h_2 p(\pi)\phi^2(\pi)$$

without boundary conditions. An analysis based on the fact that the eigenvalues become infinite as $n \to \infty$ shows that when the function q is not everywhere positive, at most a finite number of negative eigenvalues can occur. The same is true when the constants h_1, h_2 assume negative values because here, too, the eigenvalues become infinite as $n \to \infty$.

It may be noted that in the Stürm-Liouville equation (5.55) as well as in (5.39), it is assumed that $p(x) > 0$ so that the differential equation is regular at the end point. But even for Stürm-Liouville equations with singularities at end points, the eigenvalues and the eigenfunctions may be characterized by variational principles. Take, for instance, the Bessel equation of order $m \ge 1$ given by

$$(xu')' + \left(\lambda x - \frac{m^2}{x}\right)u = 0 \tag{5.57}$$

in the interval [0, 1].

In this case the functional to be extremized is

$$\bar{D}[\phi] = \int_0^1 \left(x\phi'^2 + \frac{m^2 \phi^2}{x}\right) dx$$

with $H[\phi] = 1$, where

$$H[\phi] = \int_0^1 x\phi^2\, dx$$

along with the boundary condition $\phi(0) = 0$. The boundary condition $\phi(1) = 0$ at the regular end point $x = 1$ is relevant to the problem of a clamped membrane. The Bessel function $J_0(x\sqrt{\lambda})$ of order zero arises from the variational problem for which

$$\bar{D}[\phi] = \int_0^1 x\phi'^2\, dx, \quad H[\phi] = \int_0^1 x\phi^2\, dx.$$

The asymptotic estimate of the eigenvalues is also readily carried over to singular differential equations. The solution $J_m(x\sqrt{\lambda})$ satisfying $u(0) \prec \infty$ and $u(1) = 0$ gives rise to the eigenvalues λ, which are the squares of the zeros of J_m. For $m \geq 1$, we introduce $v = \sqrt{x}\, J_m(x\sqrt{\lambda})$ with the eigenvalue equation

$$v'' + \left(\lambda - \frac{4m^2 - 1}{4x^2}\right)v = 0.$$

The eigenvalues are characterized by the maxima of minima of the quotient $D[\phi]/H[\phi]$ with

$$D[\phi] = \int_0^1 \left[\phi'^2 + \frac{(4m^2 - 1)}{4x^2}\phi^2\right] dx, \quad H[\phi] = \int_0^1 \phi^2\, dx.$$

We take the boundary conditions as $\phi(0) = \phi(1) = 0$. Since $m \geq 1$, $D[\phi] \geq \int_0^1 \phi'^2\, dx$ so that $\lambda_n \geq n^2\pi^2$. We now obtain an upper bound for λ_n by restricting the admissibility conditions as follows: In the interval $0 \leq x \leq \varepsilon$ (where ε is to be determined), we take $\phi(x) = 0$ and majorize the second term of $D[\phi]$ by the constant

$$[(4m^2 - 1)/4\varepsilon^2] \int_0^1 \phi^2\, dx = C/\varepsilon^2.$$ This gives $\lambda_n \leq [n^2\pi^2/(1 - \varepsilon)^2] + C/\varepsilon^2$. If we now

put $\varepsilon = 1/\sqrt{n}$, it follows that $\lim_{n \to \infty} \lambda_n/(n^2\pi^2) \leq 1$. We thus derive the asymptotic formula

$$\lim_{n \to \infty} \frac{\lambda_n}{n^2\pi^2} = 1$$

for the zeros $\sqrt{\lambda_{m,n}}$ of J_m. This is similar to the asymptotic formula (5.38) for non-singular problems. This result can be readily extended to the roots of the Bessel function of zeroth order.

5.5 Completeness of Eigenfunctions

In Section 5.2, we pointed out that an important consequence of the unboundedness of the eigenvalues of a Stürm-Liouville problem is the completeness of the eigenfunctions. We now wish to give this definition greater precision and furnish its proof.

A set of functions $y_1, y_2, \ldots$ is said to be complete if it is possible to 'approximate in the mean' any function $f(x)$ satisfying the same boundary conditions as the y's, with the help of a series $\sum_{i=1}^{n} a_i y_i$ such that

$$\lim_{n \to \infty} \int_a^b \left(f - \sum_{i=1}^{n} a_i y_i\right)^2 w(x)\, dx = 0, \tag{5.58}$$

where $w(x)$ appears in the Stürm-Liouville equation (5.6). Here the functions y_i are the solutions of (5.6) subject to (5.2). These functions, as shown in Section 5.1, are orthogonal in $[a, b]$. If for a given finite n, we want to make the quantity

$$N = \int_a^b \left(f - \sum_{i=1}^n a_i y_i \right)^2 w \, dx \tag{5.59}$$

as small as possible, then we have

$$\frac{\partial N}{\partial a_j} = 0 \quad \text{for } j = 1, 2, \ldots, n.$$

This gives from (5.59) the relation

$$a_j = \int_a^b f y_j w \, dx \tag{5.60}$$

after using the orthogonal properties of y_j.

Let us now introduce the following notations:

$$\Delta_n = f - \sum_{i=1}^n a_i y_i, \quad C_n = \left[\int_a^b \Delta_n^2 w \, dx \right]^{1/2}. \tag{5.61}$$

It is easy to see that Δ_n/C_n has the following properties: (i) it is normalized; and (ii) it is orthogonal to any y_i with $i \le n$. Property (i) follows from the definition of C_n above. To establish property (ii), we note that, in view of orthogonality of y_i and (5.60),

$$\int_a^b \frac{\Delta_n}{C_n} y_i w \, dx = \frac{1}{C_n} \left[\int_a^b f y_i w \, dx - \sum_{j=1}^n a_j \int_a^b y_i y_j w \, dx \right]$$

$$= \begin{cases} \dfrac{1}{C_n}(a_i - a_i) = 0 & \text{if } i \le n, \\[2mm] \dfrac{a_i}{C_n} & \text{if } i > n. \end{cases}$$

We now find that Δ_n/C_n endowed with these properties satisfies all conditions, which we have imposed on y_{n+1} in the variational problem studied in Section 5.1 except that of minimizing the functional $I[y(x)]$ given by (5.1). Hence we must have

$$I[\Delta_n/C] \ge I[y_{n+1}],$$

which implies that

$$\frac{1}{C_n^2} I[\Delta_n] \ge \lambda_{n+1}. \tag{5.62}$$

Now

$$I[\Delta_n] = \int_a^b \Delta_n L(\Delta_n) \, dx,$$

where the operator L is defined by (5.7). But

$$\int_a^b \Delta_n L(\Delta_n) \, dx = \int_a^b \left(f - \sum_{i=1}^n a_i y_i \right) \cdot L\left(f - \sum_{i=1}^n a_i y_i \right) dx$$

$$= \int_a^b f L f \, dx - \sum_{i=1}^n a_i^2 \lambda_i$$

since

$$L(y_i) = \lambda_i w y_i,$$

$$\int_a^b y_i L(f) \, dx = \int_a^b f L(y_i) \, dx = a_i \lambda_i.$$

Thus we have

$$I[\Delta_n] = I[f] - \sum_{i=1}^n a_i^2 \lambda_i.$$

It is reasonable to assume the existence of $I[f]$ or else the expansion of f in terms of y_i will not be possible. Further, f and hence $\phi_n = \sum_{i=1}^n a_i \phi_i$ both belong to L_2 (i.e., square integrable in Lebesgue sense).

Let λ_1 be the lowest of all eigenvalues. Then

$$I[\Delta_n] = I[f] - \sum_{i=1}^n a_i^2 (\lambda_i - \lambda_1) - M_n \lambda_1, \tag{5.63}$$

where M_n is given by

$$M_n = \int_a^b \phi_n^2 \, w \, dx = \sum_{i=1}^n a_i^2,$$

which is finite because $\phi_n \in L^2$. Now, $I[f] - M_n \lambda_1$ is certainly finite ($= A$, say) and the series on the right side of (5.63) consists of positive terms only. Hence (5.62) and (5.63) give

$$A/C_n^2 \geq \lambda_{n+1},$$

which, by virtue of the result $\lim_{n \to \infty} \lambda_{n+1} = \infty$, at once leads to the conclusion

$$\lim_{n \to \infty} C_n^2 = 0.$$

Using this result in (5.58) and (5.61), the completeness of eigenfunctions follows.

The above concept of completeness can be viewed in a general setting from the notion of convergence in a normed linear space. A normed linear space X is said to be complete if and only if every Cauchy sequence $\{x_n\}$, $n = 1, 2, \ldots$ in X converges to a vector $x \in X$. A sequence $\{x_n\}$ in X is Cauchy if

$\lim\limits_{m,\,n\,\to\,\infty}\ \|x_m - x_n\| \to 0$, where $\| \cdot \|$ stands for the norm. Consider the space of

Lebesgue square integrable functions $L_2[a, b]$ with norm $\|f\|_2 = \left(\displaystyle\int_a^b |f(t)|^2\, dt \right)^{1/2}$

Although this norm defines a norm in the space of continuous functions in $[a, b]$ given by $C[a, b]$, this space $C[a, b]$ fails to be complete in this norm, whereas the space $L_2[a, b]$ is complete in the same norm.

In the case of a single independent variable it is not difficult to derive from the foregoing considerations the theorems on the expansion of arbitrary functions in terms of eigenfunctions, thus supplementing the completeness theorem above. In fact, it can be proved: Every function which satisfies the admissibility conditions of an eigenvalue variational problem can be expanded in the absolutely and uniformly convergent series $\sum\limits_{n=1}^{\infty} c_n y_n$ in terms of the eigenfunctions.

These considerations and results still remain valid even if singularities occur, as in the case of Legendre and Bessel eigenfunctions. However, the proof of the expansion theorem then remains valid only when we exclude from the domain an arbitrarily small neighbourhood of the singular points since the normalized eigenfunctions may not remain bounded in such a neighbourhood.

5.6   Asymptotic Distribution of Eigenvalues in the Case of Several Independent Variables

The method of Section 5.2 concerning the asymptotic behaviour of eigenvalues for a Stürm-Liouville system involving a single independent variable can also be used for studying the asymptotic behaviour of the nth eigenvalue for several independent variables. In fact, the following result can be established: the asymptotic behaviour of the eigenvalues for partial differential equations with constant coefficients does not depend on the shape but only on the size of the fundamental domain (see [3a]).

1. Consider the equation $\nabla^2 u + \lambda u = 0$ for a rectangle of sides a and b. With boundary condition $u = 0$, the eigenfunctions are given, up to a normalizing factor, by the expressions

$$\sin \frac{l\pi x}{a} \cdot \sin \frac{m\pi y}{b}$$

and the eigenvalues by

$$\pi^2(l^2/a^2 + m^2/b^2), \qquad (l, m = 1, 2, \ldots).$$

For the boundary condition $\partial u/\partial n = 0$, the corresponding expressions are

$$\cos \frac{l\pi x}{a} \cdot \cos \frac{m\pi y}{b}, \qquad \pi^2\left(\frac{l^2}{a^2} + \frac{m^2}{b^2}\right), \qquad l, m = 0, 1, 2, \ldots.$$

If the number of eigenvalues less than a bound λ is given by $A(\lambda)$ in the first case and by $B(\lambda)$ in the second case, then $A(\lambda)$ and $B(\lambda)$ are clearly equal to the number of integral solutions of the inequality $l^2/a^2 + m^2/b^2 \leq \lambda/\pi^2$. Here, $l > 0$, $m > 0$ for the boundary condition $u = 0$, but $l \geq 0$ and $m \geq 0$ for $\partial u/\partial n = 0$. Simple asymptotic expressions for large λ can be derived for $A(\lambda)$ and $B(\lambda)$. For example, $B(\lambda)$ is precisely equal to the number of lattice points with integral coordinates in the region of the ellipse $x^2/a^2 + y^2/b^2 = \lambda/\pi^2$, which lies in the quadrant $x \geq 0$, $y \geq 0$. For sufficiently large λ, the ratio of the area of this sector to the number of lattice points with integral coordinates within this sector becomes arbitrarily close to 1. Thus,

$$B(\lambda) \sim \frac{\lambda ab}{4\pi} \text{ as } \lambda \to \infty.$$

Hence the nth eigenvalue λ_n is obtained asymptotically by setting $B(\lambda_n) = n$ giving $\lambda_n \sim (4\pi/ab)n$, which depends on the size and not on the shape of the domain. A similar formula holds for $A(\lambda)$.

2. Now consider the equation $\nabla^2\nabla^2 u - \lambda u = 0$ of a vibrating plate with the boundary conditions $u = 0$ and $\partial u/\partial n = 0$ corresponding to a clamped plate. A detailed analysis shows that with $A(\lambda)$ defined as above, the following asymptotic relation holds

$$A(\lambda) \sim \frac{f}{4\pi}\sqrt{\lambda},$$

which gives an asymptotic estimate for the nth eigenvalue λ_n as

$$y_n \sim \left(\frac{4\pi n}{f}\right)^2 \text{ as } n \to \infty,$$

where f is the area of the plate.

Comparing the results in the problems 1 and 2 above, we find that as n increases, the nth eigenvalue of the clamped plate is asymptotically equal to the square of the nth eigenvalue of the clamped membrane. An analogous statement holds in three dimensions.

Example 1. Find the upper and lower bounds for the eigenvalues of the Stürm-Liouville problem

$$y'' + \lambda(1 - x^2)y = 0, \quad y'(1) = 0, \quad y(0) = 0.$$

Solution. The base problem and the boundary conditions are

$$y'' + \Lambda y = 0, \quad y'(1) = 0, \quad y(0) = 0.$$

and the solution is (following Weinstein's method [16])

$$y_k = \sqrt{2} \sin\left[(2k - 1)\frac{\pi x}{2}\right],$$

$$\Lambda_k = (2k - 1)^2 \pi^2/4.$$

The intermediate problem is (5.45). Evaluation of the integrals in (5.53), where

$M = 1$, shows that they are not satisfied. Hence the best bounds are achieved from (5.52) and we choose α so as to satisfy a rearranged form of (5.52):

$$\frac{\Lambda_{n+1}}{\Lambda_{n+1} - \Lambda_n} = 2\alpha \int_0^1 \frac{\sin^2 [(2n - 1)\pi x/2]}{\alpha - 1 + x^2} \, dx.$$

The integrals are evaluated numerically to obtain the bounds for the eigenvalues shown in Table 1:

Table 1   Bounds for the Eigenvalues

n	Lower bounds	Upper bounds
1	5.1121	5.1217
2	30.9414	39.6610
3	81.2536	106.2502
4	153.6031	204.8600

Finally, it should be noted that in all methods for finding bounds for eigenvalues, it is of great importance to develop estimates of error. Such estimates for the Rayleigh-Ritz method were given by Krylov and Bogoliubov [1]. An elegant exposition of the upper and lower bounds for eigenvalues of differential eigenvalue problems was given by Diaz [18]. Aronszajn [19] and Weinberger [20] gave error estimates for the method due to Weinstein.

Weinstein further conjectured that the first eigenvalue of the buckling problem for a clamped plate given by

$$\nabla^4 W + \Lambda \nabla^2 W = 0$$

(subject to $W = \partial W/\partial n = 0$ on the plate boundary) is related to the second eigenvalue problem of the vibrating membrane

$$\nabla^2 u + \omega u = 0$$

(subject to $u = 0$ on the membrane boundary) by the relation $\omega_2 \le \Lambda_1$, which was found to be true by Payne [21]. Another interesting result in this connection is the following assertion made by Kornhauser and Stakgold [22]: of all simply connected domains D of a given area, the circle has the maximum value for the second eigenvalue μ_2 of the problem $\nabla^2 u + \mu u = 0$ inside a region D with $\partial u/\partial n = 0$ on the boundary of D. This statement was proved by Szegö [23] using ideas of conformal mapping. In fact, it is also true that of all membranes of a given area, the circle has the gravest fundamental tone, i.e., the lowest eigenvalue ω_1 (the lowest principal frequency) of $\nabla^2 u + \omega u = 0$ inside D with $u = 0$ on the boundary of D.

5.7   Variational Principle for Conformal Mappings

We now consider a variational principle which is quite different from the principles studied earlier, in which analytic functions were compared on the basis of certain criterion. This principle can be utilized to construct approximately a conformal mapping of one region onto another.

Consider the analytic mapping

$$f(z) = z + a_2z^2 + a_3z^3 + \ldots \tag{5.64}$$

of the circle C_R: $|z| \le R$ on a domain H. An element of area dc inside the circle undergoes $|f'(z)|^2$ — fold magnification under the mapping (5.64) and hence the area of the domain H is given by

$$H = \int_{C_R} |f'(z)|^2 \, dc = \int_{C_R} f'(z) \cdot (f'(z))^* \, \rho \, d\rho \, d\phi, \tag{5.65}$$

where $z = \rho e^{i\phi}$. Note that if the mapping is multivalent, then the area is to be counted with the corresponding multiplicity. Substitution of (5.64) in (5.65) followed by integration first with respect to ϕ and then with respect to ρ gives

$$H = \pi R^2 \, [1 + 2 \, |a_2|^2 \, R^2 + 3 \, |a_3|^2 \, R^4 + \ldots].$$

This shows that under the mapping (5.64) the area of the circle C_R always increases.

We now investigate the problem of constructing a conformal mapping $\omega = \phi_0(z)$ of a given simply connected domain G containing the origin $z = 0$ onto a circle $|\omega| \le R$ (where R is not specified beforehand) under the normalization condition

$$\phi_0(0) = 0, \quad \phi_0'(0) = 1. \tag{5.66}$$

The existence of such a mapping is guaranteed by the Riemann mapping theorem. It can be readily established that the area of the circle in the ω-plane is smaller than the area of any other region onto which the domain G is mapped by means of any other analytic function satisfying (5.66). Thus the determination of $\phi_0(z)$ reduces to the variational problem of finding $\phi_0(z)$ which minimizes the functional

$$\int_{(G)} \phi'(z) \cdot (\phi'(z))^* \, dG, \quad (z = x + iy, \quad dG = dx \, dy)$$

in the class of all analytic functions in G satisfying (5.66).

This principle can be used for approximate construction of conformal mapping of a given region onto a circle which is a modification of the Ritz method to be described in the next section. In the treatise by Kantorovich and Krylov [24], one can find another variational principle which can be used for solving the above problem: of all analytic functions in G satisfying (5.66), the function $\phi_0(z)$ is the one which renders the functional

$$\int_{(L)} |f'(z)| \, dL$$

an absolute minimum where $f(z)$ is given by (5.64). Here, L is the contour bounding the domain G. Clearly, the above integral expresses the length of the conformal image of the contour L.

CHAPTER 6

DIRECT METHODS IN VARIATIONAL PROBLEMS

6.1 Introduction to Direct Methods

We have already seen that the differential equations of variational problems can be integrated in closed form in only certain special cases. This difficulty naturally leads us to look for other methods. The essential idea for the so-called direct methods is as follows: the variational problem is considered as the limiting case of the extremum problem of a certain function of a finite number of variables. This extremum problem is solved by the standard methods for finding the extremum of a function of several variables. Then a passage to limit (if it exists) as the number of variables tends to infinity yields the desired solution of the given variational problem.

To illustrate the above ideas with regard to the extremum of a functional $I[y]$, we assume that the admissible function can be expanded in power series as

$$y(x) = a_0 + a_1 x + a_2 x^2 + \ldots + a_n x^n + \ldots$$

or, in a Fourier series,

$$y(x) = \frac{a_0}{2} + \sum_{n=1}^{\infty} (a_n \cos nx + b_n \sin nx).$$

Substitution of any one of these expressions in $I[y(x)]$ leads to

$$I[y(x)] = \phi(a_0, a_1, a_2, \ldots, a_n, \ldots),$$

which is a function of an infinite set of variables. This shows that the difference between the variational problems and the extremum problems of functions of a finite number of variables is that in the variational problem one has to deal with the extremum of a function of an infinite number of variables. The essential idea of direct methods, therefore, is based on regarding the variational problem as the limiting case of the extremum of a function of a finite number of variables.

Euler first used a method which is now known as the direct method of finite differences. This method was later on developed substantially by the Russian mathematicians L. Lyusternik, I. Petrovosky and others. This will be discussed in Section 6.2. In the remaining sections we shall examine in detail several other powerful direct methods, e.g., the Rayleigh-Ritz method, Galerkin method, Trefftz method and the method due to L. Kantorovich.

6.2 Euler's Method of Finite Difference

The essential idea of this method is that the values of the functional

$$I[y(x)] = \int_{x_1}^{x_2} F(x, y, y') \, dx, \qquad y(x_1) = a, \qquad y(x_2) = b,$$

are considered not on arbitrary curves which are admissible in the variational problem but on polygonal curves made up of a given number of line segments with specified abscissae of the vertices:

$$x_1 + \Delta x, \ x_1 + 2\Delta x, \ \dots, \ x_1 + (n - 1)\Delta x,$$

where $\Delta x = (x_2 - x_1)/n$, as shown in Fig. 6.1. On such curves the functional reduces to a function $\phi(y_1, y_2, \dots, y_{n-1})$ of the ordinates.

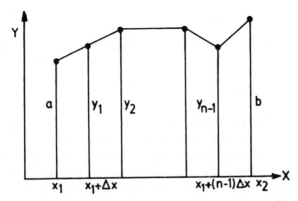

Fig. 6.1 Approximation of an extremal by a polygonal curve.

We now select the coordinates $y_1, y_2, \dots, y_{n-1}$ such that $\phi(y_1, y_2, \dots, y_{n-1})$ is extremized. Thus $y_1, y_2, \dots, y_{n-1}$ are determined from

$$\frac{\partial \phi}{\partial y_1} = 0, \frac{\partial \phi}{\partial y_2} = 0, \dots, \frac{\partial \phi}{\partial y_{n-1}} = 0.$$

If we now take the limit $n \to \infty$, we obtain the solution of the variational problem subject to certain restrictions on F.

By way of illustration, let us derive the Euler equation for the functional

$$I[y(x)] = \int_{x_1}^{x_2} F(x, y, y') \, dx.$$

Then on the polygonal curves shown in Fig. 6.1, we have

$$I[y(x)] \approx \phi(y_1, y_2, \dots, y_n) = \sum_{i=1}^{n-1} F\left(x_i, y_i, \frac{y_{i+1} - y_i}{\Delta x}\right) \Delta x.$$

Since the ith and $(i - 1)$th term in the above summation contain y_i, it follows that

$\partial \varphi / \partial y_i = 0$ $(i = 1, 2, \ldots, n - 1)$ becomes

$$F_y\left(x_i, y_i, \frac{\Delta y_i}{\Delta x}\right) - \frac{F_{y'}\left(x_i, y_i, \frac{\Delta y_i}{\Delta x}\right) - F_{y'}\left(x_{i-1}, y_{i-1}, \frac{\Delta y_{i-1}}{\Delta x}\right)}{\Delta x} = 0$$

Passage to the limit $\Delta x \to 0$ as $n \to \infty$ gives the Euler equation

$$F_y - \frac{d}{dx} F_{y'} = 0,$$

which must be satisfied by the extremizing function $y(x)$. If we do not pass to limit, the system $\partial \phi / \partial y_i = 0$ $(i = 1, 2, \ldots, n - 1)$ gives an approximate solution of the variational problem.

6.3   Rayleigh-Ritz Method

The basic idea of this method is that the values of the functional $I[y(x)]$ are taken not on arbitrary admissible curves but only on linear combinations of the form

$$y_n = \sum_{i=1}^{n} \alpha_i W_i(x),$$

where α_i's are constants and $W_1(x), W_2(x), \ldots, W_n(x) \ldots$ constitute a suitable set of functions. The above linear combination should be admissible in the given variational problem. This implies certain restrictions on the above sequence. On such linear combinations, $I[y(x)]$ reduces to a function $\phi(\alpha_1, \alpha_2, \ldots, \alpha_n)$ of the coefficients $\alpha_1, \alpha_2, \ldots, \alpha_n$. These coefficients are then selected so that ϕ is an extremum. Thus $\alpha_1, \alpha_2, \ldots, \alpha_n$ are determined from the system

$$\frac{\partial \phi}{\partial \alpha_i} = 0 \quad (i = 1, 2, \ldots, n).$$

Passing to the limit as $n \to \infty$, if the limit exists, we get the solution of the variational problem as

$$y = \sum_{i=1}^{\infty} \alpha_i W_i(x).$$

If we do not take the limit, then we obtain an approximate solution of the variational problem [15].

It should be noted that for the functions

$$y_n = \sum_{i=1}^{n} \alpha_i W_i(x)$$

to be admissible, they should satisfy the boundary conditions of the variational problem apart from satisfying the requirements of continuity or smoothness. If the boundary conditions are linear and homogeneous, e.g., $y(x_1) = 0 = y(x_2)$, then the easiest way to choose $W_i(x)$ is as follows:

$$W_i(x) = (x - x_1)(x - x_2)\phi_i(x)$$

or some other functions satisfying

$$W_i(x_1) = W_i(x_2) = 0.$$

If the conditions are not homogeneous, e.g., $y(x_1) = y_1$ and $y(x_2) = y_2$, where at least one of y_1 and y_2 is not zero, then we seek a solution of the form

$$y_n = \sum_{i=1}^{n} \alpha_i W_i(x) + W_0(x), \tag{6.1}$$

where $W_i(x)$, $i = 0, 1, 2, \ldots$, are known as coordinate functions. The boundary conditions are

$$W_0(x_1) = y_1, \qquad W_0(x_2) = y_2, \qquad W_i(x_1) = W_i(x_2) = 0 \tag{6.2}$$

for $i = 1, 2, \ldots, n$.

It is important to note that the collection of functions $W_i(x)$, $i = 1, 2, \ldots, n$, mentioned before may be regarded as a part of an infinite sequence of functions

$$W_1(x), W_2(x), \ldots, W_n(x), \ldots,$$

which are linearly independent and complete in the space of functions $y \in C^1[x_1, x_2]$, say, satisfying $y(x_1) = 0$, $y(x_2) = 0$. It may be readily shown that the system of functions

$$W_i(x) = x^{i-1}(x - x_1)(x - x_2), \qquad i = 1, 2, \ldots \tag{6.3}$$

or

$$W_k(x) = \sin \frac{k\pi (x - x_1)}{x_2 - x_1}, \qquad k = 1, 2, \ldots \tag{6.4}$$

is linearly independent and complete in $C^1[x_1, x_2]$.

If this method is employed to determine the absolute minimum of a functional, then the approximate value of the minimum of the functional is obtained in excess, since the minimum of the functional on all admissible classes of curves cannot exceed the minimum of the same functional on a subclass of the form

$$y_n = \sum_{i=1}^{n} \alpha_i W_i(x).$$

Using the same argument we may say that if the Rayleigh-Ritz method is used to obtain the maximum of the functional, then the approximate value of the maximum is obtained in defect.

The conditions for the convergence of the sequence mentioned above by the Rayleigh-Ritz method and the determination of the speed of convergence for some specific but frequently occurring functionals were worked out by N.M. Krylov and N. Bogolyubov (see [1]). However, these estimates are so complicated that they are impractical in concrete situations: For this reason, to test the accuracy of the results obtained by Rayleigh-Ritz method, one ordinarily uses the following procedure (which is mathematically not rigorous but nevertheless sufficiently reliable). After calculating $y_n(x)$ and $y_{n+1}(x)$, their values are compared at several values of the interval $[x_1, x_2]$. If their values coincide within the limits of desired accuracy, then the solution of the variational problem is taken as $y_n(x)$. But if these values do not agree at several chosen points, we compute $y_{n+2}(x)$ and compare the values of $y_{n+1}(x)$ and $y_{n+2}(x)$. This process is repeated till the values of $y_{n+k}(x)$ and $y_{n+k+1}(x)$ agree within the limits of desired accuracy.

Example 1.   Find the extremum of the functional

$$I[y(x)] = \int_0^1 (y'^2 + y^2)\, dx, \qquad y(0) = 0, \qquad y(1) = 1$$

using the Rayleigh-Ritz method.

Solution.   It can be readily shown by solving the Euler equation that the exact solution is

$$y_{ex} = \frac{\sinh x}{\sinh 1}.$$

Using the above method, we put $W_0(x) = x$ in (6.1) and take $W_i(x)$ given by (6.3) as the coordinate functions. We first take $n = 1$, which means that we seek an approximate solution of the form

$$y = x + cx(1 - x).$$

Substituting this in the given functional leads to

$$I = \frac{11}{30} c^2 + \frac{1}{6} c + \frac{4}{3}.$$

Equating dI/dc to zero, we find $c = -5/22$. Thus,

$$y_{1_{app.}} = x - \frac{5}{22} x(1 - x). \tag{6.5}$$

Next, for $n = 2$, we take the approximate solution as

$$y_{2_{app.}} = x + c_1 x(1 - x) + c_2 x^2 (1 - x). \tag{6.6}$$

Clearly, the functions $x(1 - x)$ and $x^2(1 - x)$ are linearly independent.

Substituting (6.6) in the functional and equating to zero $\partial I/\partial c_1$ and $\partial I/\partial c_2$, we get

$$\frac{11}{15} c_1 + \frac{11}{30} c_2 + \frac{1}{6} = 0,$$

$$\frac{11}{30} c_1 + \frac{2}{7} c_2 + \frac{1}{10} = 0$$

leading to $c_1 = -0.1459$, $c_2 = -0.1628$. Hence (6.6) becomes

$$y_{2_{app.}} = 0.8541x - 0.0169x^2 + 0.1628x^3 \tag{6.7}$$

It would be instructive to compare the exact solution with the approximate solutions (6.5) and (6.7). The following table gives the results of comparison:

x	0.0	0.2	0.4	0.6	0.8	1.0
y_{ex}	0.000	0.171	0.349	0.541	0.755	1
$y_{1app.}$	0.000	0.163	0.345	0.545	0.763	1
$y_{2app.}$	0.000	0.171	0.349	0.541	0.755	1

Thus we find that with a two-term approximation, the exact solution practically coincides with the approximate solution.

Example 2. Minimize the integral

$$I[y] = \int_{-l}^{l} \left(\int_{-l}^{l} \frac{y'(s)}{x-s} \, ds \right) y(x) \, dx$$

subject to the constraint

$$J[y] = \int_{-l}^{l} y(x) \, dx = S = \text{constant}$$

and the boundary conditions $y(l) = y(-l) = 0$.

Solution. This is an aerodynamic problem (see [15]) where the value of the functional $I[y]$ is proportional to the drag experienced by an aeroplane with a streamlined wing of finite span $2l$ (the compressibility of the air and the frictional force being neglected). The integral $J[y]$ is the lift force, and $y(x)$ gives the dependence of the circulation of air flux round the wing of the aeroplane. Thus the problem reduces to the determination of the distribution of circulation along the wing so that the drag of the aeroplane is minimum subject to a given lift force.

We introduce a change of the independent variable $x = -l \cos \theta$ so that the ends of the wing now correspond to $\theta = 0$ and $\theta = \pi$. We seek a solution in the form

$$y = A_1 \sin \theta + A_2 \sin 2\theta + A_3 \sin 3\theta + \dots, \tag{6.8}$$

which satisfies the boundary conditions $y = 0$ at $\theta = 0$ and π corresponding to $y(-l) = y(l) = 0$.

Substituting (6.8) in the equation of constraint $J[y] = S$, we get $A_1 = 2S/(\pi l)$. Again substitution of (6.8) in the expression for $I[y]$ gives

$$I[y] = \sum_{j=1}^{\infty} \sum_{k=1}^{\infty} A_j A_k k \int_{0}^{\pi} \left(\int_{0}^{\pi} \frac{\cos k\Psi}{\cos \Psi - \cos \theta} \right) \sin j\theta \sin \theta \, d\theta. \tag{6.9}$$

The inner integral is a singular integral for $0 < \theta < \pi$ and evaluation of its principal value gives $\pi \sin k\theta / \sin \theta$. Finally, substitution of this value in (6.9) gives

$$I[y] = \frac{\pi^2}{2} \sum_{k=1}^{\infty} k A_k^2 .$$

Since $A_1 = 2S/(\pi l)$ and the other coefficients are arbitrary, it follows that $I[y]$ attains its least value when $A_2 = A_3 = A_4 = \ldots = 0$. This leads to

$$y = \frac{2S}{\pi l} \sin \theta = \frac{2S}{\pi l^2} \cdot \sqrt{l^2 - x^2}, \tag{6.10}$$

which gives the required distribution of circulation. It is easy to see that this distribution is obtained for a wing whose shape in the xy-plane is an ellipse with semi-axes l and $2S/(\pi l)$.

The above example shows that in the Rayleigh-Ritz method, sometimes it is possible to find the general formula for the coefficients α_i in the representation (6.1) and then pass to the limit for $n \to \infty$.

Example 3.   Find the first eigenvalue of the problem

$$y''(x) + \lambda(1 + x^2)y = 0, \qquad y(-1) = y(1) = 0.$$

Solution.   Using the extremal definition of eigenvalues explained in Chapter 5, we may employ the Rayleigh-Ritz method to compute the eigenvalues of the above problem.

For the coordinate functions, choose $\phi_k(x) = 1 - x^{2k}$, $(k = 1, 2, \ldots)$, which are linearly independent and clearly satisfy the boundary conditions. Assuming

$$y(x) = C_1(1 - x^2) + C_2(1 - x^4),$$

we pose the problem of extremizing the functional

$$I[y] = \int_{-1}^{1} [y'^2 - \lambda (1 + x^2) y^2] \, dx$$

whose Euler equation coincides with the above second order differential equation. Substitution of the above expression for y in $I[y]$ yields

$$I = C_1^2 \left(\frac{8}{3} - \frac{128}{105} \lambda \right) + 2C_1 C_2 \left(\frac{16}{5} - \frac{64}{45} \lambda \right) + C_2^2 \left(\frac{32}{7} - \frac{5888}{3465} \lambda \right).$$

Now equating $\partial I/\partial C_1$ and $\partial I/\partial C_2$ to zero and using the condition for non-trivial solution yields the smallest value of λ as $\lambda_1 = 2.1775$.

6.4   Galerkin Method

The effectiveness of the Rayleigh-Ritz method gives rise to the following scheme of solving a boundary value problem: given an ordinary differential equation subject to given boundary conditions, we construct a functional whose Euler's equation coincides with the given differential equation and then apply the Rayleigh-Ritz method. Consider, for example, the differential equation

$$a(x)y'' + b(x)y' + c(x)y = f(x).$$

We multiply the equation by an arbitrary function $\mu(x)$ such that

$$-2P = a\mu, \qquad -2P' = b\mu, \qquad 2Q = c\mu, \qquad -R = f\mu$$

hold. The first two equations give

$$P = \exp \int_{x_0}^{x} \frac{b}{a} \, dx, \qquad \mu = -\frac{2}{a} P$$

so that the remaining two determine Q and R. With this choice of P, Q and R, it can be readily shown that the required functional is of the form

$$I[y] = \int [P(x)y'^2 + Q(x)y^2 + R(x)y] \, dx$$

between appropriate limits.

The boundary value problems described above can also be tackled by yet another direct method known as Galerkin's method [1], named after its discoverer B.G. Galerkin. It can be applied to both ordinary and partial differential equations (linear or nonlinear).

Consider the equation

$$y'' + p(x)y' + q(x)y = f(x) \tag{6.11a}$$

with

$$y(x_0) = 0, \qquad y(x_1) = 0. \tag{6.11b}$$

The nonhomogeneous boundary conditions $y(x_0) = y_0$, $y(x_1) = y_1$ are readily reduced to homogeneous conditions by the change of variables

$$z = y - y_0 - \frac{y_1 - y_0}{x_1 - x_0} \cdot (x - x_0).$$

We write (6.11a) in the operator form

$$Ly = f(x).$$

We now select a complete system of continuous linearly independent coordinate functions

$$W_1(x), \; W_2(x), \; ..., \; W_n(x), \; ..., \tag{6.12}$$

which satisfy $W_n(x_0) = W_n(x_1) = 0$ for $n = 1, 2, ...$ We now seek an approximate solution of the form

$$y_n = \sum_{i=1}^{n} \alpha_i W_i(x).$$

Substituting y_n in (6.11a) and choosing the coefficients α_i so that

$$L\left(\sum_{i=1}^{n} \alpha_i W_i(x)\right) - f(x)$$

is orthogonal in the interval $[x_0, x_1]$ to each of the functions $W_i(x)$, $i = 1, 2, ..., n$, we get

$$\int_{x_0}^{x_1} \left[L\left(\sum_{i=1}^{n} \alpha_i W_i(x)\right) - f(x)\right] W_i(x) \, dx = 0 \qquad i = 1, 2, ..., n. \tag{6.13}$$

We now expect that y_n tends to the exact solution

$$y_{ex} = \sum_{i=1}^{\infty} \alpha_i W_i(x)$$

as $n \to \infty$. This is due to the fact that if the series obtained converges and admits term-wise differentiation, then $Ly_{ex} - f(x)$ is orthogonal in $[x_0, x_1]$ to each function $W_i(x)$. But since the system (6.12) is complete, it follows that $L(y_{ex}) - f(x) = 0$. Clearly, y_{ex} satisfies all the boundary conditions $y_{ex}(x_0) = y_{ex}(x_1) = 0$ since $W_i(x_0) = W_i(x_1) = 0$. In actual computations, one restricts to only a finite number of coordinate functions $W_i(x)$. In this case, however, the condition of completeness is abandoned, but the functions $W_i(x)$ are assumed to be linearly independent and consistent with the boundary conditions

$$W_i(x_0) = W_i(x_1) = 0.$$

It is important to note that for Euler's equations encountered in variational problems, Galerkin's method described above coincides with Rayleigh-Ritz method. It is interesting to note that this method is also applicable to many ordinary and partial differential equations which are not Euler's equations and appear irrespective of variational problems.

Let us now illustrate Galerkin's method by considering two specific fluid flow problems. In the first problem, Djukic [25] used this technique to solve the two-dimensional stagnation point flow of a non-Newtonian power-law fluid in the presence of a uniform transverse magnetic field.

Consider the steady laminar two-dimensional stagnation point flow of a power-law non-Newtonian electrically conducting fluid towards an infinite flat plate (Fig. 6.2) coincident with the X-axis, 0 being the stagnation point. A uniform transverse magnetic field B acts along the Y-axis. The fluid is incompressible and its apparent viscosity changes with the rate of shear (power-law fluid). The external electric field is zero and the field due to polarization of charges is negligible. Further, the magnetic Reynolds number is assumed to be small so that the induced magnetic field can also be neglected. If (u, v) are the velocity components inside

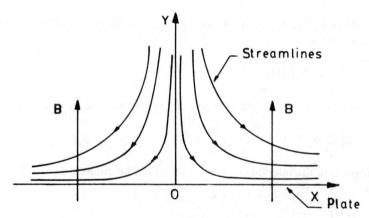

Fig. 6.2   A sketch of the physical problem.

the boundary layer and $V(x)$ is the x-component of velocity outside the boundary layer, the steady two-dimensional boundary layer equations are

$$u \frac{\partial u}{\partial x} + v \frac{\partial u}{\partial y} = V \frac{dV}{dx} + v \frac{\partial}{\partial y} \left[\left| \frac{\partial u}{\partial y} \right|^{n-1} \cdot \frac{\partial u}{\partial y} \right] + \sigma B^2 (V - u)/\rho, \qquad (6.14)$$

$$\frac{\partial u}{\partial x} + \frac{\partial v}{\partial y} = 0 \qquad (6.15)$$

The boundary conditions are

$$\begin{aligned} u = v &= 0 \quad \text{at } y = 0, \\ u &\to V(x) \quad \text{as } y \to \infty. \end{aligned} \qquad (6.16)$$

Here k is the fluid consistency index and n is the power-law index. Further, v, ρ and σ denote the constant k/ρ, the fluid density and the constant electrical conductivity of the fluid, respectively. It is well known that for a plane stagnation flow,

$$V = ax,$$

where a is a constant.

We now seek similarly a solution of the system (6.14)–(6.16) by using similarity transformations

$$\eta = \left[\frac{2a^{2-n}}{v(1+n)} \right]^{1/(1+n)} \cdot x^{(1-n)/(1+n)} \cdot y \qquad (6.17a)$$

$$u = V \frac{dF(\eta)}{d\eta}, \qquad (6.17b)$$

where $F(\eta)$ is to be determined.

Combining (6.14)–(6.17), we obtain the following ordinary differential equation for $F(\eta)$:

$$\left(\frac{d^2 F}{d\eta^2} \right)^{n-1} \cdot \frac{d^3 F}{d\eta^3} + F \frac{d^2 F}{d\eta^2} + \frac{(1+n)}{2n} \left[1 - \left(\frac{dF}{d\eta} \right)^2 + N \left(1 - \frac{dF}{d\eta} \right) \right] = 0 \qquad (6.18)$$

subject to the boundary conditions

$$\begin{aligned} F = \frac{dF}{d\eta} &= 0 \quad \text{at } \eta = 0, \\ \frac{dF}{d\eta} &\to 1 \quad \text{as } \eta \to \infty. \end{aligned} \qquad (6.19)$$

In (6.18), N stands for the magnetic parameter $\sigma B^2/(a\rho)$, which is constant.

To solve (6.18), we introduce the independent variable λ in place of η as

$$\lambda = \frac{dF}{d\eta}. \qquad (6.20)$$

Then (6.18) becomes

$$\phi \frac{d^2\phi}{d\lambda^2} - \frac{1}{n+1}\left(\frac{d\phi}{d\lambda}\right)^2 - 2\lambda\phi - (1 - \lambda^2)\frac{d\phi}{d\lambda}$$

$$- N\left[(1 - \lambda)\frac{d\phi}{d\lambda} + (n + 1)\phi\right] = 0, \tag{6.21}$$

where

$$\phi = \left(\frac{2n}{n+1}\right)\left(\frac{d^2F}{d\eta^2}\right)^{n+1} \tag{6.22}$$

is the new dependent variable. The boundary conditions for (6.21) are obtained as follows by using (6.18), (6.19) and (6.22), together with the condition of vanishing shear stress at the boundary layer edge given by $\partial u/\partial y \to 0$ as $y \to \infty$:

$$\frac{d\phi}{d\lambda} = -(n + 1)(1 + N) \quad \text{at } \lambda = 0,$$

$$\phi = 0 \quad \text{at } \lambda = 1. \tag{6.23}$$

Further, combining (6.21) and (6.23), we have the supplementary boundary conditions for (6.21) as

$$\frac{d^2\phi}{d\lambda^2} = (n + 1)N \quad \text{at } \lambda = 0,$$

$$\frac{d\phi}{d\lambda} = 0 \quad \text{at } \lambda = 1. \tag{6.24}$$

It is interesting to note that by the transformation (6.20), the infinite interval $[0, \infty]$ for η is mapped into $[0, 1]$ for λ.

To apply the Galerkin method, we seek an approximate solution of (6.21) in the form

$$\phi = (n + 1)\left[b(1 - 4\lambda^3 + 3\lambda^4) + N(1 - \lambda)^2/2 + \frac{1}{3}(2 - 3\lambda + \lambda^3)\right], \tag{6.25}$$

which satisfies the boundary conditions (6.23) and (6.24). Here b is an unknown constant. Substituting (6.25) in (6.21) and integrating the result with respect to λ from $\lambda = 0$ to 1, we obtain an equation in b whose solution is

$$b = 7\{[N + (n + 6)/(2n + 4)^2 + 4n(8 + 5N)/7(n + 2)]^{1/2}$$

$$- [N - (n + 6)/(2n + 4)]\}/48 \tag{6.26}$$

Using (6.16), (6.17a), (6.22) and (6.25), the shear stress at the wall $\tau_0 = [k(\partial u/\partial y)^n]_{y=0}$ is given in terms of shear stress coefficient $C_f(= \tau_0/\rho V^2)$ as

$$C_f = C(n, N) R_{\text{ex}}^{-1/(n+1)}, \tag{6.27}$$

where

$$C(n, N) = \left[(n + 1)\left(b + \frac{2}{3} + \frac{N}{2}\right) \bigg/ n \right]^{n/(n+1)} \tag{6.28}$$

and $R_{ex} = V^{2-n}x^n/\nu$ is the local Reynolds number.

It is important to note that the index n appearing in the constitutive relation between the shear stress and rate-of-strain given by $\tau_{xy} = k \,|\partial u/\partial y|^{n-1} \cdot \partial u/\partial y$ (within the framework of boundary layer approximations) is positive. Further, $n < 1$ for a pseudo-plastic fluid (shear-thinning) while $n > 1$ corresponds to dilatant fluids (shear-thickening). It can be seen from (6.28) that increase in the magnetic field parameter N increases the shear stress parameter C for a fixed n. It is also found that for the non-magnetic case ($N = 0$), the values of $C(n, N)$ vs. n obtained by the present method when compared with the corresponding numerical solution of Schulman and Berkovsky [26] give very good agreement for $n < 1$ although there is some error ($< 2.8\%$) for $n > 1$. This lends credence to the fact that the Galerkin method is a useful tool in handling highly nonlinear differential equations such as (6.18).

In the second problem, the same method was used by Sen Gupta and Gupta [27] who studied the stability of the flow of an electrically conducting liquid of kinematic viscosity ν and electrical conductivity σ in a channel formed by two vertical parallel plates separated by a distance D and placed on a turn table, which is rotated with angular velocity Ω about a vertical axis taken as the z-axis. The shear flow relative to the rotating frame is induced by a uniform pressure gradient P along the channel (i.e., along the z-axis) and a uniform magnetic field H_0 acts along the y-axis taken normal to the plates, the x-axis being parallel to the plates in the horizontal direction, the origin being taken in the mid-section of the channel. Neglecting the induced magnetic field in the fluid of magnetic permeability μ_e, the linearized perturbation equations for the dimensionless velocity components (u', v', w') with $v' = \partial\Psi/\partial z$,

$$w' = -\partial\Psi/\partial Y, \qquad Y = y/D_1, \qquad Z = z/D_1$$
$$\Psi = \text{Re}\{ie^{ikZ}h(Y)\}, \qquad u' = \{\text{Re } e^{ikZ}g(Y)\}$$

are

$$E(D^2 - k^2)g(Y) + \left(R_0 \frac{d\bar{U}}{dY} - 1\right)kh(Y) = 0,$$

$$E(D^2 - k^2)^2 h(Y) - kg(Y) = 0,$$

where $U(y)$ is the basic velocity distribution, k is the wave number of a disturbance and

$$E = \frac{\nu}{2\Omega D_1^2}, \qquad R_0 = \frac{U_0}{2\Omega D_1}, \qquad \bar{U}(Y) = \frac{U(y)}{U_0},$$

$$U_0 = \frac{PM(\cosh M - 1)}{\mu_e^2 \sigma H_0^2 \sinh M}, \qquad M = \frac{\mu_e H_0 D_1}{2}\left(\frac{\sigma}{\rho\nu}\right)^{1/2}$$

$$D \equiv \frac{d}{dY}.$$

The above differential equations with boundary conditions $h = Dh = g = 0$ at $Y = \pm \frac{1}{2}$ were solved by the Galerkin method and it is found that the magnetic field exerts a strong stabilizing influence on the flow. This study is of some importance in the stability problem for a zonal flow.

6.5   Methods of Projection

It is interesting to note that apart from the Rayleigh-Ritz method and Galerkin's method, other methods such as the method of least squares, or collocation methods can be viewed in a more global setting as projective methods.

Consider the equation

$$Ax = y, \tag{6.29}$$

where A maps a normed linear space X with norm $\| \ \|_X$ into the normed linear space Y with norm $\| \ \|_Y$. Let X_N be a finite-dimensional (and hence closed) subspace of X such that $X_N = \text{span}\,(\phi_1, \phi_2, \ldots, \phi_N)$. Then a direct method for solving the variational problem associated with (6.29) is simply a construction of a numerical algorithm for finding a function

$$x_N = c_1\phi_1 + c_2\phi_2 + \ldots + c_N\phi_N$$

belonging to X_N which makes

$$\| Ax_N - y \|_Y + \| x_N - x \|_X$$

small. Solution by any one of the methods mentioned above is usually (but not always) equivalent to projecting the solution or an approximate solution onto a finite-dimensional subspace of X [28].

In yet another general setting an abstract variational problem can be stated as follows: Let H be a Hilbert space and $a\,(.,.): H \times H \to R$ be a bounded bilinear functional. Further, let $f : H \to R$ be a bounded linear functional. Then the problem is to find an element $x \in H$ such that

$$a(x, y) = f(y) \quad \text{for all } y \in H. \tag{6.30}$$

It can be shown that in the above abstract setting, the variational problem has a unique solution in view of the Lax-Milgram lemma (see [29]) which we now discuss.

Lax-Milgram lemma.   If the bilinear form defined above is coercive in the sense that there exists an $\alpha > 0$ such that $a(x, x) \geq \alpha\| x \|^2$ for every $x \in H$, then the above variational problem has a unique solution.

Let us now consider an approximate problem corresponding to the variational problem given by (6.30). Suppose H^* is the space of bounded linear functionals on H. Then $f \in H^*$. Suppose that H_h is a finite-dimensional subspace of H. Then an approximate problem corresponding to the above variational problem consists of determination of a $u_h \in H_h$ such that

$$a(u_h, v_h) = f(v_h) \quad \forall\ v_h \in H_h \tag{6.31}$$

By virtue of the Lax-Milgram lemma, the above equation has a unique solution if $a(x, y)$ is coercive.

Now it can be shown that the solution of (6.31) is equivalent to the solution of the matrix equation

$$AU = b, \tag{6.32}$$

where the transpose of the matrix A, denoted by A^T, is $A^T = (a(w_i, w_j))_{i,j}$, where w_i is a basis of H_h, with $i = 1, 2, ..., N(h); j = 1, 2, ..., N(h), N(h)$ being the dimension of H_h. Further,

$$U = (\alpha_1, \alpha_2, ..., \alpha_{N(h)}), \qquad b = (f(w_1), f(w_2), ..., f(w_{N(h)}).$$

This can be shown as follows: Since $\{w_i\}$ is a basis of H_h and $u_h \in H_h$,

$$u_h = \sum_{i=1}^{N(h)} \alpha_i w_i$$

$$v_h = \sum_{j=1}^{N(h)} \beta_j w_j,$$

where α_i and $\beta_j \in R$. Substituting these in (6.31), we get

$$a\left(\sum_{i=1}^{N(h)} \alpha_i w_i, \sum_{j=1}^{N(h)} \beta_j w_j \right) = f\left(\sum_{j=1}^{N(h)} \beta_j w_j \right).$$

In view of the bilinearity of $a(.,.)$ and linearity of f, we obtain

$$\sum_{i=1}^{N(h)} \sum_{j=1}^{N(h)} \alpha_i \beta_j a(w_i, w_j) = \sum_{j=1}^{N(h)} \beta_j f(w_j).$$

Recalling the definitions of A^T, U and b mentioned above, we find that

$$V^T A U = V^T b, \tag{6.33}$$

where $V = (\beta_1, \beta_2, ..., \beta_{N(h)})$. Since (6.33) is true for all $V \in R^{N(h)}$, we get the relation (6.32), which is what we set out to prove.

The matrix equation (6.32) can be solved by any one of the standard methods such as Gauss's method of elimination, Cholesky's method etc. It may be noted that for a coercive $a(.,.)$, A is positive definite. Further, A is symmetric if the bilinear form is symmetric. Again since $a(.,.)$ is coercive, A is invertible.

The choice of the basis functions $\{w_i\}$ is of crucial importance in facilitating numerical computations. It is convenient to choose (w_i) so that A becomes a sparse matrix and the computing time is reasonably small. In the next section, we shall describe a method known as finite element method for solving the abstract variational problem in its approximate form (6.31), the method being economical from computational point of view. With reference to application of the above method to certain problems of elasticity, the matrix $a(w_i, w_j)$ and the vector $f(w_i)$ are often called the stiffness matrix and load vector, respectively.

6.6   Finite Element Method

This is essentially a projection method [30] concerned with the determination of a finite-dimensional subspace V_h of $H^1(\Omega)$, the Sobolev space of order 1 on Ω, an open subset of R^N with a smooth boundary. This space is defined by

$$H^1(\Omega) = \left\{ v \in L_2(\Omega) \Big/ \frac{\partial v}{\partial x_i} \in L_2(\Omega), 1 \le i \le n \right\},$$

where the derivatives $\partial v(x_1, x_2, \ldots, x_n)/\partial x_i$ are in the sense of distribution. This implies that

$$\langle v, \partial \phi/\partial x_i \rangle = -\langle \partial v/\partial x_i, \phi \rangle,$$

where $\phi \in D(\Omega)$, the space of infinitely differentiable functions with compact support in Ω. Further, $L_2(\Omega)$ is the space of square integrable functions in Ω in the Lebesgue sense.

To find V_h of $H^1(\Omega)$, we first define a triangulation. Let $\Omega \subset R^2$ be a given polygonal domain. A finite collection of triangles T_h is called a triangulation if the following conditions are satisfied:

(i) $\bar{\Omega} = \underset{K \in T_h}{\cup} \bar{K}$, where $\bar{K}$ denotes a triangle with boundary.

(ii) $K \cap K_1 = $ null for $K, K_1 \in T_h$, $K \ne K_1$.

(iii) $\bar{K} \cap \bar{K}_1 = $ a vertex or a side. This means that if we consider two triangles, their boundaries may have one vertex common or one side common.

We introduce $P(K)$ as a function space defined on $K \in T_h$ such that $P(K) \subset H^1(K)$. Generally, $P(K)$ is taken as a space of polynomials of some degree. The following result then holds.

Lemma. Let $C^0(\bar{\Omega})$ be the space of continuous real-valued functions on $\bar{\Omega}$ and

$$V_h = \{v_h \in C^0(\bar{\Omega}) \mid v_h/K \in P(K), K \in T_h\},$$

where v_h/K is the restriction of v_h on K and $P(K) \subset H^1(K)$. Then $V_h \subset H^1(\Omega)$.

Proof. Suppose $u \in V_h$ and v_i is a function defined on Ω such that $v_i/K = \partial/\partial x_i(u/K)$. Now v_i/K is well-defined since $u/K \subset H^1(K)$. Further, from the definition of a Sobolev space $H^1(K)$, it follows that $v_i \in L_2(\Omega)$ as $v_i/K = \partial/\partial x_i(u/K) \in L_2(K)$. The lemma is thus established if we can show that

$$v_i = \frac{\partial u}{\partial x_i} \in D^*(\Omega),$$

where $D^*(\Omega)$ is the dual space of $D(\Omega)$. This stems from the fact that $\partial u/\partial x_i \in D^*(\Omega)$ implies that $u \in H^1(\Omega)$ and this in turn implies that $V_h \in H^1(\Omega)$.

For any $\phi \in D(\Omega)$, we have

$$(v_i, \phi) = \int_\Omega v_i \phi \, dx = \sum_{K \in T_h} \int_K v_i \, \phi \, dx$$

$$= \sum_{K \in T_h} \int_K \frac{\partial}{\partial x_i} (u/K) \phi \, dx$$

$$= \sum_{K \in T_h} \left[\int_{\Gamma = \partial K} (u/K) \phi K_i d\Gamma - \int_K (u/K) \frac{\partial \phi}{\partial x_i} \, dx \right] \qquad (6.34)$$

by applying the generalized Green's formula such that Γ is the boundary of K. If η_i denotes the ith component of the outer normal at Γ, then

$$(v_i, \phi) = -\int_\Omega u \frac{\partial \phi}{\partial x_i} \, dx + \sum_{K \in T_h} \int_\Gamma (u/K) \phi \eta_i^K d\Gamma . \qquad (6.35)$$

The second integral in (6.35) vanishes since if K_1 and K_2 are two adjacent triangles, $\eta_i^{K_1} = -\eta_i^{K_2}$. Thus,

$$(v_i, \phi) = -\int_\Omega u \frac{\partial \phi}{\partial x_i} \, dx = \left(\frac{\partial u}{\partial x_i}, \phi \right),$$

which shows that $v_i = \dfrac{\partial u}{\partial x_i} \in D*(\Omega)$. This completes the proof.

Definition of an n-simplex

In R^n, a (non-degenerate) n-simplex is the convex hull K of $n + 1$ points $a_j = (a_{ij})_{i=1}^n \in R^n$, which are known as the vertices of the n-simplex such that the matrix

$$A = \begin{vmatrix} a_{11} & a_{12} & \cdots & a_{1\,n+1} \\ a_{21} & a_{22} & \cdots & a_{2\,n+1} \\ \vdots & \vdots & & \vdots \\ a_{n1} & a_{n2} & \cdots & a_{n\,n+1} \\ 1 & 1 & \cdots & 1 \end{vmatrix}$$

is regular, i.e., $(n + 1)$ points a_j are not contained in a hyperplane. In other words, K is said to be an n-simplex if

$$K = \left\{ x = \sum_{j=1}^{n+1} \lambda_j a_j / 0 \le \lambda_j \le 1, \sum_1^{n+1} \lambda_j = 1 \right\}.$$

Hence a 2-simplex is a triangle and a 3-simplex is a tetrahedron.

Following Ciarlet [30], we now introduce the concept of a finite element. Let K be a polyhedron in R^n, P_K the space of polynomials with dimension m and Σ_K

a set of distributions (i.e., continuous linear functionals on $D(\Omega)$ of cardinality m). The triplet (K, P_K, Σ_K) is called a finite element if

$$\Sigma_K = \{L_i \in D^*/i = 1, 2, ..., m\}$$

is such that for given $\alpha_i \in R$, $1 \leq i \leq m$, the system of equations

$$L_i(p) = \alpha_i, \qquad 1 \leq i \leq m$$

admits of a unique solution $p \in P_K$. The elements $L_i(i = 1, 2, ..., m)$ are known as the degrees of freedom of P_K.

If K is 2-simplex, then (K, P_K, Σ_K) is called a triangular finite element and if K is a 3-simplex, then (K, P_K, Σ_K) is known as tetrahedral.

We now show by considering an example how the finite element method can be applied to solve boundary value problems. We shall use triangular finite elements defined above.

Example 4.   We consider the Neumann boundary value problem

$$- \nabla^2 u + u = f \text{ in } \Omega, \qquad \Omega \subset R^2, \tag{6.36a}$$

$$\frac{\partial u}{\partial n} = 0 \quad \text{on the boundary } \Gamma. \tag{6.36b}$$

The variational formulation for the above problem is as follows:

$$V = H^1(\Omega), \tag{6.37a}$$

$$a(u, v) = \int_\Omega \left\{ \sum_{i=1}^2 \frac{\partial u}{\partial x_i} \frac{\partial v}{\partial x_i} + uv \right\} dx$$

$$= \int_\Omega (\nabla u \cdot \nabla v + uv) \, dx, \tag{6.37b}$$

$$L(v) = \int_\Omega fv \, dx. \tag{6.37c}$$

An internal approximation of this problem is the following:

$$V_h = \{v_h \in C^0(\overline{\Omega}) \, /\forall \, K \in T_h, \, v_h/K \in P_1(K)\}$$

as already pointed out in the lemma of this section. We choose a basis for V_h as follows:

$$w_i(a_j) = \delta_{ij}, \qquad 1 \leq i \leq N(h), \qquad 1 \leq j \leq N(h),$$

where δ_{ij} is the Kronecker delta and $a_1, a_2, ..., a_{N(h)}$ are the vertices of the triangulation T_h. We then have for every $v_h \in V_h$,

$$v_h = \sum_{i=1}^{N(h)} v_h(a_i)w_i.$$

Then (6.37) is equivalent to determining the value of u_h such that

$$a(u_h, v_h) = L(v_h) \ \forall \ v_h \in V_h. \tag{6.38}$$

Since $w_i (i = 1, 2, \ldots, N(h))$ is a basis for V_h, the solution of (6.38) is taken as

$$u_h = \sum_{k=1}^{N(h)} \beta_k w_k. \tag{6.39}$$

Hence β_k are the solutions of the following linear system:

$$\sum_{k=1}^{N(h)} a(w_k, w_l)\beta_k = L(w_l) \quad \text{for } 1 \le l \le N(h) \tag{6.40}$$

with

$$a(w_k, w_l) = \sum_{K \in T_h} \int_K \left(\sum_{i=1}^{2} \frac{\partial w_k}{\partial x_i} \frac{\partial w_l}{\partial x_i} + w_k w_l \right) dx \tag{6.41}$$

$$L(w_l) = \sum_{K \in T_h} \int_K f(w_l) \, dx. \tag{6.42}$$

Hence if we know the stiffness matrix $a(w_k, w_l)$ and the load vector $L(w_l)$, β_k can be found from (6.40). Putting these values in (5.39), the solution of (6.38) can be found.

6.7 Trefftz Method

If the Euler-Ostrogradsky equation arising in the problem of extremum of a functional depending on functions of two or more independent variables is linear and homogeneous but the domain of integration is bounded by a complex contour, the Trefftz method (see [15]) proves very effective. We shall demonstrate this method by considering the problem of finding a stationary value of the Dirichlet integral

$$I[u(x, y)] = \iint\limits_G \left[\left(\frac{\partial u}{\partial x} \right)^2 + \left(\frac{\partial u}{\partial y} \right)^2 \right] dx \, dy \tag{6.43}$$

satisfying the boundary condition

$$u |_\Gamma = f, \tag{6.44}$$

where f is a given function on the boundary Γ of the domain G. This problem arises in the solution of Laplace's equation $\nabla^2 u = 0$ in a domain G with the boundary condition given above.

Let $u_0(x, y)$ be the unknown solution of the problem. We seek an approximate solution of the form

$$u_{\text{app.}} = \sum_{k=1}^{n} c_k u_k(x, y), \tag{6.45}$$

where u_k are solutions of $\nabla^2 u = 0$. If u_0 were known, we could pose the problem of finding the coefficients c_k in such a way that $u_{\text{app.}}$ minimizes the integral

$$I\{u_{\text{app.}} - u_0\} = \iint \left[\left(\frac{\partial}{\partial x} u_{\text{app.}} - \frac{\partial u_0}{\partial x} \right)^2 + \left(\frac{\partial u_{\text{app.}}}{\partial y} - \frac{\partial u_0}{\partial y} \right)^2 \right] dx\, dy. \quad (6.46)$$

It appears natural to try to construct the approximate solution of the form (6.45) minimizing the functional (6.46). Equating the partial derivatives of the expression in (6.46) with respect to c_j ($j = 1, 2, \ldots, n$), we get

$$\sum_{k=1}^{n} \iint_G \left(\frac{\partial u_j}{\partial x} \frac{\partial u_k}{\partial x} + \frac{\partial u_j}{\partial y} \frac{\partial u_k}{\partial y} \right) c_k\, dx\, dy$$

$$= \iint_G \left(\frac{\partial u_j}{\partial x} \frac{\partial u_0}{\partial x} + \frac{\partial u_j}{\partial y} \frac{\partial u_0}{\partial y} \right) dx\, dy \quad (j = 1, 2, \ldots, n). \quad (6.47)$$

But for any harmonic function v and an arbitrary function u, we have

$$\iint_G \nabla u \cdot \nabla v\, dx\, dy = \int_\Gamma u \frac{\partial v}{\partial n}\, dS.$$

Using (6.44) and the above relation, we get from (6.47), the equation

$$\sum_{k=1}^{n} \left(\int_\Gamma \frac{\partial u_j}{\partial n} u_k\, d\Gamma \right) c_k = \int_\Gamma f \frac{\partial u_j}{\partial n}\, d\Gamma \quad (j = 1, 2, \ldots, n), \quad (6.48)$$

which only involves the value of u_0 on the boundary Γ. Thus (6.48) can be used when u_0 is unknown in the domain G. When the values of c_k determined from (6.48) are substituted in (6.45), we obtain the same expression as if we have minimized the integral (6.46) and thus determine an approximate solution of the original problem.

It should be noted that the method is also applicable when we have the boundary condition $[\partial u/\partial n]_\Gamma = f$ instead of (6.44). Numerical calculations reveal that the Trefftz method is highly effective.

6.8   Synge's Method of the Hypercircle

The Trefftz method described in Section 6.7 is best illustrated by considering the problem of finding the bounds on the flow rate in the steady laminar motion of a Newtonian fluid through a square duct under a uniform pressure gradient. We take the origin at the centre of the duct, x_3-axis along the axis of the duct and x_1 and x_2 axes in a transverse section of the duct such that the duct sides are $x_1 = \pm a$ and $x_2 = \pm a$. If v_3 is the velocity along the duct, the governing equation is

$$\frac{\partial^2 v_3}{\partial x_1^2} + \frac{\partial^2 v_3}{\partial x_2^2} = \frac{1}{\mu} \frac{\partial p}{\partial x_3} \quad (6.49)$$

subject to the no slip condition at the duct boundary Γ:

$$v_3 = 0 \quad \text{at } x_1 = \pm a,$$

$$v_3 = 0 \quad \text{at } x_2 = \pm a. \tag{6.50}$$

Define a functional of two variables u and v:

$$M(u, v) = \int\int_{-a}^{a} \left(\frac{\partial v}{\partial x_1} \frac{\partial u}{\partial x_1} + \frac{\partial v}{\partial x_2} \frac{\partial u}{\partial x_2} \right) dx_1 \, dx_2, \tag{6.51}$$

where the integration is over the cross-section of the duct. It is evident from (6.51) that $M(u, u) \geq 0$ and that

$$M(u - v, u) = M(u, u) - M(v, u). \tag{6.52}$$

This equation is inherent in the definition of a linear function space which arises in the problem of fixing bounds. By Schwarz inequality, we have

$$M(v, v)M(u, u) \geq [M(u, v)]^2. \tag{6.53}$$

Consider now the class of functions u satisfying

$$\frac{\partial^2 u}{\partial x_1^2} + \frac{\partial^2 u}{\partial x_2^2} = 0. \tag{6.54}$$

Further, we define another class of functions v which vanish on the duct boundary Γ:

$$v(x_1, x_2) = 0 \quad \text{at } x_1 = \pm a, \; x_2 = \pm a. \tag{6.55}$$

Now using (6.51) and (6.54), we find that

$$M(u, v) = \int\int_{-a}^{a} \left[\frac{\partial}{\partial x_1} \left(v \frac{\partial u}{\partial x_1} \right) + \frac{\partial}{\partial x_2} \left(v \frac{\partial u}{\partial x_2} \right) \right] dx_1 \, dx_2$$

$$- \int\int_{-a}^{a} v \left(\frac{\partial^2 u}{\partial x_1^2} + \frac{\partial^2 u}{\partial x_2^2} \right) dx_1 \, dx_2 = 0 \tag{6.56}$$

because the first integral on the right side can be reduced to a line integral (by Green's theorem) which vanishes by virtue of (6.55). Since

$$\int\int_{-a}^{a} v_3 \left(\frac{\partial^2 v_3}{\partial x_1^2} + \frac{\partial^2 v_3}{\partial x_2^2} \right) dx_1 \, dx_2 + \int\int_{-a}^{a} \left[\left(\frac{\partial v_3}{\partial x_1} \right)^2 + \left(\frac{\partial v_3}{\partial x_2} \right)^2 \right] dx_1 \, dx_2$$

$$= \int_{\Gamma} v_3 \frac{\partial v_3}{\partial n} \, dS = 0,$$

we find, on using (6.49) and (6.51), that $M(v_3, v_3)$ is proportional to the flow rate

$\iint\limits_{-a}^{a} v_3 \, dx_1 \, dx_2$. Note that v_3 is a member of the set v, since v_3 vanishes on Γ.

Now consider a function w satisfying

$$\frac{\partial^2 w}{\partial x_1^2} + \frac{\partial^2 w}{\partial x_2^2} = \frac{1}{\mu}\frac{\partial p}{\partial x_3} \tag{6.57}$$

such that w need not satisfy the boundary condition (6.55). Clearly, $v_3 - w$ is a member of the class u satisfying (6.54). Further, it follows from (6.56) that $M(v_3 - w, v_3) = 0$, which implies that

$$M(v_3, v_3) = M(v_3, w). \tag{6.58}$$

Using (6.53) and (6.58), we find

$$M(v_3, v_3) \le M(w, w), \tag{6.59}$$

which provides an upper bound for the flow rate.

We now proceed to find the lower bound. Expanding

$$M(v_3 - \alpha v, v_3 - \alpha v) \ge 0 \ (\alpha \text{ is a real number}),$$

we find that

$$M(v_3, v_3) \ge 2\alpha M(v, v_3) - \alpha^2 M(v, v). \tag{6.60}$$

Since $v_3 - w$ belongs to the class u, (6.56) gives $M(v_3 - w, v) = 0$, leading to

$$M(v, v_3) = M(v, w). \tag{6.61}$$

Combining (6.60) and (6.61), we get

$$M(v_3, v_3) \ge 2\alpha M(v, w) - \alpha^2 M(v, v), \tag{6.62}$$

which yields a lower bound for the flow rate. Maximizing the right-hand side of (6.62) with respect to α, we can sharpen the lower bound as

$$M(v_3, v_3) \ge [M(v, w)]^2/M(v, v). \tag{6.63}$$

The results (6.59) and (6.63) giving the upper and lower bounds are indeed very satisfying since these give a good idea about the validity of the approximation. However, no method exists for finding these bounds in the general case. For a certain class of linear problems, Synge [31] devised a very interesting and useful geometry applicable in function space.

We think of a function space where the functions are regarded as vectors. This space is infinite-dimensional but many of the vector operations can be translated so that comparison is fruitful. We introduce a measure of length in this function space. This metric has certain properties such as satisfying the commutative and distributive laws and is also positive definite. Equation (6.51) provides a suitable metric for a function space and (6.53) gives the basis for defining the angle β between two vectors u and v as follows:

$$\cos \beta = \frac{M(u, v)}{\sqrt{M(u, u)M(v, v)}}, \qquad 0 \leq \beta \leq \pi. \qquad (6.64)$$

Thus (6.56) is the condition of orthogonality of the vectors u and v. Further, using concepts of geometry, we can interpret the bounds obtained in this section.

Equation (6.61) implies that $v_3 - w$ and v are orthogonal, and this is illustrated in Fig. 6.3. Since v_3 is in class v, it is shown parallel to v. The vector w is neither

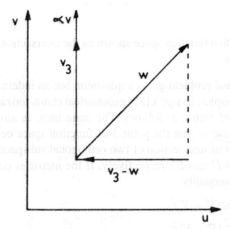

Fig. 6.3 A geometric interpretation of the upper bound of a solution in a function space.

in u nor in v and is shown skew to both axes. Thus we have a picture of the mathematical machinery which was used to develop upper and lower bounds. Indeed it is clear that w must be 'longer' than v_3 if $v_3 - w$ is orthogonal to v. This gives the geometric interpretation of the upper bounds. Further, Fig. 6.3 shows that the shortest distance from αv to the vector w is along $v_3 - w$, since this vector is orthogonal to αv. This implies that

$$M(w - v_3, w - v_3) \leq M(w - \alpha v, w - \alpha v).$$

This result suggested by geometry gives

$$M(w, v_3) \geq 2\alpha M(w, v) - \alpha^2 M(v, v), \qquad (6.65)$$

since $w - v_3$ is orthogonal to v_3. But due to orthogonality, we have $M(w - v_3, v_3)$ = 0, leading to

$$M(w, v_3) = M(v_3, v_3). \qquad (6.66)$$

Combining (6.65) and (6.66), we get the lower bound (6.62).

In the above discussion the metric of the function space is assumed to be positive definite. Such a positive-definite metric also occurs in problems of elasticity involving equilibrium, the positive-definite character being due to the positive-definite nature of the energy of the system. However, in certain physical problems involving forced vibrations, the appropriate metric is indefinite, similar to the metric in a Minkowski space-time. It may be noted that with a positive-definite

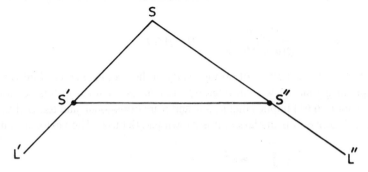

Fig. 6.4 Solution in a function space shown as the intersection of two orthogonal subspaces.

metric, the variational problem gives a minimum but an indefinite metric leads to only stationary principles. Synge's [31] geometrical characterization however takes care of both types of metric as follows: The main idea, as already stated before, is to split the problem so that the point S of function space corresponding to the solution is the point of intersection of two orthogonal subspaces L' and L''. Let S' and S'' be points on L' and L'', respectively. If the metric is positive-definite, we have by Schwarz inequality

$$(S - S'')^2 \leq (S' - S'')^2, \tag{6.67a}$$

$$(S - S')^2 \leq (S' - S'')^2. \tag{6.67b}$$

Define Φ by

$$\Phi = (S' - S'')^2. \tag{6.68}$$

Thus we have the following two minimum principles:

(i) If S' is fixed, Φ is minimized for $S' = S$.
(ii) If S'' is fixed, Φ is minimized for $S'' = S$.

If the metric is indefinite, (6.67a) and (6.67b) no longer hold but we have an orthogonality condition

$$(S - S') \cdot (S - S'') = 0,$$

which gives

$$(S - S'') \cdot \delta S' = 0, \qquad (S - S') \cdot \delta S'' = 0 \tag{6.69}$$

corresponding to arbitrary variations of S' and S'' on L' and L'', respectively. But (6.68) yields

$$\delta\Phi = 2(S' - S'') \cdot (\delta S' - \delta S''),$$

which gives the following two stationary principles:

(i) For S'' fixed, Φ is stationary if $S' = S$.
(ii) For S' fixed, Φ is stationary if $S'' = S$.

We now apply the Trefftz method to obtain approximate bounds for the flow rate. In dimensionless form, (6.49) and the boundary conditions (6.50) become

$$\nabla^2 u = -1 \text{ in the duct cross-section } A \tag{6.70}$$

with

$$u = 0 \text{ on the duct boundary } \Gamma. \tag{6.71}$$

Here

$$\nabla^2 = \partial^2/\partial x^2 + \partial^2/\partial y^2,$$

$$x = x_1/a, \qquad y = x_2/a$$

and

$$u = v_3/u_1 \text{ with } u_1 = -(a^2/\mu)(dp/dx_3).$$

It is clear from the geometry of the flow that the trial functions must be symmetric in x and y, i.e.,

$$(x, y) \leftrightarrow (-x, y), (x, y) \leftrightarrow (x, -y), (x, y) \leftrightarrow (y, x).$$

Using this symmetry property, the non-homogeneous solution to (6.67) is $u_2(x, y)$ $= -(x^2 + y^2)/4$. For finding the solution of (6.70) with -1 replaced by 0 on the right-hand side, we consider the real and imaginary parts of $(x + iy)^n$. Thus the trial functions satisfying the above symmetry property are $1 (= u_0(x, y))$, $x^4 - 6x^2y^2 + y^4 (= u_4(x, y))$, ... corresponding to $n = 0, 4, ...$ in $(x + iy)^n$, the quadratic terms corresponding to $n = 2$ being already considered in the non-homogeneous solution. Thus the trial function u_N is taken as

$$u_N = c_0 - \frac{1}{4}(x^2 + y^2) + \sum_{i=4}^{N} c_i u_i(x, y). \tag{6.72}$$

We drop the constant c_0 in (6.72) since it does not make any contribution to the integral in (6.51).

Now substituting (6.72) in (6.51) and minimizing $M(u_N, u_N)$ with respect to c_i, following the Trefftz method, we get

$$\frac{\partial M}{\partial c_i} = 2 \int \left[\sum_{i=4}^{N} c_i u_i - \frac{1}{4}(x^2 + y^2) \right] \mathbf{n} \cdot \nabla u_j \, dA = 0. \tag{6.73}$$

It is found from (6.73) that $N = 4$ gives fairly accurate result (see [16]) for the bounds on the flow rate as

$$0.5622 \leq QL/(a^4 \Delta p) \leq 0.5630.$$

6.9 Kantorovich Method

While applying the Rayleigh-Ritz method to functionals $I[z(x_1, x_2, ..., x_n)]$ depending on the functions of several variables, the coordinate system of functions is chosen as $W_1(x_1, x_2, ..., x_n)$, $W_2(x_1, x_2, ..., x_n)$, ..., $W_n(x_1, x_2, ..., x_n)$, ... and an approximate solution is sought in the form

$$z_m = \sum_{k=1}^{m} \alpha_k W_k(x_1, x_2, ..., x_n),$$

where α_k's are constants and W_k's are linearly independent.

In Kantorovich's method [1] also, one chooses the coordinate system of functions as above but the approximate solution is sought in the form

$$z_m = \sum_{k=1}^{m} \alpha_k(x_i) W_k(x_1, x_2, ..., x_n), \tag{6.74}$$

where the coefficients $\alpha_k(x_i)$ are unknown functions of one of the independent variables. On the class of functions of the type (6.74), the functional $I[z]$ is transformed into a functional of the form $I[\alpha_1(x_i), \alpha_2(x_i), ..., \alpha_m(x_i)]$, which depends on $\alpha_1(x_i), \alpha_2(x_i), ..., \alpha_m(x_i)$. These functions are then chosen so as to extremize the functional I.

If we proceed to the limit as $m \to \infty$, then subject to certain conditions one can obtain an exact solution. But if such limit is not taken, then the method will give an approximate solution which is generally more accurate than that obtained by Ritz method with the same coordinate functions and the same number of terms. The greater precision of Kantorovich's method stems from the fact that the class of functions given by (6.74) is considerably broader than the class with the same coordinate functions but with constant α_k's. Thus it is possible to find functions that approximate better the solution of the variational problem than the functions from the class $\sum_{k=1}^{m} \alpha_k W_k(x_1, x_2, ..., x_n)$, where the α_k's are constants.

Example 5.   Find an approximate solution of Poisson's equation

$$\frac{\partial^2 z}{\partial x^2} + \frac{\partial^2 z}{\partial y^2} = -1 \text{ in the rectangle } D \begin{cases} -a \leq x \leq a, \\ -b \leq y \leq b \end{cases}$$

with $z = 0$ on the boundary of D.

Solution.   It may be readily shown that Poisson's equation is the Euler-Ostrogradsky equation for the extremum of the functional

$$I[z] = \iint_D \left[\left(\frac{\partial z}{\partial x} \right)^2 + \left(\frac{\partial z}{\partial y} \right)^2 - 2z \right] dx \, dy.$$

We seek an approximate solution in the form

$$z_1(x, y) = (b^2 - y^2)\alpha(x),$$

which clearly satisfies $z_1 = 0$ on $y = \pm b$.

Substituting this in the expression for I, we get

$$I[z_1] = \int_{-a}^{a} \left[\frac{16}{15} b^5 \alpha'^2 + \frac{8}{3} b^3 \alpha^2 - \frac{8}{3} b^3 \alpha \right] dx$$

whose Euler equation is

$$\alpha''(x) - \frac{5\alpha}{2b^2} = -\frac{5}{4b^2}. \tag{6.75}$$

Its solution satisfying $\alpha(-a) = \alpha(a) = 0$ is

$$\alpha(x) = \frac{1}{2}\left[1 - \frac{\cosh\sqrt{\frac{5}{2}}\cdot\frac{x}{b}}{\cosh\sqrt{\frac{5}{2}}\frac{a}{b}}\right].$$

Thus the approximate solution is

$$z_1(x, y) = \frac{b^2 - y^2}{2}\left[1 - \frac{\cosh\sqrt{\frac{5}{2}}\cdot\frac{x}{b}}{\cosh\sqrt{\frac{5}{2}}\cdot\frac{a}{b}}\right].$$

To obtain a more accurate solution we may try a solution of the form

$$z_2(x, y) = (b^2 - y^2)\alpha_1(x) + (b^2 - y^2)^2\alpha_2(x).$$

6.10 Variational Proofs of Certain Important Inequalities

Let us first prove the following results: If $y(0) = 0$ and $2k$ is an even positive integer, then

$$\int_0^1 y^{2k}\,dx \le C\int_0^1 y'^{2k}\,dx, \tag{6.76}$$

where

$$C = \frac{1}{2k - 1}\cdot\left(\frac{2k}{\pi}\sin\frac{\pi}{2k}\right)^{2k} \tag{6.77}$$

To prove this we suppose first that $y(1) \ne 0$ and we take $y(1) = 1$. Now consider the extremum of the functional

$$I[y(x)] = \int_0^1 (Cy'^{2k} - y^{2k})\,dx.$$

Euler's equation is

$$(2k - 1)Cy'^{2k-2}y'' + y^{2k-1} = 0,$$

which gives, on integration, the relation

$$(2k - 1)Cy'^{2k} = C_1 - y^{2k},$$

where C_1 is a constant of integration.

There exists one extremal which passes through $(0, 0)$ and $(1, 1)$ and cuts $x = 1$ at right angles. In fact, if we take $C_1 = 1$, then $y' = 0$ at $y = 1$, and hence

$$x = [(2k - 1)C]^{1/(2k)}\int \frac{dy}{(1 - y^{2k})^{1/(2k)}}. \tag{6.78}$$

Further, since

$$\int_0^1 \frac{dy}{(1 - y^{2k})^{1/(2k)}} = \frac{\pi}{2k} \cosec \frac{\pi}{2k},$$

it follows from (6.78) that C has the value given by (6.77). If we denote this extremal by Y, then using $Y'(1) = 0$, we have

$$I[Y] = [CYY'^{2k-1}]_0^1 - \int_0^1 Y[(2k - 1)CY'^{2k-2}Y'' + Y^{2k-1}]\,dx = 0.$$

To establish the inequality (6.76), we have to show that $y = Y$ gives a strong minimum. The extremal is a rising curve of the same general form as the curve $y = \sin(\pi x/2)$, corresponding to the form of the above extremal for $k = 1$. Now clearly, $y = \alpha Y$ defines a central field of extremals and invoking the Weirstrass excess function W (defined in Section 3.3), we have

$$W = y'^{2k} - p^{2k} - 2k(y' - p)p^{2k-1},$$

which is positive. Hence the sufficient conditions for a strong minimum are satisfied.

The case in which $y(1) = 0$ can also be analyzed similarly since $y = 0$ is then an extremal satisfying the boundary conditions and can be embedded in the field $y = \alpha Y$ mentioned above.

An inequality similar to (6.76) corresponding to $k = 1$ is

$$\int_0^{\pi/2} y^2\,dx < \int_0^{\pi/2} y'^2\,dx \tag{6.79}$$

if $y(0) = 0$, y is not a multiple of $\sin x$ and y' belongs to L_2 (see [32]).

The proof is as follows: Consider an identity of the form

$$\int_0^{\pi/2} (y'^2 - y^2)\,dx = \int_0^{\pi/2} [y' - y\Psi(x)]^2,$$

which implies

$$\int_0^{\pi/2} [y^2(1 + \Psi^2) - 2yy'\Psi]\,dx = 0.$$

The above result is evidently true if the integrand is an exact differential dz with z vanishing at the limits. This requires $-\Psi'(x) = 1 + \Psi^2$ so that $\Psi = -\tan(x + k_1)$. In this case, $z = -\Psi y^2$. If we take $k_1 = \pi/2$, then $\Psi = \cot x$. Hence z vanishes when $x = \pi/2$. Further, since y' is L_2, $y = o(x^{1/2})$. So z also vanishes at $x = 0$. We then get

$$\int_0^{\pi/2} (y'^2 - y^2)\,dx = \int_0^{\pi/2} (y' - y\cot x)^2\,dx \tag{6.80}$$

and the inequality (6.79) follows. A slight modification of the above result is as follows: If $y(0) = y(\pi) = 0$ and y' is L_2, then

$$\int_0^\pi y^2 \, dx < \int_0^\pi y'^2 \, dx \qquad\qquad (6.81)$$

unless $y = C \sin x$.

Since y' is L_2, $y = o(x^{1/2})$ for small x and $y = o\{(\pi - x)^{1/2}\}$ for x close to π. Hence $y^2 \cot x$ vanishes at both the limits. Thus as before,

$$\int_0^\pi (y'^2 - y^2) \, dx = \int_0^\pi (y' - y \cot x)^2 \, dx$$

and the result follows.

A variational proof of (6.81) is as follows: We find the minimum of $\int_0^\pi y'^2 \, dx$ subject to

$$\int_0^\pi y^2 \, dx = 1, \qquad y(0) = y(\pi) = 0.$$

Euler's equation for the functional

$$I[y] = \int_0^\pi [y'^2 - \lambda y^2] \, dx$$

is of the form

$$y'' + \lambda y = 0$$

with $y(0) = y(\pi) = 0$. The eigenfunctions and eigenvalues of this problem are

$$y_n(x) = \sin nx, \qquad \lambda_n = n^2.$$

The smallest eigenvalue is 1 and hence by the extremal properties of eigenvalues described in Chapter 5, we have

$$\min \int_0^\pi y'^2(x) \, dx = 1.$$

Thus for any function $y(x)$ for which $\int_0^\pi y^2(x) \, dx = 1$, we find that

$$\int_0^\pi y'^2 \, dx \geq \int_0^\pi y^2 \, dx.$$

This inequality cannot be sharpened since for $y_1(x) = \sin x / \sqrt{\pi}$, we have

$$\int_0^\pi y_1'^2 \, dx = \int_0^\pi y_1^2 \, dx = 1.$$

If $\int_0^\pi y^2 \, dx = k^2 \neq 1$, then the problem reduces to the preceding one if we introduce the function $z(x) = y(x)/k$.

The following result is also true:

$$\left(\frac{l}{\pi}\right)^2 \int_0^l y'^2 \, dx \ge \int_0^l y^2 \, dx \tag{6.82}$$

if $y(0) = y(l) = 0$ and $y' \in L_2[0, l]$. Here equality is attained only for $y = A \sin(\pi x/l)$.

While the above inequalities refer only to a function of a single variable, a more general result for a function of several variables known as Steklov's inequality (see [33]) is the following: There exists a positive constant c such that

$$\int_Q f^2 \, dx \le c \int_Q |\nabla f|^2 \, dx$$

for every function $f \in H^{01}(Q)$. Here Q is a bounded region of space R^n with a piecewise smooth boundary Γ. Further, $H^k(Q)$ is the Sobolev space consisting of all functions $f \in L_2(Q)$ that have generalized derivatives up to order k inclusive and belong to $L_2(Q)$. In particular, $H^{01}(Q)$ denotes the set of functions belonging to $H^1(Q)$, whose traces on Γ are zero almost everywhere.

It is interesting to note that by using Steklov's inequality, one can prove the existence and uniqueness of the generalized solution to Poisson's equation $\nabla^2 u = -f$ in a bounded region $Q \subset R^n$ subject to the boundary conditions on the smooth boundary Γ of Q given by $u|_\Gamma = 0$ with $f \in L_2(Q)$.

Finally, a modification of (6.80) leads to an interesting inequality known as Wirtinger's inequality.

Wirtinger's Inequality [32]

If $y(x)$ has period 2π, y' is L_2 and

$$\int_0^{2\pi} y \, dx = 0, \tag{6.83}$$

then the following inequality holds:

$$\int_0^{2\pi} y^2 \, dx < \int_0^{2\pi} y'^2 \, dx$$

unless $y = A \cos x + B \sin x$.

To prove this result we cannot at once write down an identity similar to (6.80) because $y \cot x$ will have infinities in the range of integration $\langle 0, 2\pi \rangle$. However, we may argue as follows. Consider the function

$$z(x) = y(x + \pi) - y(x). \tag{6.84}$$

Clearly, $z(x)$ has opposite signs at x and $x + \pi$ by virtue of the periodicity of $y(x)$ and, therefore, it vanishes at least once in $\langle 0, \pi \rangle$. Let $z(\alpha) = 0$ where $0 \le \alpha < \pi$, and put $y(\alpha) = a$. Since y' is L_2, it follows that $(y - a)^2 \cdot \cot(x - \alpha)$ vanishes for $x = \alpha$ and $x = \alpha + \pi$. Hence

$$\int_0^{2\pi} [y'^2 - (y-a)^2 - \{y' - (y-a)\cot(x-\alpha)\}^2]\,dx$$

$$= [(y-a)^2 \cot(x-\alpha)]_0^{2\pi} = 0.$$

Thus using (6.83), we get

$$\int_0^{2\pi} (y'^2 - y^2)\,dx = 2\pi a^2 + \int_0^{2\pi} [y' - (y-a)\cot(x-\alpha)]^2\,dx,$$

which is positive unless $a = 0$ and $y' = y\cot(x-\alpha)$, leading to $y = C\sin(x-\alpha)$. This proves the result.

An important application of this inequality lies in the establishment of the classical isoperimetric property of the circle. Consider a simple closed curve C with area A and perimeter L and take $\phi = 2\pi s/L$, where s is the arc of the curve given by $x = x(\phi)$, $y = y(\phi)$ with $0 \le \phi \le 2\pi$. Further we assume, without loss of generality, that the centre of gravity of the perimeter lies on the x-axis so that

$$\int_0^{2\pi} y\,d\phi = 0.$$

Now we have

$$\left(\frac{dx}{d\phi}\right)^2 + \left(\frac{dy}{d\phi}\right)^2 = \left[\left(\frac{dx}{ds}\right)^2 + \left(\frac{dy}{ds}\right)^2\right]\frac{L^2}{4\pi^2} = \frac{L^2}{4\pi^2}.$$

Hence

$$\frac{L^2}{2\pi} - 2A = \int_0^{2\pi}\left[\left(\frac{dx}{d\phi}\right)^2 + \left(\frac{dy}{d\phi}\right)^2\right]d\phi + 2\int_0^{2\pi} y\,\frac{dx}{d\phi}\,d\phi$$

$$= \int_0^{2\pi}\left(\frac{dx}{d\phi} + y\right)^2 d\phi + \int_0^{2\pi}\left[\left(\frac{dy}{d\phi}\right)^2 - y^2\right]d\phi$$

$$\ge \int_0^{2\pi}\left[\left(\frac{dy}{d\phi}\right)^2 - y^2\right]d\phi.$$

Thus by Wirtinger's inequality, $(L^2/2\pi) - 2A$ is always positive unless $y = A_1\cos\phi + B_1\sin\phi$, in which case the above expression for $(L^2/2\pi) - 2A$ implies

$$\frac{dx}{d\phi} + y = 0.$$

This leads to

$$x = -\int y\,d\phi = -A_1\sin\phi + B_1\cos\phi + C_1$$

and the curve is then clearly a circle. Thus a closed curve of given perimeter encloses maximum area when it is a circle. Although the above proof is based on the assumption that $x'(\phi)$ and $y'(\phi)$ are continuous, the same result can be obtained for more general x and y.

Another result similar to Wirtinger's inequality is as follows: Let $y(x)$ be a function defined on $[0, 2\pi]$ with $y'(x) \in L_2[0, 2\pi]$ satisfying $\int_0^{2\pi} y(x) \, dx = 0$. Now if $y'(0) = y'(2\pi) = 0$, then $\int_0^{2\pi} y'^2 \, dx \geq \int_0^{2\pi} y^2 \, dx$.

In 1905, Almansi (see Komkov [34]) proved the following result: Let f be a function belonging to $C^1[a, b]$ such that $f(a) = f(b)$ and $\int_a^b f(x) \, dx = 0$. Then

$$\int_a^b [f'(x)]^2 \, dx \geq \left(\frac{2\pi}{b-a} \right)^2 \int_a^b [f(x)]^2 \, dx.$$

This is, in fact, a generalization of Wirtinger's inequality stated above. It can be regarded as a special (one-dimensional) case of Poincare's inequality.

It may be remarked in this connection that if a differential system is strongly elliptic, its strong ellipticity sometimes permits us to estimate high order derivatives of solutions in terms of the lower derivatives (see [34]).

An application of the inequality (6.82) to the problem of hydromagnetic thermal convection in an electrically conducting fluid layer heated from below is now described below.

•Magnetoconvection in a Horizontal Layer Heated from Below

Consider a horizontal layer of an electrically conducting fluid heated from below. The layer is permeated by a uniform magnetic field along the vertical. In the undisturbed state the fluid is at rest and heat flows by conduction. Convection sets in when the adverse temperature gradient due to heating exceeds a critical value. The eigenvalue problem involving the growth rate p of a disturbance of small amplitude with time dependence e^{pt} is governed by the following linearized stability equations (Chandrasekhar [60]):

$$(D^2 - a^2)(D^2 - a^2 - p/\sigma)w = Ra^2\theta - QD(D^2 - a^2)h_z, \tag{6.85}$$

$$(D^2 - a^2 - p)\theta = -w, \tag{6.86}$$

$$(D^2 - a^2 - p\sigma_1/\sigma)h_z = -Dw, \tag{6.87}$$

where θ, w and h_z stand for the amplitudes of perturbations in temperature, vertical velocity and the vertical component of the induced magnetic field, respectively. Further, $D = d/dz$, z being the dimensionless vertical distance and a, σ, σ_1, R and Q stand for the horizontal disturbance wave number, Prandtl number, magnetic Prandtl number, Rayleigh number (characterizing the temperature gradient) and Chandrasekhar number (characterizing the strength of the imposed magnetic field), respectively. With the bounding surfaces of the layer at $z = 0$ and 1, the boundary conditions for velocity are

$$w = Dw = 0 \quad \text{at a rigid wall} \tag{6.88}$$

$$w = D^2w = 0 \quad \text{at a free surface.} \tag{6.89}$$

The boundary conditions for θ are

$$\theta = 0 \quad \text{at } z = 0 \quad \text{and } 1. \tag{6.90}$$

Further, the boundary conditions for h_z at perfectly electrically conducting surfaces are

$$h_z = 0 \quad \text{at } z = 0 \quad \text{and } 1 \tag{6.91a}$$

and the boundary conditions at electrically insulated surfaces are

$$\begin{aligned} Dh_z &= ah_z \quad \text{at } z = 0 \\ Dh_z &= -ah_z \quad \text{at } z = 1. \end{aligned} \tag{6.91b}$$

We now consider two cases.

Case 1: **Perfectly conducting boundaries**

When (6.85) is multiplied by w^* (the complex conjugate of w) and the resulting equation is integrated with respect to z from $z = 0$ to 1 and using (6.86), (6.87) and the boundary conditions (6.88) (or (6.89)), (6.90) and (6.91a), we get

$$\int_0^1 [|D^2w|^2 + 2a^2 |Dw|^2 + a^4 |w|^2] \, dz + (p/\sigma) \int_0^1 [|Dw|^2 + a^2 |w|^2] \, dz$$

$$= Ra^2 \int_0^1 [|D\theta|^2 + a^2 |\theta|^2 + p^* |\theta|^2] \, dz \; - Q \int_0^1 |(D^2 - a^2) \, h_z|^2 \, dz$$

$$- (Qp^*\sigma_1/\sigma) \int_0^1 [|Dh_z|^2 + a^2 |h_z|^2] \, dz. \tag{6.92}$$

Equating the imaginary part of (6.92) and cancelling the factor p_i (where $p = p_r + ip_i$ with $p_i \neq 0$), we obtain

$$(1/\sigma) \int_0^1 [|Dw|^2 + a^2 |w|^2] \, dz - (Q\sigma_1/\sigma) \int_0^1 [|Dh_z|^2 + a^2 |h_z|^2] \, dz$$

$$= - Ra^2 \int_0^1 |\theta|^2 \, dz. \tag{6.93}$$

Similarly, (6.87) leads to

$$\int_0^1 [|Dh_z|^2 + a^2 |h_z|^2] \, dz + (p\sigma_1/\sigma) \int_0^1 |h_z|^2 \, dz = \int_0^1 h_z^* Dw \, dz \tag{6.94}$$

whose real part gives

$$\int_0^1 [|Dh_z|^2 + a^2|h_z|^2]\,dz + (p_r\sigma_1/\sigma)\int_0^1 |h_z|^2\,dz$$

$$= \text{Re}\int_0^1 h_z^* Dw\,dz. \tag{6.95}$$

Now

$$\text{Re}\int_0^1 h_z^* Dw\,dz \le \int_0^1 |h_z||Dw|\,dz \le \frac{1}{2}\int_0^1 [|h_z|^2 + |Dw|^2]\,dz. \tag{6.96}$$

At the onset of convection, $p_r = 0$ ($p_r > 0$ for instability) and this condition, combined with (6.95) and (6.96), gives

$$\int_0^1 [|Dh_z|^2 + a^2|h_z|^2]\,dz \le \frac{1}{2}\int_0^1 [|h_z|^2 + |Dw|^2]\,dz. \tag{6.97}$$

Since $h_z(0) = h_z(1) = 0$ ((6.91a)), we get from (6.82) with $l = 1$,

$$\int_0^1 |Dh_z|^2\,dz \ge \pi^2\int_0^1 |h_z|^2\,dz. \tag{6.98}$$

Equations (6.97) and (6.98) give

$$\int_0^1 |h_z|^2\,dz \le \frac{1}{[2(\pi^2 + a^2) - 1]}\int_0^1 |Dw|^2\,dz. \tag{6.99}$$

Finally, when (6.98) and (6.99) are used in (6.93), we obtain

$$\frac{1}{\sigma}\left[1 - \frac{Q\sigma_1(\pi^2 + a^2)}{2(\pi^2 + a^2) - 1}\right]\int_0^1 |Dw|^2\,dz + \frac{a^2}{\sigma}\int_0^1 |w|^2\,dz \le -Ra^2\int_0^1 |\theta|^2\,dz$$

and this demands that

$$1 - \frac{Q\sigma_1(\pi^2 + a^2)}{2(\pi^2 + a^2) - 1} < 0.$$

This leads to

$$a^2(2 - Q\sigma_1) < Q\sigma_1\pi^2 - (2\pi^2 - 1)$$

which clearly does not hold if

$$Q\sigma_1 < (2\pi^2 - 1)/\pi^2. \tag{6.100}$$

Thus, if (6.100) holds at the onset of convection, then p_i must vanish for all a^2 so that a steady state prevails. Hence a sufficient condition for the validity of the principle of exchange of stabilities (i.e., onset of steady convection) is $Q\sigma_1 < (2\pi^2 - 1)/\pi^2$. This result is due to Banerjee and Banerjee ([35], p. 28).

Case 2: Electrically insulated boundaries

In this case the governing equations are still (6.85)–(6.87), but the boundary conditions are (6.88) (or (6.89)), (6.90) and (6.91b). Multiplying (6.85) by w^* and integrating the resulting equation from $z = 0$ to 1, we get, by using (6.86) and (6.87) and the above boundary conditions,

$$\int_0^1 [|D^2 w|^2 + 2a^2 |Dw|^2 + a^4 |w|^2] \, dz + \frac{p}{\sigma} \int_0^1 [|Dw|^2 + a^2 |w|^2] \, dz$$

$$= Ra^2 \int_0^1 [|D\theta|^2 + a^2 |\theta|^2] \, dz + Ra^2 p^* \int_0^1 |\theta|^2 \, dz$$

$$- Q \int_0^1 |(D^2 - a^2) h_z|^2 \, dz - (Qp^* \sigma_1 / \sigma) \left[a(|h_z|_0^2 + |h_z|_1^2) \right.$$

$$\left. + \int_0^1 (|Dh_z|^2 + a^2 |h_z|^2) \, dz \right], \tag{6.101}$$

where the subscripts 0 and 1 refer to conditions at $z = 0$ and 1, respectively. Equating the imaginary part of (6.101), we obtain

$$(1/\sigma) \int_0^1 [|Dw|^2 + a^2 |w|^2] \, dz - (Q\sigma_1 / \sigma) \left[a(|h_z|_0^2 + |h_z|_1^2) \right.$$

$$\left. + \int_0^1 (|Dh_z|^2 + a^2 |h_z|^2) \, dz \right] = - Ra^2 \int_0^1 |\theta|^2 \, dz. \tag{6.102}$$

Again multiplying (6.87) by h_z^* and integrating the resulting equation from $z = 0$ to 1, we derive the following equation on using the boundary conditions (6.88) (or (6.89)) and (6.91b):

$$a[|h_z|_0^2 + |h_z|_1^2] + \int_0^1 [|Dh_z|^2 + a^2 |h_z|^2] \, dz$$

$$+ (p\sigma_1 / \sigma) \int_0^1 |h_z|^2 \, dz = - \int_0^1 w Dh_z^* \, dz. \tag{6.103}$$

Equating the real part of (6.103) and assuming $p_r = 0$ (at the onset of convection), one readily finds from (6.103) that

$$a[|h_z|_0^2 + |h_z|_1^2] + \int_0^1 [|Dh_z|^2 + a^2 |h_z|^2] \, dz$$

$$\leq \int_0^1 |w|^2 \, dz - a[|h_z|_0^2 + |h_z|_1^2] - a^2 \int_0^1 |h_z|^2 \, dz. \tag{6.104}$$

Again, since $w(0) = w(1) = 0$ by (6.88) or (6.89), we have by (6.82) with $l = 1$,

$$\int_0^1 |Dw|^2 \, dz \geq \pi^2 \int_0^1 |w|^2 \, dz. \tag{6.105}$$

Finally, using (6.104) and (6.105) in (6.102), we get

$$[(\pi^2/\sigma) - (Q\sigma_1/\sigma)] \int_0^1 |w|^2 \, dz + \frac{a^2}{\sigma} \int_0^1 |w|^2 \, dz + (Q\sigma_1/\sigma)\left[a(|h_z|_0^2 \right.$$

$$\left. + |h_z|_1^2) + a^2 \int_0^1 |h_z|^2 \right] dz \leq - Ra^2 \int_0^1 |\theta|^2 \, dz, \tag{6.106}$$

which demands that

$$(\pi^2/\sigma) - (Q\sigma_1/\sigma) < 0. \tag{6.107}$$

Clearly, (6.107) does not hold if

$$Q\sigma_1 < \pi^2. \tag{6.108}$$

This result is due to Banerjee et al. ([35], p. 32).

Now since $(2\pi^2 - 1)/\pi^2 < \pi^2$, it clearly follows from (6.100) and (6.108) that a sufficient condition for the validity of the principle of exchange of stabilities for hydromagnetic thermal convection is that

$$Q\sigma_1 < (2\pi^2 - 1)/\pi^2 \tag{6.109}$$

regardless of whether the boundary surfaces are electrically insulated or perfectly conducting. Chandrasekhar [60] first studied this problem of hydromagnetic thermal convection and conjectured that the principle of exchange of stabilities holds if the total kinetic energy associated with a disturbance given by

$$\int_0^1 [|Dw|^2 + a^2|w|^2] \, dz \text{ exceeds its total magnetic energy given by}$$

$$(Q\sigma_1/\sigma) \int_0^1 [|Dh_z|^2 + a^2|h_z|^2] \, dz.$$

A little calculation will show that this conjecture is valid if (6.109) holds.

PROBLEMS

1. Using the Rayleigh-Ritz method, find an approximate solution of $\nabla^2 z = -1$ inside the square $-a \leq x \leq a, -a \leq y \leq a$ which vanishes on the boundary of the square.

   Ans.   Seeking an approximate solution of the form

   $$z = \alpha(x^2 - a^2)(y^2 - a^2), \text{ one finds that } \alpha = \frac{5}{16a^2}.$$

2. Using the Rayleigh-Ritz method, find an approximate solution of the differential equation $y'' + x^2 y = x$, $y(0) = y(1) = 0$. Determine $y_2(x)$ and $y_3(x)$ and compare their values at the points $x = 0.25$, $x = 0.5$ and $x = 0.75$.

Ans.   Seek the solution in the form

$$y_2(x) = x(x - 1)(\alpha_1 + \alpha_2 x), \quad y_3(x) = x(x - 1)(\beta_1 + \beta_2 x + \beta_3 x^2).$$

Then it is found that $\alpha_1 = 0.1708$, $\alpha_2 = 0.1744$. Further, $\beta_1 = 0.1705$, $\beta_2 = 0.1760$, $\beta_3 = -0.0018$. The values of y_2 and y_3 agree at the specified points to within 0.0001.

3. Approximate the first eigenvalue of the Mathieu equation

$$y'' + \lambda(2 + \cos x)y = 0, \qquad y(0) = y(\pi) = 0.$$

Ans. $\lambda_1 = 0.493$.

4. Approximate the first eigenvalue of the problem

$$\nabla^2 z + \lambda z = 0$$

with $z = 0$ on the boundary of the domain D, which is a circle of unit radius with centre at the origin.

Ans. $\lambda_1 = 6$ with $z_1 = \alpha(x^2 + y^2 - 1)$.

5. Let Q be the square $\{0 < x_1 < 1, 0 < x_2 < 1\}$. Prove that

$$\int_Q f^2 \, dx \le \frac{1}{2\pi^2} \int_Q |\nabla f|^2 \, dx$$

for every f that belongs to $H^{01}(Q)$ and that the constant in the inequality is exact.

6. Let Q be the cube

$$\{0 < x_1 < 1, 0 < x_2 < 1, 0 < x_3 < 1\}.$$

Prove that

$$\|f\|_{L_2}^2 \le \frac{1}{3\pi^2} \|\nabla f\|_{L_2}^2$$

for every function $f \in H^{01}(Q)$.

7. Prove Poincare's inequality: Let Ω be a bounded open set in R^n and $W^{1,p}(\Omega)$ be the Sobolev space of order 1 for $1 \le p \le \infty$ with semi-norm $|\cdot|_{1,p,\Omega}$. Further, let $W_0^{1,p}(\Omega)$ be the closure of $D(\Omega)$ (which is the space of infinitely differentiable functions with compact support in Ω) in $W^{1,p}(\Omega)$. Then there exists a positive constant $C = C(\Omega, p)$ such that

$$|u|_{0,p,\Omega} \le C|u|_{1,p,\Omega} \quad \text{for every } u \in W_0^{1,p}(\Omega).$$

(It should be noted that this inequality is fundamental in studying weak solutions of Dirichlet boundary value problems.)

8. Prove the following important inequality (Korn's inequality (see [34])). Let Ω be a bounded open subset of R^3 of class C^1 and let V be the space $(H^1(\Omega))^3$, where $H^1(\Omega)$ is the Sobolev space $W^{1,2}(\Omega)$. If $v \in V$ with $v = (v_1, v_2, v_3)$ with

$$\varepsilon_{ij}(v) = \frac{1}{2}\left(\frac{\partial v_i}{\partial x_j} + \frac{\partial v_j}{\partial x_i}\right), \quad 1 \le i, j \le 3,$$

then there exists a positive constant C depending only on Ω, such that

$$\int_\Omega \varepsilon_{ij}(v)\varepsilon_{ij}(v) + \int v_i v_i \geq C \|v\|_V^2$$

for every $v \in V$ with $\| \cdot \|_V$ denoting the usual product norm on V. (Korn's inequality plays an important role in the weak formulation of the equation of linear elasticity).

9. Let Lu denote the operator

$$Lu = \sum_{0 \leq |r|, |s| \leq m} (-1)^r D^{|r|}(a_{rs}(\mathbf{x}) D^s \mathbf{u}),$$

where $\mathbf{u}$ and $\mathbf{x}$ are vectors, D is the differential operator and $a_{rs}(\mathbf{x})$ are sufficiently smooth. Further,

(a) L is strongly elliptic with a modulus of ellipticity independent of $\mathbf{x}$ in a domain Ω;

(b) the coefficients a_{rs} are bounded, i.e., there exists a positive constant C_1 such that $|a_{rs}| < C_1$; and

(c) the highest order coefficients have a bounded modulus of continuity, i.e., there exists a positive constant C_2 such that

$$| a_{rs}(\mathbf{x}_1) - a_{rs}(\mathbf{x}_2) | < C_2 | \mathbf{x}_1 - \mathbf{x}_2 | \quad \text{for } |r| = m$$

and $|s| = m$ and for $\mathbf{x}_1$ and $\mathbf{x}_2$ in Ω and C_2 is small in a small neighbourhood of the origin. Show that there exist positive constants C_3 and C_4 such that

$$\|\mathbf{u}\|_m^2 \leq C_3 B(u, u) + C_4 \|\mathbf{u}\|_0^2,$$

where $\| \mathbf{u} \|_0$ denotes the usual $L_2(\Omega)$ norm of $\mathbf{u}(\mathbf{x})$ and $B(u, v)$ is the bilinear form

$$B(\mathbf{u}, \mathbf{v}) = \sum_{0 \leq |r|, |s| \leq m} D^r \mathbf{v}(a_{rs} D^s \mathbf{u}).$$

(The above inequality is known as the Garding inequality [34] and finds applications in the solution of elliptic partial differential equations.)

10. Using variational methods, establish the inequality

$$\int_0^\infty (y^2 - y'^2 + y''^2) \, dx > 0$$

unless

$$y(x) = A \exp\left(-\frac{1}{2}x\right) \sin\left(\frac{\sqrt{3}x}{2} - \frac{\pi}{3}\right)$$

when there is equality. Assume that y and y'' are L_2 in $(0, \infty)$.

11. In the problem

$$\int_{-\infty}^{\infty} y^2 \, dx \text{ maximum}, \quad \int_{-\infty}^{\infty} x^2 y^2 \, dx \text{ and } \int_{-\infty}^{\infty} y'^2 \, dx \text{ given},$$

the Euler equation is

$$y'' + (a + bx^2)y = 0,$$

which can be solved in terms of parabolic cylinder functions. Show that this gives the variational basis for Weyl's inequality (useful in quantum mechanics [32])

$$\int_0^{\infty} f^2 \, dx < 2 \left(\int_0^{\infty} x^2 f^2 \, dx \right)^{1/2} \left(\int_0^{\infty} f'^2 \, dx \right)^{1/2}$$

unless $f = Be^{-Cx^2}$, B and C being constants.

APPENDIX

A NOTE ON VARIATIONAL INEQUALITIES

In Section 6.5, we have already seen by Lax-Milgram lemma that if H is a (real) Hilbert space and $a(.,.)$ is a bounded coercive bilinear functional, then there exists a unique $x \in H$ such that

$$a(x, y) = f(y) \quad \text{for all } y \in H, \tag{A6.1}$$

where $f : H \to R$ is a bounded linear functional. In particular, if $a(.,.)$ is also symmetric, then the functional $I : H \to R$ defined by

$$I(y) = \frac{1}{2} a(y, y) - (f, y) \tag{A6.2}$$

attains its minimum at x. Thus, (A6.1) can be regarded as the Euler equation of the above unconstrained variational problem.

However, if we consider a constrained variational problem, i.e., we minimize I over a closed convex subset K of the Hilbert space H, then we get an inequality instead of (A6.1). This is known as a variational inequality (see [30]). We have the following theorem.

Theorem.   Let $a(.,.)$ be a bounded symmetric and coercive bilinear functional on a Hilbert space H and $K \subset H$ be a closed convex subset. Let $f : H \to R$ be a bounded linear functional. Then there exists a unique $x \in H$ such that

$$a(x, y - x) \geq (f, y - x) \quad \text{for all } y \in K. \tag{A6.3}$$

To prove this we consider

$$\langle x, y \rangle = a(x, y) \quad \text{for } x, y \in H.$$

Then from the bilinearity and symmetry of $a(.,.)$, it follows that $\langle x, y \rangle$ is an inner product for H. Let

$$||| x |||^2 = \langle x, x \rangle = a(x, x). \tag{A6.4}$$

Now since $a(.,.)$ is bounded and coercive, we may write

$$\alpha || x ||^2 \leq ||| x |||^2 \leq M || x ||^2, \qquad \alpha > 0, M > 0$$

and hence the new norm $||| \cdot |||$ is equivalent to the original one. Thus H is also a Hilbert space with respect to the new inner product. Now by Riesz representation theorem, we can find $\overline{f} \in H$ such that for any $y \in H$,

$$a(\overline{f}, y) = \langle \overline{f}, y \rangle = (f, y). \tag{A6.5}$$

Let us now consider

$$\frac{1}{2} ||| y - \overline{f} |||^2 = \frac{1}{2} a(y - \overline{f}, y - \overline{f})$$

$$= \frac{1}{2} a(y, y) - a(y, \overline{f}) + \frac{1}{2} a(\overline{f}, \overline{f})$$

$$= \frac{1}{2} a(y, y) - (f, y) + \frac{1}{2} \| \overline{f} \|^2 \qquad (\text{A6.6})$$

$$= I(y) + \frac{1}{2} \| \overline{f} \|^2 .$$

Since $\| \overline{f} \|^2$ is a constant, minimizing $I(y)$ over K is equivalent to minimizing $\| y - \overline{f} \|^2$ over K. Now one of the classical results of functional analysis is the minimization of the norm in a Hilbert space which is embodied in the following result: Let H be a real Hilbert space and $K \subset H$ be a closed convex subset. Then there exists a unique $y \in K$ such that

$$\| x - y \| = \underset{z \in K}{\text{minimum}} \, \| x - z \|. \qquad (\text{A6.7})$$

Further, y can be characterized by

$$y \in K, \qquad (x - y, z - y) \leq 0 \quad \text{for all } z \in K. \qquad (\text{A6.8})$$

Hence using the above characteristic in our foregoing analysis, it follows from (A6.6) that

$$\langle \overline{f} - x, y - x \rangle \leq 0 \quad \text{for every } y \in K$$

leading to $a(x, y - x) \geq (f, y - x)$, which is what we set out to prove.

However, the symmetry condition on $a(.,.)$ in the above theorem can be relaxed and we state (without proof) the following important theorem due to Stampacchia (see [36]): Let H be a Hilbert space and let $a(.,.)$ be a bounded coercive bilinear form on H. Then given $f : H \to R$, a bounded linear functional, there exists a unique $x \in K$ (a closed convex subset of H) such that

$$a(x, y - x) \geq (f, y - x)$$

for every $y \in K$. Of course, in this case we will not be able to identify the problem with one of minimization. Variational inequalities have enormous applications to the study of free boundary problems (e.g., Stefan problems) in mechanics and physics. However, we will not pursue this matter any further as it is beyond the scope of this book. The interested reader will find a complete account of the theory and applications of variational inequalities in Duvaut and Lions [37].

CHAPTER 7

VARIATIONAL FORMULATION FOR LINEAR AND NONLINEAR PROBLEMS

7.1 Variational Formulation for Linear and Nonlinear Problems

The problem of giving variational formulation for all linear or nonlinear problems has so far eluded solution. As a matter of fact, variational principles do not exist for many heat and mass transfer problems of interest. We now wish to examine the question of the existence of a variational principle in a more systematic way. We first introduce the notions of Gateaux differentials and Gateaux derivatives in order to be able to give a general treatment of variational formulation for nonlinear differential equations.

7.2 Gateaux Derivatives

We begin by considering a vector field $\mathbf{v}$ and we ask the question: Can $\mathbf{v}$ be derived from a potential? It is well known that if $\nabla \times \mathbf{v} = 0$, then $\mathbf{v}$ can be represented as the gradient of a potential, i.e., $\mathbf{v} = \nabla \phi$.

It is clear from this elementary concept in vector calculus that if we regard the Euler equation in a variational principle as the gradient of a functional, analogous to a potential, then we should not expect every differential equation to be derivable from a potential for the simple reason that every vector field cannot be derived from a potential. In order to make these concepts clearer we should define the gradient of a functional and the derivative of a differential operator.

An equation (or a differential equation, to be more specific) is generally associated with additional conditions which specify initial, boundary and regularity conditions, as well as the functional class. The set formed by an equation and all additional conditions constitutes a problem. Every problem may be expressed in the general form

$$N(u) = \phi_v, \tag{7.1}$$

where N denotes an operator which may be nonlinear. The set of elements u that satisfies the given initial or boundary conditions and the given functional class is called the domain of the operator and is denoted by $D(N)$ which can be considered as a subset of a vector space U. The set of elements $v = N(u)$ constitutes the range of N denoted by $R(N)$. This is supposed to be embedded in another vector space V and ϕ_v in (7.1) is the null element of V. Suppose

$$N'_u \phi = \lim_{\varepsilon \to 0} \frac{N(u + \varepsilon \phi) - N(u)}{\varepsilon} = \left[\frac{\partial}{\partial \varepsilon} N(u + \varepsilon \phi) \right]_{\varepsilon = 0} \tag{7.2}$$

exists. The limit is defined by the topology of the V-space. Then $N'_u \phi$ is called the Gateaux differential of the operator N in the direction ϕ and N'_u is called the Gateaux derivative of the operator N. The subscript u means that the differentiation of the operator is with respect to the argument u.

We now introduce a bilinear functional $\langle v, u \rangle$, which is a map $B: V \times U \rightarrow R$. The expression $\langle v, u \rangle$ satisfies the following requirements:

(i) It must be real-valued even if U and V are vector spaces over the complex number field.

(ii) It must be bilinear over the real number field.

(iii) It must be non-degenerate. This implies that

if $\langle v, u_0 \rangle = 0$ for every $v \in V$, then $u_0 = \phi_u$;

if $\langle v_0, u \rangle = 0$ for every $u \in U$, then $v_0 = \phi_v$.

The real number $s = \langle v, u \rangle$ is called the scalar product of the elements $v \in V$ and $u \in U$. The V-space is called the dual or the conjugate of the U-space and one writes $V = U^*$.

In practice, one can take the bilinear functional as follows. In many physical problems one can take the bilinear functional $\langle v, u \rangle$ as

$$\langle v, u \rangle = \int \mathbf{v}(\mathbf{x}) \cdot \mathbf{u}(\mathbf{x}) \, d\Omega, \tag{7.3}$$

where Ω is a subset of R^N and $\mathbf{x}$ is a point of Ω with $\mathbf{x} = (x_1, x_2, ..., x_n)$. Here $\mathbf{v} \cdot \mathbf{u}$ is the scalar-product, i.e., a scalar-valued function formed of two vector-values or two tensor-valued functions such as

$$\sum_k v_k(\mathbf{x}) u^k(\mathbf{x}) \quad \text{or} \quad \sum_{h,k} v_{hk}(\mathbf{x}) u^{hk}(\mathbf{x}),$$

where the two tensors must have the same symmetry. Of course, a more general bilinear functional can be constructed as follows: If $A: U \rightarrow U$ and $B: V \rightarrow V$ are two linear invertible operators whose domains are the entire U and V spaces respectively, then the bilinear functional is

$$\langle v, u \rangle = \int B \mathbf{v}(\mathbf{x}) \cdot A\mathbf{u}(\mathbf{x}) \, d\Omega.$$

Once a bilinear functional is introduced, it is natural to introduce a topology in both the spaces such that the bilinear functional becomes continuous with respect to both the arguments. Such a topology is said to be compatible with duality. For instance, consider the operator N whose domain is that of differentiable functions over $[0, 1]$ which vanish at $x = 0$. Suppose the bilinear functional is the usual one given by (7.3). We may choose $D(N) = U = C^1(0, 1)$ and $R(N) = V = C(0,1)$. The topologies induced by the norms

$$\|u\| = \max_{x \in [0, 1]} [|u(x)| + |u'(x)|]$$

$$\|v\| = \max_{x \in [0, 1]} |v(x)|$$

are compatible with duality. To show this we first note that the two spaces are complete and if $\| u_n - u_0 \| < \varepsilon$, then

$$| \langle v, u_n \rangle - \langle v, u_0 \rangle | = | \langle v, u_n - u_0 \rangle |$$

$$= \left| \int_0^1 v(u_n - u_0) \, dx \right| \le (\max |v|) \cdot \varepsilon \cdot 1$$

Since v is continuous and the interval is finite, the property follows. Once the continuity is ensured, if u belongs to a dense subset D of a linear space U, the condition $\langle v_0, u \rangle = 0$ for every $u \in D$ assures that v_0 is ϕ_v.

The gradient of a functional is defined as follows: Given a functional $F(u)$ such that

$$F(u) = \int L(u) \, dV, \tag{7.4}$$

its Gateaux differential in the direction ϕ is

$$\lim_{\varepsilon \to 0} \frac{F(u + \varepsilon\phi) - F(u)}{\varepsilon} = \int \lim_{\varepsilon \to 0} \frac{L(u + \varepsilon\phi) - L(u)}{\varepsilon} \, dV$$

$$= \int L'_u \phi \, dV.$$

Now the Gateaux differential $F'_u \phi$ defined by the limit on the left-hand side depends on u and ϕ. Integration by parts gives

$$F'_u \phi = \int L'_u \phi \, dV = \int \phi N(u) \, dV + \text{boundary terms} \tag{7.5}$$

and the operator $N(u)$ is called the gradient of the functional.

To see if an operator $N(u)$ is the gradient of a functional, we should see whether the path integral in (7.5) depends on the path of integration. Consider two paths

$$\text{I} : u \to u + \varepsilon\phi \to u + \varepsilon\phi + v\Psi,$$

$$\text{II} : u \to u + v\Psi \to u + v\Psi + \varepsilon\phi,$$

where u, ϕ and $\Psi \in X$ and ε and v are constants.

If the path integral is independent of the path chosen, then the following equation must hold:

$$\int N(u)\varepsilon\phi \, dV + \int N(u + \varepsilon\phi)v\Psi \, dV = \int v\Psi N(u) \, dV + \int N(u + v\Psi)\varepsilon\phi \, dV.$$

We can rearrange this equation as

$$\int \left[\frac{N(u + \varepsilon\phi) - N(u)}{\varepsilon} \right] \Psi \, dV = \int \left[\frac{N(u + v\Psi) - N(u)}{v} \right] \phi \, dV.$$

When $\varepsilon \to 0$ and $v \to 0$, we have from above,

$$\int \Psi N_u' \phi \, dV = \int \phi N_u' \Psi \, dV. \tag{7.6}$$

This implies that the operator N_u' is symmetric. The fact that (7.6) is the condition for the existence of a functional having the operator $N(u)$ as its gradient follows from the following theorem given by Vainberg [38]:

Theorem 1. Suppose that the following conditions are satisfied:

(i) N is an operator from a normed space E into its conjugate space E^*.

(ii) N has a linear Gateaux differential $DN(x, h)$ at every point of the ball S: $\| x - x_0 \| < r$.

(iii) The bilinear functional $(DN(x, h_1), h_2)$ is continuous in x for every point x in S.

Then in order that the operator N be potential in the ball S, it is necessary and sufficient that the bilinear functional $(DN(x, h_1), h_2)$ be symmetric for every x in S, i.e.,

$$(DN(x, h_1), h_2) = (DN(x, h_2), h_1) \tag{7.7}$$

for every h_1 and h_2 in E and every x in D.

Equation (7.7) is just the symmetry condition (7.6). Provided that an operator $N(u)$ is the gradient of a functional, i.e.,

$$N(u) = \nabla F(u),$$

the functional F can be written as

$$F(u) = \int u \int_0^1 N(\lambda u) \, d\lambda \, dV. \tag{7.8}$$

The variation of $F(u)$ due to a variation δu in u is

$$\delta F = \int N(u) \, \delta u \, dV.$$

Clearly, if F is the functional arising in a variational principle, then $N(u) = 0$ is the corresponding Euler equation. Consequently, the question as to whether a variational principle exists for a given operator N depends on whether the operator has a symmetric Gateaux differential expressed by the condition (7.6).

As an example, consider the following equation (see [16])

$$f(u; u_{,j}; u_{,jk}) = 0. \tag{7.9}$$

Now from (7.2), we have

$$N_u' \phi = \left[\frac{\partial}{\partial \varepsilon} f(u + \varepsilon \phi, u_{,j} + \varepsilon \phi_{,j}, u_{,jk} + \varepsilon \phi_{,jk}) \right]_{\varepsilon=0}$$

$$= \frac{\partial f}{\partial u} \phi + \frac{\partial f}{\partial u_{,j}} \phi_{,j} + \frac{\partial f}{\partial u_{,jk}} \phi_{,jk}. \tag{7.10}$$

To test the symmetry requirement, we now integrate the following by parts

$$\int \Psi N_u' \phi \, dV = \int \Psi \left[\frac{\partial f}{\partial u} \phi + \frac{\partial f}{\partial u_{,j}} \phi_{,j} + \frac{\partial f}{\partial u_{,jk}} \phi_{,jk} \right] dV$$

$$= \int \phi \left\{ \left[\frac{\partial f}{\partial u} - \nabla_j \left(\frac{\partial f}{\partial u_{,j}} \right) + \nabla_k \nabla_j \left(\frac{\partial f}{\partial u_{,jk}} \right) \right] \Psi \right.$$

$$+ \left[- \frac{\partial f}{\partial u_{,j}} + 2\nabla_k \left(\frac{\partial f}{\partial u_{,jk}} \right) \right] \nabla_j \Psi$$

$$+ \left. \frac{\partial f}{\partial u_{,jk}} \nabla_k \nabla_j \Psi \right\} dV + \text{boundary terms}$$

$$= \int \phi \bar{N}_u' \Psi \, dV + \text{boundary terms.} \tag{7.11}$$

Equation (7.11) defines the Gateaux derivative $\bar{N}_u'$, which may be regarded as the adjoint to N_u. It should be noted that an adjoint is generally defined for a linear operator but the notion of an adjoint is also useful for nonlinear operators.

Suppose the nonlinear operator N has a Gateaux derivative N_u' which is not symmetric. We then define its adjoint $N^*(u, v) = \bar{N}_u'(v)$ by (7.11). Hence the boundary value problem in a region D with boundary Γ given by

$$N(u) = f \quad \text{in } D,$$

$$B_i(u) = 0 \quad \text{on } \Gamma$$

admits of a variational principle $\delta I = 0$ with

$$I(u, v) = \int_D [vN(u) - ug - vf] \, dV.$$

Here the Euler equations are

$$N(u) = f, \quad N^* (u, v) = g.$$

Now using (7.10) and the symmetry condition (7.6), we get

$$\int \phi \bar{N}_u' \Psi \, dV = \int \phi N_u' \Psi \, dV = \int \phi \left[\frac{\partial f}{\partial u} + \frac{\partial f}{\partial u_{,j}} \nabla_j + \frac{\partial f}{\partial u_{,jk}} \nabla_j \nabla_k \right] \Psi \, dV.$$

Since this relation holds for arbitrary ϕ and Ψ, we must have

$$\frac{\partial f}{\partial u} - \nabla_j \left(\frac{\partial f}{\partial u_{,j}} \right) + \nabla_k \nabla_j \left(\frac{\partial f}{\partial u_{,jk}} \right) = \frac{\partial f}{\partial u},$$

$$- \frac{\partial f}{\partial u_{,j}} + 2\nabla_k \left(\frac{\partial f}{\partial u_{,jk}} \right) = \frac{\partial f}{\partial u_{,j}}.$$

These two equations are equivalent to

$$\frac{\partial f}{\partial u_{,j}} - \nabla_k \left(\frac{\partial f}{\partial u_{,jk}} \right) = 0 \qquad (7.12)$$

and this is the required condition for (7.9) to be derivable from a potential.

We now introduce the concept of Frechét derivative (see [39]). Suppose X and Y are Banach spaces, Ω is an open subset of X, F maps Ω into Y, and $a \in \Omega$. If there exists $\Lambda \in B(X, Y)$ (the Banach space of all bounded linear mappings of X into Y) such that

$$\lim_{x \to 0} \frac{\| F(a + x) - F(a) - \Lambda x \|}{\| x \|} = 0,$$

then Λ is called the Frechét derivative of F at a.

It is well known that if a Frechét differential exists then so does a Gateaux differential. Hence if the operator has a symmetric Frechét differential, then a variational principle exists for (7.1).

It may be noted that many natural functionals which we may encounter may not be bounded at all, neither from above nor from below. So we cannot look for maxima or minima. Instead we seek saddle points by a min-max argument. The notion of Frechét derivative plays an important role here. In this context it may be pertinent to recall from the Lax-Milgram lemma of Section 6.5 that if $J(v)$ is a coercive functional on a Hilbert space V, i.e. $J(v) \to +\infty$ when $\| v \| \to \infty$ and is weakly lower semicontinuous, then J attains a global minimum, i.e., we can find $u \in V$ such that

$$J(u) = \lim_{v \in V} J(V).$$

Let us consider now the problem of finding a nontrivial stationary point of a given real C^1 functional J defined in a Banach space X and state the following (Nirenberg [40]):

Mountain pass lemma (MPL)

Let $J: X \to R$ be a C^1 functional. Further, let $u_0, u_1 \in X$, $c_0 \in R$ and $R_1 > 0$ such that

(i) $\| u_1 - u_0 \| > R_1$,

(ii) $J(u_0), J(u_1) < c_0 \leq J(v)$ for all v

such that $\| v - u_0 \| = R_1$. Then J has a stationary value $c \geq c_0$ defined by

$$c = \inf_{p} \max_{u \in p} J(u).$$

Here, p represents any continuous path joining u_0 to u_1 in X. We take the maximum J over p and then take the infimum with respect to all possible paths. Since every such path must cross the sphere $\{ v \mid \| v - u_0 \| = R_1 \}$, where we have $J \geq c_0$, we see that $\max_{p} J \geq c_0$. Think of J as representing the height of land at a point u.

Then u_0 is a point in a valley U bounded by a mountain range ∂U which is the boundary $\|v - u_0\| = R_1$. For any path p joining u_0 to u_1, $\max_p J$ represents how high we have to go on that path. Taking the infimum then minimizes this. But, c is the height of the lowest mountain pass crossing the mountain range. When we are at that mountain pass the earth is level, so that the Frechét derivative J' vanishes.

Although this result is intuitively obvious, it is false even in finite dimensions. For example, in the complex plane, consider the non-negative function

$$F(z) = |\, e^z - 1\,|^2.$$

Obviously, F achieves the minimum at 0 and $2\pi i$. One can show that for small $r > 0$,

$$F(z) \geq c_0 > 0 \quad \text{for } |z| = r.$$

On the other hand, zero is the only critical value of F. Thus F satisfies condition (ii) of MPL above, but the conclusion of MPL does not hold. For the validity of MPL, we have to add an additional condition to MPL. This is known as Palais-Smale condition $(PS)_c$ (a kind of compactness condition mentioned in Chapter 1), and is defined as follows:

 $(PS)_c$: Any sequence $\{u_i\}$ in X for which $F(u_i) \to c$ and the Frechét derivatives $F'(u_i) \to 0$ strongly in X^* (the dual space of X) has a strongly convergent subsequence $\{u_{i_j}\}$ in X.

It may be noted that the Frechét derivative $F'(u)$ of F at u represents a continuous linear functional on X, i.e., an element in X^*. It may be shown that MPL formulation above along with $(PS)c$ gives the correct MPL.

If N is a linear operator, i.e., $N = L$, then

$$L'_u \phi = \lim_{\varepsilon \to 0} \frac{L(u + \varepsilon\phi) - L(u)}{\varepsilon} = L\phi.$$

Consequently, $L'_u = L$ and the symmetry condition (7.6) becomes

$$\int \Psi L\phi \, dV = \int \phi L\Psi \, dV \tag{7.13}$$

and the functional (7.8) then reduces to

$$F(u) = \frac{1}{2} \int uLu \, dV. \tag{7.14}$$

7.3   Variational Principles for Non-Self-Adjoint Equations

Let H be a Hilbert space and A be a continuous linear operator such that $A: H \to H$ and $y \in H$. We introduce a functional f_y on H by

$$f_y(x) = (Ax, y).$$

Clearly, $f_y(x)$ is a linear functional and for $x \in H$,

$$|f_y(x)| = |(Ax, y)| \leq \|Ax\| \cdot \|y\| \leq \|A\| \cdot \|y\| \cdot \|x\|.$$

Thus f_y is bounded and so f_y is a continuous linear functional defined everywhere on H and $\|f_y\| \leq \|A\| \cdot \|y\|$. Hence by the Riesz representation theorem (Rudin [40]),

$$f_y(x) = (x, y^*)$$

for all $x \in H$ such that $y^* \in H$ is uniquely determined by f_y. Clearly, if y changes, then y^* also changes. So we introduce an operator A^* such that

$$y^* = A^*y.$$

Here, A^* is defined everywhere on H and its range is also in H. This operator A^* is called the adjoint operator to A. From the above equations we find that A and A^* are connected by

$$(Ax, y) = (x, A^*y).$$

Now we define a self-adjoint operator A^* as follows: A continuous linear operator $A: H \to H$ is called self-adjoint if $A^* = A$.

Given a linear differential operator L, we define the adjoint operator as above. When $L = L^*$, (7.13) holds and a variational principle exists with the functional given by (7.14), provided the boundary conditions are appropriate. When L is not self-adjoint, (7.13) does not hold. For such an operator let the linear boundary value problem be

$$Lu = f \quad \text{in } V \tag{7.15a}$$

with

$$B_i u = 0 \quad \text{on } S, \tag{7.15b}$$

where S is the piece-wise smooth boundary of the domain V. For a linear boundary value problem with a non-homogeneous boundary condition given by

$$Lw = h \quad \text{in } V,$$
$$B_i w = g_i \quad \text{on } S, \tag{7.16}$$

we assume that a function v can be found such that v satisfies $B_i v = g_i$ on S and v can be extended into the region V. Then it is clear that the function u given by $u = w - v$ satisfies (7.15a) and (7.15b).

A variational principle for a non-self-adjoint problem (7.15) can be found by a method closely related to the least squares method. This method minimizes the mean-square residual

$$J(u) = \int_V (Lu - f)^2 \, dV \tag{7.17}$$

among functions satisfying $B_i u = 0$. The variation of J is given by

$$\delta J = 2 \int_V (Lu - f)L\,\delta u\,dV$$

$$= 2 \int \delta u(L^*Lu - L^*f)\,dV + B(\delta u, Lu - f).$$

(7.18)

Thus, the Euler equation with the essential and the natural boundary conditions is given by

$$L^*\,Lu = L^*f \text{ in } V$$

(7.19a)

subject to

$$B_i u = 0, \quad B_j^*\,Lu = B_j^*f \text{ on } S.$$

(7.19b)

Mikhlin [41] studied the conditions under which the solution of (7.19) reduces to the solution of (7.15). If the system (7.15) admits of a solution and the inequality

$$(u, u) \le K(Lu, Lu)$$

(7.20)

holds, then the least-squares method using (7.17) is equivalent to the variational method applied to (7.19). When the adjoint problem is unique, i.e. when the system

$$L^*v = 0 \quad \text{in } V,$$

$$B_j^*\,v = 0 \text{ on } S$$

(7.21)

has the trivial solution $v = 0$, then solving (7.19) is equivalent to solving (7.15). An equation similar to (7.19a) is given by

$$Ax = f, \quad A = T^*T.$$

(7.22)

An equation of this type arises in a variety of problems in physics and mechanics. Laplace's equation, the biharmonic equation, and the Lagrange-Germain equation describing a static deflection of a thin plate are all of this type.

Let us consider a linear operator A mapping a subset D_A of a Hilbert space H_1 into H_1. We assume that A is positive definite, so that $A = T^*T$. Further, the domain of T is dense in H_1 and hence T^* is uniquely defined. Clearly, T and T^* are the linear maps given by

$$T: D_T, H_1 \to H_2, \quad T^*: H_2 \to H_1.$$

Thus (7.22) in the space H_1 can be rewritten as a pair of equations

$$Tx = p \quad \text{in } H_2,$$

$$T^*p = f \text{ in } H_1.$$

(7.23)

The system (7.23) has been designated by Rall [42] as a Hamiltonian system.

Let us introduce a new Hilbert space $H = H_1 \oplus H_2$, such that every element h of H is an ordered pair $h = (x, p)$ with x in H_1 and p in H_2. We define the inner product in H as follows:

$$\{h_1, h_2\} = (x_1, x_2)_{H_1} + \langle p_1, p_2 \rangle_{H_2},$$

where $(\cdot)_{H_1}$ and $\langle \rangle_{H_2}$ denote respectively the inner product in H_1 and H_2. Let $\tilde{p} \in H_2, \tilde{x} \in H_1, x \in H_1$ be arbitrary vectors and $\tilde{w} = (\tilde{x}, \tilde{p})$ a vector in H. The corresponding value of the functional $L : H \to R$ is given by

$$L(x, Tx) = \langle T\tilde{x}, \tilde{p} \rangle - \frac{1}{2} \langle \tilde{p}, \tilde{p} \rangle - (f, \tilde{x}). \tag{7.24}$$

If the gradient L_w of the above functional is uniquely defined at $w_0 = (x_0, p_0) \in H$, then equations (7.23) are the necessary and sufficient conditions for the vanishing of $L_{\tilde{w}}$. Thus the functional has a critical point (or an extremum) at w_0 if and only if these equations are satisfied.

Further, in the context of complementary variational principle, the system (7.23) has been designated by Noble (see [11]) as a Hamiltonian system. This can be easily seen if one introduces the functional

$$W(x, p) = \frac{1}{2} \langle p, p \rangle + (f, x), \tag{7.25}$$

which can be regarded as the Hamiltonian such that the system (7.23) can be written as

$$Tx = W_p, \qquad T^*p = W_x. \tag{7.26}$$

These are Hamilton's canónical equations in the special case when

$$T = \frac{d}{dt}, \qquad T^* = -\frac{d}{dt}.$$

Here, x and p denote the vectors of generalized displacement and momenta, respectively.

Let the Hamiltonian system (7.26) (with Hamiltonian $H = W(x, p)$) be satisfied at the critical point $x = \bar{x}$, $p = \bar{p}$. But if $W(x, p)$ fails to be convex at some neighbourhood of $p = \bar{p}$ for fixed $\bar{x}$ (or vice versa), then we do not have an obvious way of formulating complementary variational principles ([11]), or deriving two-sided bounds on the value of the Lagrangian. A remedy for this was suggested by Komkov [34] who pointed out that in such cases complementary variational principles could be formulated by altering the rules of multiplication of some vector-valued functions. The appropriate algebra for such problems was shown by him to be the quaternionic algebra of Hamilton. But we do not pursue it here because this will take us too far from our discussion.

Further, a standard technique introduced by Kato [43] is to write (7.22) in terms of Lagrangian coordinates q, $\dot{q}$ and t with the Lagrangian $L(q, \dot{q}, t)$ as

$$T^* Tq = f$$

and then rewrite it as a system of two equations as before:

$$Tq = p(t), \qquad T^*p = f(q(t), t).$$

The Hamiltonian is similar to (7.24) and is given by

$$H = \frac{1}{2} \langle p, p \rangle + V(q, t), \qquad \frac{\partial V}{\partial q} = f(q, t).$$

The Legendre transformation is defined by the mapping

$$\{q, Aq\} \rightarrow \{q, p\}$$

with

$$p = \frac{\partial L}{\partial (Aq)}, \qquad H = L - \langle Aq, p \rangle.$$

This establishes the duality between a Lagrangian and a Hamiltonian formulation.

To sum up, we may say that if a linear operator is self-adjoint, then a variational principle exists. For a linear non-self-adjoint operator, a variational principle can be constructed by least squares method as explained above. We have also seen that for a non-linear operator, a variational principle exists if the Gateaux differential of the operator is symmetric.

7.4 Variational Formulation for Any Nonlinear Problem

The question now naturally arises: Does there exist a variational principle for a nonlinear operator whose Gateaux differential is not symmetric? We now address this question.

We begin by observing that the symmetry of a linear operator, like that of a matrix, is not an absolute concept; it is related to a bilinear form. If a given problem does not meet the symmetry requirement, one may try to convert it into another which meets this requirement. The following methods can be used:

(i) To transform the given problem into another with the same solutions.

(ii) To change the bilinear form.

It can be shown that these two methods are essentially equivalent. This means that every transformation of the original equation corresponds to a bilinear form and vice versa.

It may be noted that for a long period, several problems resisted formulation as variational problems. Take, for instance, the heat conduction equation (due to Fourier) whose first variational formulation was given by Gurtin [44]. His idea was to make a preliminary transformation of an equation into an integro-differential form along with the introduction of the convolution product of two functions. This method was simplified by Tonti [45] who showed that one may introduce a convolutive bilinear form to give a variational formulation to linear initial value problems having an equation with constant coefficients. The idea of adapting a bilinear form to a given operator was investigated by Magri [46] who showed that every linear equation admits of a variational formulation, giving an explicit method for obtaining the functional. However, every linear problem may be associated with many functionals such that for each of these, a stationary value is attained in correspondence to the solution of the problem. In general, such functionals do not have extremum at this point.

The method of Magri [46] for giving a variational formulation to linear problems involves two steps: (a) The linear problem is written in the form

$$Lu = f,$$

where $L: D(L) \in U \to V$ is a linear operator, and (b) the domain $D(L)$ is a subset of the vector space U. In the step (i), one defines a symmetric non-degenerate bilinear form on $V \times V$, denoted by (v_1, v_2); in step (ii), one introduces a bilinear form on $U \times V$ by the relation

$$\langle v, u \rangle = (v, Lu).$$

The first bilinear form is chosen as

$$(v_1, v_2) = \int_0^T v_1(t) \int_0^T k(t, \tau) v_2(\tau) \, d\tau \, dt, \tag{7.27}$$

where k is a symmetric positive-definite kernel. The second form is

$$\langle v, u \rangle = (v, Lu) = \int_0^T v(t) \int_0^T k(t, \tau) Lu(\tau) \, d\tau \, dt \tag{7.28}$$

and the functional is

$$F(u) = \frac{1}{2} \langle Lu, u \rangle = \frac{1}{2} \int_0^T Lu(t) \int_0^T k(t, \tau) Lu(\tau) \, d\tau \, dt. \tag{7.29}$$

To get an idea of the method for transforming the given problem into another with the same solution but such that it admits of variational formulation, we may introduce the notion of an integrating factor. By integrating factor is generally meant a function or a matrix whose elements are functions such that an essential requirement is that the factor is invertible. This ensures that no new solutions are added to the given problem. For example, in the boundary value problem

$$m\ddot{q} + h\dot{q} + kq = f, \quad 0 \le t \le T,$$

$$q(0) = 0, \quad q(T) = 0, \quad q(t) \in C^2(0, T),$$

the operator is not symmetric and the problem does not admit of a variational formulation. Multiplying the above differential equation by the integrating factor $\exp (ht/m)$, the problem becomes

$$m \frac{d}{dt} \left[\exp \left(\frac{ht}{m} \right) \frac{dq}{dt} \right] + k \exp \left(\frac{ht}{m} \right) q = \exp \left(\frac{ht}{m} \right) \cdot f,$$

which is symmetric. Hence a variational formulation is possible and the functional is

$$F(q) = \int_0^T \exp \left(\frac{ht}{m} \right) \left[\frac{1}{2} m\dot{q}^2 - \frac{1}{2} kq^2 - fq \right] dt.$$

In general, the existence of the integrating factor for the problem

$$f(t; q, \dot{q}, \ddot{q}) = 0 \tag{7.30}$$

may be put in the following form: Does there exist a function $r(t; q, \dot{q})$ such that the equation

$$r(t; q, \dot{q}) \cdot f(t; q, \dot{q}, \ddot{q}) = 0$$

is the Euler-Lagrange equation of a functional? An obvious restriction on $r(t; q, \dot{q})$ is that it should not vanish identically for some function $q(t)$.

Let us now generalize the above concept and introduce the notion of an integrating operator. We seek for an integrating operator R such that

$$R(q; f(t; q, \dot{q}, \ddot{q})) = 0 \tag{7.31}$$

has the same solution as that of (7.30). We may consider the Laplace transform as an example of an integrating operator. It turns out that (7.31) has the form of the following integro-differential equation

$$\int_0^T r(t; q(t), \dot{q}(t); \tau, q(\tau), \dot{q}(\tau)) \cdot f(\tau; q(\tau), \dot{q}(\tau), \ddot{q}(\tau)) \, d\tau = 0. \tag{7.32}$$

Further, integrating operators can be obtained such that the functional is an extremum at the solution and hence direct methods of the calculus of variations may be applied. This statement is valid for linear or nonlinear equations, with total or partial derivatives of any order. In this manner, we can derive a variational formulation for nonlinear problems.

Let us now consider two kinds of variation formulation, i.e. variational formulation in the restricted sense and in the extended sense.

Variational Formulation in the Restricted Sense

Given a problem $N(u) = \phi_v$ with the operator N (which may be nonlinear): $D(N) \subset U \to V = U^*$, find a functional F, if any, such that the operator N is the gradient of F, i.e.,

$$\delta F = \langle N(u), \delta u \rangle .$$

This means that the solutions to the problem are the critical points of F and vice versa.

We have already discussed this problem in detail in Section 7.1. It is found that in order that an operator $N: D(N) \subset U \to R(N) \subset V = U^*$ be the gradient of a functional, it is necessary that $N'_u(u; \cdot)$ must be symmetric. This also implies that the circulation of the element $v = N(u)$ along any reducible closed line contained in $D(N)$ vanishes, i.e.,

$$\langle N'_u \phi, \Psi \rangle = \langle N'_u \Psi, \phi \rangle.$$

If the domain $D(N)$ is simply connected, then the above condition becomes sufficient. Here the important observation is that the symmetry condition involves the use of a bilinear functional. This means that if the operator does not satisfy the symmetry condition, then we change the bilinear functional. This holds one of the keys for providing a variational formulation to problems which do not admit of such formulation with classical bilinear functionals.

Variational Problem in the Extended Sense

Given a problem $N(u) = \phi_v$ with $N: D(N) \subset U \rightarrow V = U^*$, determine a functional $\bar{F}$, if any, whose critical points are solutions to the problem and vice versa. This means that for a given operator N, there exists an operator $\bar{N}$ such that

$$\delta \bar{F} = \langle \bar{N}(u), \delta u \rangle$$

and the problems $N(u) = \phi_v$ and $\bar{N}(u) = \phi_v$ have the same solutions.

It is clear that the above problem in the extended sense is less restrictive than the former one, because the above problem requires only that critical points should coincide with the solutions, without imposing the additional requirement that N should be the gradient of a functional. The following figure displays the relation between the two formulations.

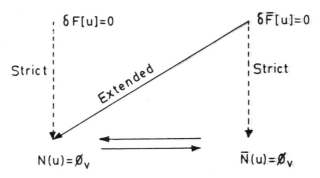

Fig. 7.1   An illustration of the restricted and the extended variational formulation.

Let us consider an example. The operator D defined by

$$D = \left\{ \frac{d}{dt}, u(0) = 0, u \in C^1(0, T) \right\} \tag{7.33}$$

is not symmetric with respect to the usual bilinear functional

$$\langle v, u \rangle = \int_0^T v(t)u(t)\, dt. \tag{7.34}$$

But it becomes symmetric with respect to the convolution bilinear functional

$$\langle v, u \rangle_c = \int_0^T v(T-t)u(t)\, dt = \int_0^T v(t)u\,(T-t)\, dt. \tag{7.35}$$

Let us introduce the convolution operator

$$Cv(t) = v(T - t) \tag{7.36}$$

and we may write

$$\langle v, u \rangle_c = \langle Cv, u \rangle = \langle v, Cu \rangle.$$

Now the symmetry of D with respect to the convolution

$$\langle Du, u' \rangle_c = \langle Du', u \rangle_c$$

implies that CD is symmetric with respect to the canonical bilinear functional

$$\langle CDu, u' \rangle = \langle Du, u' \rangle_c = \langle Du', u \rangle_c = \langle CDu', u \rangle.$$

Thus the change in bilinear functional is equivalent to premultiplication by an operator. Hence, if we say that the symmetry of an operator is related to a bilinear functional, it means that the operator may be made symmetric by application of an integrating operator.

We now explore the possibility of determining an integrating operator for a given operator.

From matrix theory we know that if a matrix C is invertible, then equations $CAu = Cb$ and $Au = b$ have the same solutions. In particular, if the adjoint matrix A^* is invertible then the system reduces to $A^*Au = A^*b$. In this case the solution u of $Au = b$ makes

$$f(u) = \| Au - b \|^2$$

stationary and this is the essence of the least square method explained in Section 7.2.

However, the above procedure cannot be extended to system containing a differential operator. Consider the differential operator

$$D = \left\{ \frac{d}{dt}, u(0) = 0, u \in C^1(0, T) \right\} \tag{7.37}$$

and the differential system

$$Du = f \text{ with } f \in C(0, T). \tag{7.38}$$

The adjoint operator is

$$D^* = \left\{ -\frac{d}{dt}, v\,(T) = 0, v \in AC(0, T) \right\}. \tag{7.39}$$

Here, $AC(0, T)$ denotes the class of absolutely continuous functions. Although D^*D is a symmetric operator, D^* cannot be applied to (7.38) because f does not satisfy $f(T) = 0$, and hence does not belong to the domain of definition of D^*. Thus the domain of the operator D^*D is a restriction on the domain of D. Thus if $Du = f$ represents a physical law, all elements $f \in R(D)$ describe possible sources.

We may, however, think of applying an integral operator K. In other words, we may try to apply an integral transformation such that f is transformed to $\bar{f}$ satisfying $\bar{f}(T) = 0$. We may select the operator as follows:

$$\hat{f}(t) = \int_0^T k(t, \tau) f(\tau) \, d\tau \tag{7.40}$$

subject to the condition $k(T, \tau) = 0$. We may also select an integral operator of the kind

$$\bar{f}(t) = \int_0^t k(t, \tau) f(\tau) \, d\tau. \tag{7.41}$$

Then the system (7.38) reduces to

$$KDu = Kf. \tag{7.42}$$

We are now able to apply the operator D^* such that

$$D^*KDu = D^*Kf. \tag{7.43}$$

Equation (7.43) has the same solutions as the given one if both D^* and K are invertible. Further, if the integral operator K is symmetric, then D^*KD is also symmetric. Thus the problem (7.43) admits of an extended variational formulation. Hence we find that the role of K is to modify the range of D so that it becomes acceptable to D^*. This problem, however, does not arise in the matrix theory because the domain of the matrix is the whole vector space.

This idea can now be extended to nonlinear operators and expressed in the following theorem due to Tonti [47].

Theorem 2. Consider the system

$$N(u) = \phi_v, \tag{7.44}$$

where N is a nonlinear operator: $D(N) \subset U \to R(N) \subset U^*$ such that (i) the solution of the problem exists and (ii) it is unique; (iii) $D(N)$ is simply connected; (iv) the Gateaux derivative $N_u'(u; .)$ exists; (v) $D(N_u')$ is dense in U; (vi) $N_u'^*(u; .)$ is invertible for every $u \in D(N)$.

Then for every operator K that satisfies the conditions: (vii) $D(K) \supset R(N)$; (viii) $R(K) \subset D(N_u'^*)$; (ix) it is linear, (x) it is invertible; (xi) it is symmetric, the operator $\bar{N}$ defined by

$$\bar{N}(u) = N_u'^*(u; KN(u)) \tag{7.45}$$

has the following properties: (a) its domain coincides with that of N; (b) the problem $N(u) = \phi_v$ and $\bar{N}(u) = \bar{\phi}_v$ admit of the same solution, (c) it is a potential operator.

From properties (b) and (c), it is clear that the solution of (7.44) is the critical point of the functional

$$\bar{F}_1 [u] = \frac{1}{2} \langle N(u), KN(u) \rangle \tag{7.46}$$

whose gradient is the operator $\bar{N}$. The functional vanishes when the solution is attained. Further, if K is positive definite, then $\bar{F}_1[u]$ is minimum at the critical point.

To prove the above theorem we begin with a geometrical sketch following Tonti [47]. Here the operators are represented by pipes, the ingress stands for the domain and the egress for the range. It is clear that conditions (vii) and (viii) in the theorem simply indicate that the ingress to the second pipe contains the egress from the first. Further, Fig. 7.2 shows that the operators N and $\bar{N}$ have the same domain thus proving (a). The linearity of N'_u and N'^*_u together with the linearity

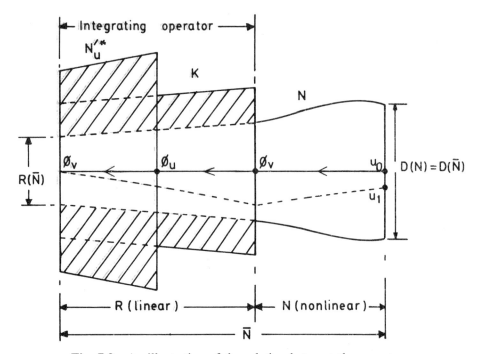

Fig. 7.2   An illustration of the relation between the operators.

of K also shows that $N'^*_u(u; K\phi)$ is linear with respect to ϕ. Thus ϕ_v is mapped into itself. Hence if u_0 is the solution of the problem (7.37), we find that

$$\bar{N}(u_0) = N'^*_u(u_0; KN(u_0)) = N'^*_u(u_0; K\phi_v)$$

$$= N'^*_u(u_0; \phi_v) = \phi_v. \tag{7.47}$$

Thus u_0 is also a solution of $\bar{N}(u) = \phi_v$.

Conversely, we suppose that u_0 is a solution of $\bar{N}(u) = \phi_v$. Conditions (vi) and (x) ensure that ϕ_v is mapped into itself. Now since

$$N'^*_u(u_0; KN(u_0)) = \phi_v, \tag{7.48}$$

if we apply $(N'^*_u)^{-1}$ to both sides, we get

$$KN(u_0) = (N'^*_u)^{-1}\phi_v = \phi_v. \tag{7.49}$$

If we again apply K^{-1} to (7.42), we obtain

$$N(u_0) = K^{-1}\phi_v = \phi_v,$$

which proves that u_0 is a solution of (7.44). It should be noted that conditions (ii), (vi) and (x) ensure that a sequence beginning from u_1 and represented by a dashed line is not possible, and this proves (b).

To prove the existence of the potential one may perform the test of symmetry of N'_u given by (7.6). This can be established (proof is omitted), and since the domain is simply connected due to the condition (iii) of the theorem, the existence of potential is established.

Now we establish that the gradient of $\bar{F}_1$ is $\bar{N}$. In fact,

$$\delta\bar{F}_1[u] = \langle N(u), \delta KN(u)\rangle = \langle N(u), K\delta N(u)\rangle$$

$$= \langle N(u), KN'_u(u; \delta u)\rangle = \langle N'_u(u; \delta u), KN(u)\rangle$$

$$= \langle N'_u*(u; KN(u)), \delta u\rangle$$

$$= \langle \bar{N}(u), \delta u\rangle. \tag{7.50}$$

Thus the vanishing of $\delta\bar{F}_1[u]$ implies the vanishing of the last term in (7.50) for every δu. Since $\delta u \in D(N'_u)$, which is dense in U and since the bilinear functional is continuous, it follows that $\delta\bar{F}_1[u] = 0$ implies $\bar{N}[u] = \phi_v$. Hence the critical point of the functional $\bar{F}_1[u]$ coincides with the solution of $N(u) = \phi_v$.

Further, if condition (xii) is satisfied, we have, on using the property of a positive definite operator, the relations

$$\bar{F}_1[u] = \frac{1}{2}\langle N(u), KN(u)\rangle = \frac{1}{2}\langle v, Kv\rangle > 0$$

for every $v \in D(K)$ and $v \neq \phi_v$. Since $\bar{F}_1[u_0] = 0$, it follows that $\bar{F}_1$ is minimum at u_0. This completes the proof of the theorem.

It may be noted that the linear operator

$$R(u, v) = N'_u*(u; Kv) \tag{7.51}$$

transforms a given operator N into a potential operator $\bar{N}(u) = R(u; Nu)$, and hence can be regarded as an integrating operator.

Finally, we discuss the method of choosing the integrating operator. Now the integrating operator for N has the general form (7.51), where K must be invertible, symmetric with a range contained in $D(N'_u*)$.

We first consider problems in one variable t and let the interval be [0,1]. Take a function $\phi(t) \in D(N'_u*)$. In practice, since N'_u* is a linear operator, the boundary/initial conditions involved in the problem must be homogeneous. Let $\phi(t)$ satisfy these conditions. Consider the integral transform

$$W(t) = Kv = \int_0^1 f(t, \tau)\phi(t)\phi(\tau)v(\tau)\,d\tau, \tag{7.52}$$

where $W(0) = W(1) = 0$ and $f(t, \tau)$ is an arbitrary symmetric function in t and τ, to be specified later on. Since $W(t)$ satisfies the same homogeneous boundary conditions as $\phi(t)$, $W(t) \in D(N_u'^*)$. If we can find a function $f(t, \tau)$ which makes the operator K positive definite, K will surely be invertible. It should be noted that $f(t, \tau)$ must not be a polynomial because in this case the kernel would be degenerate. We take $f(t, \tau) = \exp(t\tau)$. Then

$$\langle v, Kv \rangle = \int_0^1 v(t) \int_0^1 \exp(t\tau)\phi(t)\phi(\tau)v(\tau) \, d\tau \, dt$$

$$= \sum_{k=0}^\infty \frac{1}{k!} \int_0^1 t^k \phi(t)v(t) \, dt \int_0^1 \tau^k \phi(\tau)v(\tau) \, d\tau$$

$$= \sum_{k=0}^\infty \frac{1}{k!} M_k^2 \geq 0,$$

(7.53a)

where

$$M_k = \int_0^1 t^k \phi(t)v(t) \, dt.$$

(7.53b)

It is now clear from (7.53) that

$$\langle v, Kv \rangle > 0$$

unless v is identically zero. Hence we have found an integral operator which satisfies all the conditions of Theorem 7.2.

If the boundary/initial conditions involve the vanishing of the derivatives, e.g., $W'(0) = 0$, we select $\phi(t)$ so that $\phi(0) = 0$ and $\phi'(0) = 0$. Now from

$$W'(t) = \int_0^1 [f'\phi(t) + f\phi'(t)]\phi(\tau)v(\tau) \, d\tau,$$

it follows that $W'(0) = 0$.

A simple extension of K to two-dimensional problems is

$$Kv = \int_0^1 \int_0^1 \exp(xy\xi\eta) \, \phi(x, y)\phi(\xi, \eta)v(\xi, \eta) \, d\xi \, d\eta,$$

where $\phi(x, y)$ satisfies the homogeneous and initial/boundary conditions of $D(N_u'^*)$.

When N is linear and symmetric, a restricted variational formulation exists and the extended variational problem contains it as a particular case. In this case, if we take $K = L^{-1}$, the functional $\bar{F}_1(u)$ becomes

$$\bar{F}_1(u) = \frac{1}{2}\langle Lu, KLu \rangle = \frac{1}{2}\langle Lu, u \rangle = F(u)$$

and this proves the assertion made above.

Let us now illustrate the above method by considering an example involving a nonlinear operator.

Example. Consider the first-order nonlinear differential equation with the initial condition given by

$$\dot{u}(t) = f(t; u(t)), \qquad u(0) = a, \qquad u \in C^1(0, T), \tag{7.54}$$

where f is a prescribed function. Obtain a variational formulation of this problem.

Solution. Clearly, this is a Cauchy problem so that its existence and uniqueness are guaranteed under the usual hypothesis. Here we have, on comparing with (7.44), the relation

$$N(u) = \left\{ \frac{du(t)}{dt} - f(t; u(t)); u(0) = a; u \in C^1(0, T) \right\} \tag{7.55}$$

$$N_u' \phi = \left\{ \frac{d}{dt} \phi(t) - \frac{\partial f}{\partial u} \phi(t); \phi(0) = 0; \phi \in C^1(0, T) \right\}. \tag{7.56}$$

$$N_u'^* \Psi = \left\{ -\frac{d}{dt} \Psi(t) - \frac{\partial f}{\partial u} \Psi(t); \Psi(T) = 0; \Psi \in AC(0, T) \right\}. \tag{7.57}$$

The adjoint homogeneous problem is

$$-\frac{d}{dt} \Psi(t) - \frac{\partial f}{\partial u} \cdot \Psi(t) = 0, \qquad \Psi(T) = 0. \tag{7.58}$$

This equation is linear in Ψ with variable coefficients containing $u(t)$. It can be easily shown that it has only null solution and so the operator $N_u'^*$ is invertible. Thus the conditions of Theorem 2 are fulfilled. Let us introduce the function h as follows

$$h(t; u(t); \dot{u}(t)) = \dot{u}(t) - f(t; u(t)). \tag{7.59}$$

We now recall the fact that the operator K appearing in the integral operator (7.51) should be invertible, symmetric with a range contained in $D(N_u'^*)$. One convenient source of such operators is the inverse of symmetric positive definite differential operators: these are integral operators whose kernel is the Green's function of such a differential operator. Take, for instance, the operator

$$L = \left\{ -\frac{d^2}{dt^2}; \dot{u}(0) = 0, u(T) = 0, u \in C^2(0, T) \right\}, \tag{7.60}$$

which is clearly symmetric and positive-definite (and hence invertible). Its inverse is

$$Kv = \int_0^T [-(t - \tau)H(t - \tau) + (T - \tau)]v(\tau) \, d\tau, \tag{7.61}$$

where $H(t)$ is the Heaviside unit step function with the Green's function

$$g(t, \tau) = -(t - \tau)H(t - \tau) + (T - \tau). \tag{7.62}$$

Using (7.46), we now have the variational formulation of the problem (7.54) with the required functional given by

$$\bar{F}_1(u) = \frac{1}{2} \int_0^T h(t, u(t), \dot{u}(t)) \int_0^T g(t, \tau) h(t, u(\tau), \dot{u}(\tau)) \, d\tau \, dt, \tag{7.63}$$

where h and g are given by (7.59) and (7.62). Further using (7.51), the integrating operator $R(u, v)$ is given by

$$R(u, v) = \left[-\frac{d}{dt} - \frac{\partial f}{\partial u} \right] \int_0^T [-(t - \tau) H(t - \tau) + (T - \tau)] v(\tau) \, d\tau$$

which, after integration by parts, reduces to

$$R(u, v) = \int_0^T v(\tau) \, d\tau - \frac{\partial f}{\partial u} \cdot \int_0^T [-(t - \tau) H(t - \tau) + (T - \tau)] v(\tau) \, d\tau.$$

If we use the Green's function for the operator

$$L = \left\{ -\frac{d^2}{dt^2}, u(0) = 0, u(T) = 0, u \in C^2(0, T) \right\}$$

(instead of (7.60)) in (7.63) and perform two integrations by parts, we obtain the functional $\bar{F}_1(u)$ as

$$\bar{F}_1(u) = \frac{1}{2} \int_0^T u(t) \int_0^T \frac{\partial^2 g}{\partial \tau \partial t} u(\tau) \, d\tau \, dt + \int_0^T f(t, u(t)) \int_0^T \frac{\partial g}{\partial \tau} u(\tau) \, d\tau \, dt$$

$$+ \frac{1}{2} \int_0^T f(t, u(t)) \int_0^T g(t, \tau) f(\tau, u(\tau)) \, d\tau \, dt, \tag{7.64}$$

where $g(t, \tau)$ is given by

$$g(t, \tau) = -(t - \tau) H(t - \tau) + (T - \tau) \frac{t}{T}. \tag{7.65}$$

It is interesting to note that $\bar{F}_1(u)$ in (7.64) is free from $\dot{u}(t)$ which is 'absorbed' by the kernel $g(t, \tau)$.

7.5   Concluding Remarks

The method described in Section 7.4 is particularly suitable for the equations of fluid dynamics since it is applicable to nonlinear and evolutionary type of equations. This also provides a procedure for obtaining the required functional for both homogeneous and non-homogeneous boundary conditions.

Theorem 2 shows that the variational characterization of a problem depends on the form of the equation underlying the problem. It proves that it is possible to change the form of the equation so that the modified equation admits of variational formulation.

To elucidate this point we consider two classical variational formulations: Dirichlet's principle for Poisson's equation and Hamilton's principle for the equation of motion of a particle. In the first case the equation being elliptic, the boundary conditions play an important part in the variational formulation and the solution makes the functional minimum. In fact, the solution may be obtained by direct methods of calculus of variations.

In the second case, however, the initial conditions arising in the problem do not form an essential part of the variational formulation. One has to ignore the initial condition on velocity arising from the physics of the problems and introduce a fictitious final condition. The natural motion is characterized by the stationary property of the functional (in Hamilton's principle) over a class of functions satisfying one given initial condition and one fictitious final condition. Thus an essentially initial value problem for the motion of a particle is artificially changed into a boundary value problem. As a consequence one cannot use Hamilton's principle to obtain the solution by direct methods since the final condition is not known. From a classical point of view, boundary value problems can, in general, be characterized by a variational principle and not the initial value problems. This is because one has to artificially change, as mentioned above, an initial value problem to a boundary value problem to be able to derive a variational formulation. It is more natural to change the form of the equation in an initial value problem, preserving both the solution and the given initial conditions (arising from physical considerations) and then apply the method of solution described in Section 7.4.

CHAPTER 8

VARIATIONAL PROBLEMS IN FLUID FLOW AND HEAT TRANSFER

In this chapter, we shall consider applications of variational methods to some specific problems of mechanics with particular reference to fluid mechanics and heat transfer. In fact, there are many areas in these fields which are governed by variational principles. For applications of variational principles to continuum mechanics, reference may be made to Langhaar [48] and Oden and Reddy [49]. An excellent exposition of the applications of variational principles to modern physics can be found in Yourgrau and Mandelstam [50].

In fluid mechanics, principles exist for flows of perfect fluids, and for viscous flows with such Reynolds number for which the solution of the Navier-Stokes equation is stable. Certain problems in magnetohydrodynamics (MHD) and non-Newtonian fluids as well as flows around suspended drops and particles admit of variational formulation.

In particular, Lundgren [51] gave a variational principle for the time-dependent hydromagnetic flow (governed by equations in Lagrangian form) of a perfectly conducting, inviscid compressible fluid bounded partly by a stationary rigid perfect conductor and partly by a vacuum. The corresponding variational principle for steady flow of a compressible perfectly conducting fluid (with Eulerian form of governing equations) was given by Green and Karlson [52]. Wenger [53], on the other hand, presented a variational principle for magnetohydrodynamic channel flow of a viscous fluid.

Variational methods were used to find the drag in the flow of a non-Newtonian power law fluid past a rigid sphere by Wasserman and Slattery [54] and by Nakano and Tien [55] for the creeping flow of a power-law fluid past a Newtonian fluid sphere. Keller, Rubenfeld and Molyneux [56] used variational principles to obtain bounds for the viscosity of a suspension. Water waves are governed by variational principles (Luke [57], Whitham [58a], [58b], and Simmons [59]), and many problems of hydrodynamic stability (e.g., the Rayleigh-Taylor instability of two superposed fluids of different densities) are characterized by these principles (Chandrasekhar [60]). Further, variational principles have also been found for some problems in rarefied gas flow (Cercignani and Pagani [61]) and rocket exhaust nozzles designed for optimum thrust (Rao [62], Kraiko and Osipov [63], Guderley and Armitage [64]).

In the field of heat transfer, Gurtin [44] used convolution integrals (as described in Section 7.4) to reduce an initial value problem involving unsteady heat transfer to an integral equation for which he formulated a variational principle. Variational principles also govern heat transfer by radiation, where the problems are usually formulated as integral equations (Sparrow [65]). It is important to note that variational principles applicable to heat transfer are obviously applicable to mass transfer (with or without chemical reaction) since both are diffusion processes. Finally, bounds on heat (or mass) transport in turbulent convection can also be found using variational methods (Howard [66] and Busse [67]).

8.1 Basic Equations of Fluid Flows

Following the usual notation, the Navier-Stokes equation governing the conservation of momentum is

$$\rho\left(\frac{\partial u_i}{\partial t} + u_j u_{i,j}\right) = \rho\bar{F}_i + T_{ji,j}, \tag{8.1}$$

where for a Newtonian viscous fluid, the stress tensor T_{ji} is given by

$$T_{ji} = -p\delta_{ji} + g_{ji} \tag{8.2a}$$

with g_{ji} given by

$$g_{ji} = 2\mu d_{ji}, \qquad d_{ji} = \frac{1}{2}(u_{i,j} + u_{j,i}). \tag{8.2b}$$

For a certain type of non-Newtonian fluid, the deviatoric tensor g_{ji} is a function of the rate of deformation. For a perfect fluid,

$$T_{ji} = -p\delta_{ji}. \tag{8.3}$$

The equation of conservation of mass is

$$\frac{\partial \rho}{\partial t} + (\rho u_i)_{,i} = 0. \tag{8.4}$$

If the fluid is electrically conducting (with electrical conductivity σ) and is permeated by a magnetic field, then the force per unit volume given by $\rho\bar{F}_i$ in (8.1) becomes

$$\rho\bar{F}_i = (\rho_e \, \mathbf{E} + \mu_e \, \mathbf{j} \times \mathbf{H})_i, \tag{8.5}$$

where ρ_e, μ_e, $\mathbf{E}$, $\mathbf{j}$ and $\mathbf{H}$ denote the charge density, magnetic permeability, electric field, current density and magnetic field, respectively. In this case the above equations must be supplemented by Maxwell's equations

$$\nabla \times \mathbf{H} = \mathbf{j} + \frac{\partial \mathbf{D}}{\partial t}, \tag{8.6}$$

$$\nabla \cdot \mathbf{D} = \rho_e, \tag{8.7}$$

$$\nabla \times \mathbf{E} = -\frac{\partial \mathbf{B}}{\partial t}, \tag{8.8}$$

$$\nabla \cdot \mathbf{B} = 0, \tag{8.9}$$

$$\mathbf{j} = \rho_e\mathbf{E} + \sigma(\mathbf{E} + \mu_e \, \mathbf{u} \times \mathbf{H}), \tag{8.10}$$

$$\mathbf{B} = \mu_e\mathbf{H}, \tag{8.11}$$

where **u** is the velocity with components u_j. In (8.6), $\partial \mathbf{D}/\partial t$ stands for the displacement current (which may be neglected in low frequency approximation), **D** being the displacement vector.

8.2   Variational Principles for Perfect Fluids

Several attempts were made to derive the aforementioned governing equations of fluid flow from the variational principle of Hamilton which proves, as shown earlier, to be a powerful tool in particle mechanics. Unfortunately, however, these attempts were not very successful. In fact, Truesdell and Toupin [68] remarked "the lines of thought which have led to beautiful variational statements for systems of mass points have been applied in continuum mechanics also, but only rarely are the results beautiful or useful".

Let us consider first the steady irrotational flow of an incompressible perfect fluid and assume that the body force is derivable from a potential, i.e., $\rho \mathbf{F} = - \nabla \Phi$. Using (8.2a) with $\mu = 0$, (8.1) can be written as

$$\nabla \left(\frac{1}{2} \mathbf{u} \cdot \mathbf{u} \right) = - \nabla \cdot \Phi - \nabla (p/\rho),$$

which gives, on integration, Bernoulli's equation

$$\frac{1}{2} \mathbf{u} \cdot \mathbf{u} + \Phi + p/\rho = \text{constant}. \tag{8.12}$$

This gives the pressure distribution once the velocity field is known. Since the motion is irrotational, we have

$$\mathbf{u} = \nabla \phi \tag{8.13}$$

along with the equation of continuity

$$\nabla \cdot \mathbf{u} = 0 \tag{8.14}$$

and the boundary condition

$$\rho \mathbf{n} \cdot \mathbf{u} = f \quad \text{on } S, \tag{8.15}$$

where S is the boundary of the region V in which the flow takes place.

We now state the first variational principle due to Thomson [16].

Among all possible motions of an incompressible fluid in V with a specified mass flux on S ((8.15)), the irrotational motion has the least kinetic energy T, where

$$T(\mathbf{u}) = \frac{1}{2} \rho \int_V \mathbf{u} \cdot \mathbf{u} \, dV. \tag{8.16}$$

Consider the variational integral

$$I = \frac{1}{2} \rho \int \mathbf{u} \cdot \mathbf{u} \, dV + \rho \int \lambda \nabla \cdot \mathbf{u} \, dV$$

whose first variation gives, after using divergence theorem, the relation

$$\delta I = \rho \int_V [\delta \mathbf{u} \cdot (\mathbf{u} - \nabla \lambda) + \delta \lambda \nabla \cdot \mathbf{u}] \, dV + \int_S \lambda \rho \mathbf{n} \cdot \delta \mathbf{u} \, dS. \tag{8.17}$$

In view of the boundary condition (8.15), the surface integral in (8.17) vanishes and the Euler equations are given by (8.13) and (8.14).

We can establish the minimum property by considering a motion $\mathbf{u} = \nabla \phi + \mathbf{u}_0$, where ϕ satisfies $\nabla^2 \phi = 0$ and $\mathbf{u}_0$ satisfies $\nabla \cdot \mathbf{u}_0 = 0$ in V subject to $\mathbf{n} \cdot \mathbf{u}_0 = 0$ on S. Then

$$T(\nabla \phi + \mathbf{u}_0) = \frac{1}{2} \rho \int_V (\nabla \phi \cdot \nabla \phi + 2 \mathbf{u}_0 \cdot \nabla \phi + \mathbf{u}_0 \cdot \mathbf{u}_0) \, dV.$$

Now by divergence theorem and using $\mathbf{n} \cdot \mathbf{u}_0 = 0$ on S,

$$\int_V \mathbf{u}_0 \cdot \nabla \phi \, dV = \int_V \nabla \cdot (\phi \mathbf{u}_0) \, dV - \int_V \phi \nabla \cdot \mathbf{u}_0 \, dV$$

$$= \int_S \phi \mathbf{n} \cdot \mathbf{u}_0 \, dS = 0$$

Hence

$$T(\nabla \phi + \mathbf{u}_0) = T(\nabla \phi) + T(\mathbf{u}_0). \tag{8.18}$$

Since T is positive, it follows that the kinetic energy of any other motion consistent with the boundary condition is greater than that corresponding to the irrotational motion. The above principle is derived by embedding the problem in a vector space which is solenoidal, but not irrotational. In the reciprocal (or complementary) variational principle, one uses a vector space which is irrotational but not solenoidal. Using this principle it can be shown that among all irrotational motions in V, the one satisfying (8.13)–(8.15) maximizes the functional

$$J(\phi) = -\frac{1}{2} \int_V \rho \nabla \phi \cdot \nabla \phi \, dV + \int_S \phi f \, dS.$$

Here the Euler equation is clearly $\nabla^2 \phi = 0$ with the natural boundary condition $\rho \mathbf{n} \cdot \nabla \phi = f$ on S. The above two variational principles give upper and lower bounds on the kinetic energy

$$J(\phi) \le \text{kinetic energy} \le T(\mathbf{u}).$$

Analogous variational principles exist for steady irrotational flows of compressible fluid. We present here the variational formulation due to Lush and Cherry [69].

We consider the non-dissipative flow of a compressible fluid in which the entropy is assumed constant. The density ρ is variable and pressure is a definite function of density given by an equation of state. If U, V and S denote the internal energy, specific volume and the specific entropy per unit mass, we have from thermodynamic considerations

$$dU = -p \, dV = \frac{p \, d\rho}{\rho^2}, \qquad p = \left(\frac{\partial U}{\partial V} \right)_S. \tag{8.19}$$

Taking the dot product of the velocity **u** with the momentum equation and adding it to the energy equation

$$\rho \mathbf{u} \cdot \nabla U = -T_{ji}u_{ji},$$

we get on using (8.3) the relation

$$\mathbf{u} \cdot \nabla\left(\frac{1}{2}|\mathbf{u}|^2 + U + p/\rho\right) = -\frac{p}{\rho^2}\mathbf{u} \cdot \nabla\rho - \frac{p}{\rho}\nabla \cdot \mathbf{u} = 0. \tag{8.20}$$

From (8.19) and (8.20), we obtain a particular integral of the governing equations in the form of Bernoulli's theorem, as

$$\frac{1}{2}u^2 + \frac{d}{d\rho}(\rho U) = 0. \tag{8.21}$$

Let us now maximize the integral

$$J = \int_V p\, dV + \int_S \phi f\, dS \tag{8.22}$$

among all continuous functions ϕ satisfying the following equations (see (8.19) and (8.21)):

$$p = \rho^2 U', \quad \frac{1}{2}\mathbf{u} \cdot \mathbf{u} + (\rho U)' = 0, \quad \mathbf{u} = \nabla\phi. \tag{8.23}$$

Here the prime denotes differentiation with respect to ρ. The first variation of J is now

$$\delta J = \int_V \delta p\, dV + \int_S f\,\delta\phi\, dS.$$

From (8.23) we have

$$\delta p = 2\rho U'\delta p + \rho^2 U''\,\delta\rho = p'\,\delta\rho = c^2\,\delta\rho, \tag{824a}$$

$$\mathbf{u} \cdot \delta\mathbf{u} = -2U'\,\delta\rho - \rho U''\delta\rho = -\delta p/\rho = -c^2\,\delta\rho/\rho, \tag{8.24b}$$

where $(dp/d\rho)_S = c^2$, the square of the sound velocity. The first variation then becomes

$$\delta J = -\int_V \rho\mathbf{u} \cdot \delta\mathbf{u}\, dV + \int_S f\,\delta\phi\, dS. \tag{8.25}$$

Putting $\mathbf{u} = \nabla\phi$ and integrating by parts, the above equation gives, on using the divergence theorem, the relation

$$\delta J = \int_V (\nabla \cdot (\rho\mathbf{u}))\,\delta\phi\, dV + \int_S (f - \rho\mathbf{n} \cdot \nabla\phi)\,\delta\phi\, dS,$$

which gives the Euler equation and the natural boundary conditions as

$$\nabla \cdot (\rho\mathbf{u}) = 0 \quad \text{in } V,$$

$$f - \rho\mathbf{n} \cdot \nabla\phi = 0 \quad \text{on } S.$$

To investigate the maximum property, we consider the second variation in (8.25):

$$\delta^2 J = - \int_V \rho \, \delta \mathbf{u} \cdot \delta \mathbf{u} \, dV - \int_V \mathbf{u} \cdot \delta \mathbf{u} \, \delta\rho \, dV .$$

By using (8.24), the above equation gives

$$\delta^2 J = - \int_V \frac{\rho}{c^2} \sum_{i,j=1}^{3} (c^2 \, \delta_{ij} - u_i u_j) \, \delta u_i \, \delta u_j \, dV,$$

which is negative definite for a subsonic flow with $c^2 > \mathbf{u} \cdot \mathbf{u}$. Thus the above principle satisfies the necessary condition for a maximum. The corresponding reciprocal variational principle was established by Bateman [70] as follows: Minimize the integral

$$I(\mathbf{u}) = \int_V (p + \rho \mathbf{u} \cdot \mathbf{u}) \, dV$$

among all velocity fields satisfying

$$p = \rho^2 U', \quad \frac{1}{2} \mathbf{u} \cdot \mathbf{u} + (\rho U)' = 0, \quad \nabla \cdot (\rho \mathbf{U}) = 0 \quad \text{in } V$$

$$\rho \mathbf{n} \cdot \mathbf{u} = f \text{ on } S.$$

It is found that the velocity fields which fulfil the above requirements are irrotational. Further, as in the case of incompressible fluids, $J(\phi)$ and $I(\mathbf{u})$ provide the lower and upper bounds on the sum of pressure and twice the kinetic energy of the flow:

$$J(\phi) \leq \int_V (p + \rho \mathbf{u} \cdot \mathbf{u}) \, dV \leq I(\mathbf{u}).$$

In the general case of unsteady compressible flows of a perfect fluid, the following variational integral is stationary (see [16]):

$$I = \int_{t_1}^{t_2} \int_V \left[\frac{1}{2} \rho \mathbf{u} \cdot \mathbf{u} - \rho(U + \Phi) \right] dV \, dt$$

when the external force has a potential Φ.

8.3   Variational Principle for Viscous Fluids

We now consider steady flow of an incompressible Newtonian viscous fluid with constant physical properties and a conservative body force field. Then the equation of motion (8.1) is

$$\mathbf{u} \cdot \nabla \mathbf{u} = - \frac{1}{\rho} \nabla p - \nabla \phi + \nu \nabla^2 \mathbf{u},$$

which can be re-written as

$$\nabla\left(\frac{1}{2}\,\mathbf{u}\mathbf{u}\right) - \mathbf{u} \times (\nabla \times \mathbf{u}) = -\frac{1}{\rho}\nabla p - \nabla\phi + \nu\nabla^2 u. \tag{8.26}$$

Now if the inertial term $\mathbf{u} \cdot \nabla\mathbf{u}$ is absent or even $\mathbf{u} \times (\nabla \times \mathbf{u})$ only vanishes, it follows from the above equations with $\nabla \cdot \mathbf{u} = 0$ (the equation of continuity) that

$$\nabla^2\mathbf{u} = \nabla H, \quad \nabla^2 H = 0. \tag{8.27a}$$

where

$$H = \frac{1}{\nu}\left[\frac{\mathbf{u} \cdot \mathbf{u}}{2} + p/\rho + \phi\right] \tag{8.27b}$$

In this case a variational principle for (8.26) exists and is known as the Helmholtz-Korteweg principle.

Minimize the functional

$$J(\mathbf{u}) = \nu \int_V d_{ij}d_{ij}\, dV \tag{8.28}$$

among velocity functions $\mathbf{u} \in C^2$ which satisfy $u = f$ on S and $\nabla \cdot \mathbf{u} = 0$ in V.

Using the Lagrange multiplier, we add $\int \lambda \nabla \cdot \mathbf{u}\, dV$ to the above integral and derive the Euler equations in the usual manner. It is easy to see that the multiplier $\lambda = -u^2 - 2(p/\rho) - 2\Phi$ gives (8.26) without the term $\mathbf{u} \times (\nabla \times \mathbf{u})$.

An interesting physical interpretation of the above minimum principle is (see Batchelor [71]) that the steady flow of an incompressible viscous fluid with negligible inertia forces has a smaller total rate of dissipation of energy than any other incompressible flow in the same region with the same values of the velocity vector everywhere on the boundary of the region. The integral in (8.28) is proportional to the total rate of dissipation of mechanical energy by the action of viscosity in the whole region.

The above result can be generalized to steady flows of a certain class of non-Newtonian fluids without inertial terms. The governing equations in usual notations are

$$T_{ji,j} - p_{,i} + \rho F_i = 0, \tag{8.29a}$$

$$u_{i,i} = 0 \tag{8.29b}$$

with the constitutive relation ([16])

$$T_{ji} = \partial\Gamma(d_{pq}, x_r)/\partial d_{ij}, \tag{8.30}$$

where Γ is a given symmetric function of the rate-of-deformation tensor d_{pq} and the position x_r. The boundary conditions are: the velocity is specified on S_u and the surface traction is prescribed on S_t with $S = S_u \cup S_t$ as follows:

$$u_i = f_i \quad \text{on } S_u, \tag{8.31a}$$

$$T_{ji}n_j - pn_i = g_i \quad \text{on } S_i. \tag{8.31b}$$

The variational principle (Hill [72]) in terms of velocity is as follows: Make $J(\mathbf{u})$ stationary among all velocity functions $\mathbf{u} \in C^2$ subject to (8.29)–(8.31) with

$$J(\mathbf{u}) = \int_V (\Gamma - \rho F_i u_i)\, dV - \int_{S_t} g_i u_i\, dS. \tag{8.32}$$

A complementary variational principle is obtained by making a functional $I(T)$ stationary to tensor functions $T \in C^1$ subject to (8.29) and (8.31b) with

$$I(T) = -\int_V \hat{\Gamma}\, dV + \int_{S_u} (T_{ji} n_j - pn_i) f_i\, dS. \tag{8.33}$$

Under the conditions that J and I give minimum and maximum principles, respectively, one can derive the upper and lower bounds as

$$I(T) \le I(\bar{T}) = J(\mathbf{u}_1) \le J(\mathbf{u}), \tag{8.34}$$

where $\bar{T}$ is the tensor function T at the extremum $\mathbf{u}_1$. Further, $\hat{\Gamma}$ in (8.33) is given by inverting (8.30) as

$$d_{ij} = \partial\hat{\Gamma}(T_{pq}, x_r)/\partial T_{ji}. \tag{8.35}$$

It would be illuminating to apply the foregoing results to steady rectilinear flow of a non-Newtonian fluid in a duct in the absence of body forces. Taking the scalar product of (8.29a) with $\mathbf{u}$, integrating by parts and applying divergence theorem, we get (on using $F_i = 0$)

$$0 = -\int pu_i n_i\, dS - \int u_{i,j} T_{ji}\, dV + \int T_{ji} u_i n_j\, dS. \tag{8.36}$$

As the deviatoric stress tensor T_{ij} is symmetric, $u_{i,j} T_{ij} = d_{ij} T_{ij}$. Further, since $\mathbf{u} = 0$ on the sides of the duct, the surface integral vanishes there. On the ends of the duct, the last surface integral involves T_{zz} (z-axis is taken along the duct) which vanishes for a Newtonian or a power-law non-Newtonian fluid. At the ends, pressure is constant so that

$$\int_{\text{ends}} pu_i n_i\, dS = -p_0 \int_{S_0} u_z\, dS + p_L \int_{S_L} u_z\, dS \tag{8.37}$$
$$= (p_L - p_0)Q,$$

where S_0 and S_L are the surfaces at $z = 0$ and $z = L$.

Now from (8.36) and (8.37), we have

$$\int d_{ij} T_{ij}\, dV = (p_0 - p_L)Q = Q\Delta p.$$

For a Newtonian fluid,

$$d_{ij} T_{ij} = 2\mu d_{ij} d_{ij} = 2\Gamma$$

so that the variational integral (8.32) is proportional to the flow rate Q. Thus the two variational principles provide upper and lower bounds on the flow rate. The same result applies to a non-Newtonian fluid also provided that $d_{ij}T_{ij}$ is proportional to Γ. For a power-law fluid (see [54]), this is true since $d_{ij}T_{ij} = (n + 1)\ \Gamma$.

Suppose U and U' denote the class of vector functions which vanish on S and S' respectively. Suppose $S \subset S'$, then $U \subset U'$. This means that any function in U vanishing on S can also be extended to be zero on S' and hence is in U'. Thus as the cross-section of the duct increases, the admissible class of functions is extended, and this results in a decrease in $J(u)$. We thus arrive at the following important result: For steady rectilinear flow of a Newtonian or a power-law fluid, the product of the pressure drop per unit length times the flow rate decreases as the duct cross-section increases.

Using the above ideas, bounds on the drag on a particle in an incompressible flow (with negligible inertia) of a power-law fluid can be found as was done for the pressure drop through ducts. In fact, the variational integral (8.32) is now proportional to the drag when the external forces are conservative and the particle is stationary. We denote by U and U' the class of vector functions which vanish on S and S', respectively. If S is contained in S', then $U' \subset U$. Hence as the size of the particle is increased, the class of admissible functions decreases resulting in an increase in the minimum of the functional. Thus in a power-law (or Newtonian) fluid, the drag is increased as the particle size increases provided the inertial forces are negligible.

This result can be utilized to find bounds on the drag for irregularly shaped particles in slow flow, provided that we know the solution for a particle which either contains or is contained by the irregularly shaped particle (see Happel and Brenner [73]). For example, let us give an estimate of the drag on an oblate spheroid with major axis $2a$ and minor axis $\sqrt{2}a$ moving slowly in a viscous fluid with velocity U. This body can clearly be contained within a sphere of radius a and can contain a sphere of radius $a/\sqrt{2}$. Since the drag on a sphere of radius a moving with velocity U is $6\pi a\mu U$ (μ is the dynamic viscosity coefficient), it follows that the drag F experienced by the above body satisfies

$$\frac{6\pi a\mu U}{\sqrt{2}} < F < 6\pi a\mu U.$$

This gives

$$F \approx 3\frac{1 + \sqrt{2}}{\sqrt{2}} \cdot \pi a\mu U \pm \frac{3\,(\sqrt{2} - 1)}{\sqrt{2}} \cdot \pi a\mu U$$

$$= 5.12\ \pi a\mu U \pm 0.89\ \pi a\mu U,$$

which may be compared with the exact solution $5.67\pi\mu aU$ (see Lamb [74]).

Further, the drag on a particle in slow flow taking place in a rigid container is increased as compared with the corresponding value in the absence of the container. This follows from the fact that the velocity has to vanish on the container wall and hence the class of admissible functions decreases, resulting in an increase in the minimum of the functional.

8.4 Energy Methods for Stability of Fluid Motion

In Section 8.3 it was pointed out that a variational principle exists for the flow of an incompressible viscous fluid if the inertial terms are absent. However, it was shown by Millikan (see [16]) that it is not possible to find a Lagrangian L such that the variational integral $J = \int_V L \, dV$ gives as Euler equations the full Navier-Stokes equation (8.26). Despite this limitation there are stability theorems applicable to these equations. Serrin [75] developed an energy method for finding the stability of solutions of the full Navier-Stokes equations with respect to disturbances of arbitrary amplitude. We now analyze this method.

Consider a definite flow of an incompressible viscous fluid occupying a region V and subject to prescribed velocity distribution on the boundary S of V. Now suppose the velocity field at the instant $t = 0$ in the flow is slightly changed subject to the same boundary conditions. The question arises whether the subsequent motion changes only a little from what it was or whether it changes radically in character. There are two methods of studying this problem. The first one involves the well known normal mode analysis based on small perturbations of the basic flow. In the second method we assume, following Serrin, that $\mathbf{v}$ is the velocity of the basic flow and $\mathbf{v}^*$ is the velocity of the perturbed motion. Since $\mathbf{v}$ and $\mathbf{v}^*$ are both solutions of (8.1) written in the form

$$\rho\left(\frac{\partial \mathbf{v}}{\partial t} + \mathbf{v} \cdot \nabla \mathbf{v}\right) = -\nabla p + \mu \nabla^2 \mathbf{v}, \tag{8.38}$$

we find that the perturbation $\mathbf{u}$ $(= \mathbf{v}^* - \mathbf{v})$ satisfies

$$\frac{\partial \mathbf{u}}{\partial t} + \mathbf{u} \cdot \nabla \mathbf{v} + \mathbf{v}^* \cdot \nabla \mathbf{u} = -\nabla\left(\frac{p^* - p}{\rho}\right) + \nu \nabla^2 \mathbf{u}. \tag{8.39}$$

Taking the scalar product of (8.39) with $\mathbf{u}$ and then integrating over the region V of the flow, we get, on using the divergence theorem and $\nabla \cdot \mathbf{v} = \nabla \cdot \mathbf{v}^* = 0$ and the boundary condition $\mathbf{u} = 0$ on S, the relation

$$\frac{d}{dt} \int_V \frac{1}{2} u^2 \, dV = -\int_V (\mathbf{u} \cdot \mathbf{D} \cdot \mathbf{u} + \nu \nabla \mathbf{u} : \nabla \mathbf{u}) \, dV, \tag{8.40}$$

where the components D_{ij} of $\mathbf{D}$ form the rate-of-strain matrix of the basic flow $\mathbf{v}$. It is clear from (8.40) that while viscosity tends to damp out any disturbances, large enough values of the rate of shear of the basic flow ($\mathbf{D}$) may foster the growth of disturbances. The relative importance of these two terms determines the stability of the flow. In (8.40), the notation ':' stands for a dyadic product.

Using the divergence theorem and the result

$$\frac{1}{2} u_i(v_{i,k} + v_{k,i}) u_k = (v_i u_i u_k)_{,k} - u_k u_{i,k} v_k,$$

we obtain from (8.40) the relation

$$\frac{dK}{dt} = \int_V [\mathbf{u} \cdot \nabla \mathbf{u} \cdot \mathbf{v} - \nu \nabla \mathbf{u} : \nabla \mathbf{u}] \, dV, \tag{8.41}$$

where $K = \int_V \frac{1}{2} u^2 \, dV$. Hence if $K \to 0$, then $\mathbf{u}$ also tends to zero almost everywhere. Thus the basic flow will be stable in the mean provided that the energy of the disturbance tends to zero as time increases.

It is clear that if the first term on the right of (8.41) is less than the second term, then the basic flow is stable. It also follows that high speeds of the basic flow as well as high rates of shear tend to destabilize the flow. However, it is important to remember that the present energy method cannot provide accurate knowledge of the limits of stability, which can be gained from the normal mode analysis of disturbances of small amplitude.

Let the length scale of the region V be d. Consider an arbitrary differentiable vector field $\mathbf{h}$ in V. Obviously,

$$0 \le (\nabla \mathbf{u} + \mathbf{h} u) : (\nabla \mathbf{u} + \mathbf{h} u) = \nabla \mathbf{u} : \nabla \mathbf{u} + \mathbf{h} \cdot \nabla u^2 + h^2 u^2,$$

which, when integrated over V along with $\mathbf{u} = 0$ on S, gives

$$\int_V \nabla \mathbf{u} : \nabla \mathbf{u} \, dV \ge \int_V (\nabla \cdot \mathbf{h} - h^2) u^2 \, dV. \tag{8.42}$$

Now the specific vector field $\mathbf{h} = C \tan (Cr) \cdot \mathbf{r}/r$ is differentiable in a sphere of radius $\pi/2C$ about the origin. We set $C = \pi/d$ and suitably locate the origin in V. Equation (8.42) then gives

$$\int_V \nabla \mathbf{u} : \nabla \mathbf{u} \, dV \ge 3C^2 \int_V u^2 \, dv = \frac{6\pi^2}{d^2} K. \tag{8.43}$$

Now for any dyadic $\mathbf{A}$,

$$\mathbf{A} : \mathbf{A} - 2\mathbf{u} \cdot \mathbf{A} \cdot \mathbf{v} + u^2 v^2 = (\mathbf{A} - \mathbf{u}\mathbf{v}) : (\mathbf{A} - \mathbf{u}\mathbf{v}) \ge 0$$

leading to

$$\mathbf{u} \cdot \mathbf{A} \cdot \mathbf{v} \le \frac{1}{2} (\mathbf{A} : \mathbf{A} + u^2 v^2). \tag{8.44}$$

Putting $\mathbf{A} = v\nabla\mathbf{u}$ in (8.44) and using this result in (8.41), we get on using (8.43) the relation

$$\frac{dK}{dt} \le \frac{1}{v} (V^2 - 3\pi^2 v^2 d^{-2}) K, \tag{8.45}$$

where V is the maximum speed of the basic flow in the time interval 0 to t. Integration of (8.45) gives

$$K \le K_0 \exp [(V^2 - 3\pi^2 v^2/d^2) t / v], \tag{8.46}$$

where K_0 is the initial energy of the disturbance. Thus if $V < \sqrt{3} \cdot \pi v/d$, then $K \to 0$ at $t \to \infty$ and the basic flow is stable. Although this result is obtained for a bounded region, similar results also hold when the region is enclosed in an infinite cylinder or between two infinite plates and the disturbances are assumed periodic. The above stability criterion for finite disturbances can be rephrased in terms of a Reynolds number Re ($= \rho V d / \mu$) such that $Re \leq \sqrt{3}\,\pi$ implies stability of the motion.

In the foregoing analysis we have found stability criteria based on arbitrary perturbations $\mathbf{u}$. In reality, however, not all vector fields $\mathbf{u}$ are permissible. To investigate this situation more fully, we consider the maximum of the right side of (8.40) under the constraint $\nabla \cdot \mathbf{u} = 0$. After introducing a suitable normalization, we consider the following variational problem:

$$\text{Maximize} - \int_V \mathbf{u} \cdot \mathbf{D} \cdot \mathbf{u}\, dV \tag{8.47}$$

subject to the constraints

$$\nabla \cdot \mathbf{u} = 0, \quad \int_V \nabla \mathbf{u} : \nabla \mathbf{u}\, dV = 1, \quad \text{on } S, \mathbf{u} = 0 \tag{8.48}$$

Introducing the Lagrange multipliers v^* and $\lambda = \lambda(\mathbf{x})$, the above variational problem may be formulated as

$$\delta \int_V (\mathbf{u} \cdot \mathbf{D} \cdot \mathbf{u} + v^*\, \nabla \mathbf{u} : \nabla \mathbf{u} - \lambda\, \nabla \cdot \mathbf{u})\, dV. \tag{8.49}$$

The Euler equation gives

$$\mathbf{u} \cdot \mathbf{D} = -\nabla \lambda + v^* \nabla^2 \mathbf{u}, \quad \nabla \cdot \mathbf{u} = 0 \tag{8.50}$$

These relations are to be solved subject to the boundary condition $\mathbf{u} = 0$ on S. The linear system (8.50) has presumably non-trivial solutions for a bounded set of eigenvalues. If $\bar{v}$ be the greatest of these eigenvalues, then using the variational properties of eigenvalues described in Section 5.3, we get

$$-\int_V \mathbf{u} \cdot \mathbf{D} \cdot \mathbf{u}\, dV \leq \bar{v}$$

for all $\mathbf{u}$ satisfying (8.48). This now leads to the following result: Let $\bar{v}$ be the maximum eigenvalue of the system (8.50). Then the basic flow $\mathbf{v}$ in V is stable provided that $\bar{v} < v$.

Serrin applied the above technique to investigate the stability of the flow between two concentric rotating circular cylinders. It is found that complete stability to all disturbances is ensured if

$$|\,(\Omega_2 - \Omega_1)/v\,| < C(R_1, R_2),$$

where $C(R_1, R_2)$ is a known function of R_1 and R_2 which form the inner and outer radii of the cylinders rotating with angular velocities Ω_1 (>0) and Ω_2, respectively. It is well known from the celebrated experiments of Taylor [76] that the flow becomes unstable in the form of toroidal vortices provided that the inner cylinder rotates much faster than the outer one causing an adverse distribution of angular momentum.

The energy method was also applied to the problem of thermal instability of a fluid layer of depth d heated from below (with temperature gradient β) in the presence of a shear flow by Joseph [77] who found accurate bounds ensuring stability for finite amplitude disturbances by variational methods. For Couette flow between two parallel plates heated from below, he found that the flow is stable provided that $Ra + Re^2 < 1708$, where Ra is the Rayleigh number $g\alpha\beta d^4/kv$ and Re is the Reynolds number Vd/v where the fluid has thermal expansion coefficient α and the upper and lower plates have velocities $\pm V$. In the absence of shear ($V = 0$), it is found that subcritical nonlinear instabilities cannot occur. This means that the flow does not become unstable with respect to finite amplitude disturbances before it becomes unstable with respect to infinitesimal perturbation.

8.5   Variational Methods Applied to Some Stability Problems in Hydrodynamics and Hydromagnetics

In this section we shall study several problems of hydrodynamic and hydromagnetic stability using variational methods.

Stability of Hydromagnetic Flow Past a Porous Plate

We shall examine the nonlinear stability of the flow of an electrically conducting fluid past a porous infinite flat plate in the presence of a uniform transverse magnetic field, the plate being subjected to uniform suction. Serrin's energy method is applied to this problem (see Rajagopal, Gupta and Dandapat [78]), which has an important bearing on magneto-aerodynamic flow past a body subjected to suction to reduce the frictional resistance by preventing separation and to stabilize the boundary layer. The technique essentially considers the time rate of change of the kinetic and magnetic energy of an arbitrary disturbance. If the total energy decreases with time, the flow is stable and we derive a universal stability estimate which provides a sufficient condition for asymptotic stability in the mean.

The basic equations of hydromagnetics for an incompressible viscous fluid are the equations of continuity, momentum and magnetic induction given in Section 8.1, which may be written as

$$\nabla \cdot \mathbf{q} = 0, \tag{8.51}$$

$$\frac{\partial \mathbf{q}}{\partial t} + \mathbf{q} \cdot \nabla \mathbf{q} = -\frac{1}{\rho} \nabla p + \frac{\mu_e}{4\pi\rho}(\nabla \times \mathbf{H}) \times \mathbf{H} + v\nabla^2 \mathbf{q}, \tag{8.52}$$

$$\frac{\partial \mathbf{H}}{\partial t} = \nabla \times (\mathbf{q} \times \mathbf{H}) + \eta\nabla^2 \mathbf{H} \tag{8.53}$$

along with $\nabla \cdot \mathbf{H} = 0$, η being the magnetic diffusivity $1/(4\pi\mu_e\,\sigma)$.

Consider the flow of this fluid past an infinite porous flat plate $y = 0$ (Fig. 8.1) (which is electrically non-conducting) in the presence of a uniform transverse magnetic field H_0, the plate being subjected to uniform suction velocity V_0. This flow problem was first studied by Gupta [79] and then by Kakutani [80], who found that an asymptotic solution for velocity and magnetic field exists if the suction is strong enough to check the propagation of vorticity due to Alfvén waves away from the plate. The velocity and the magnetic field for this flow are

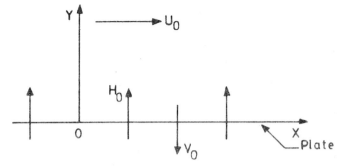

Fig. 8.1   A sketch of the physical problem.

given by

$$\frac{u_0(y)}{U_0} = 1 + \frac{1}{2\alpha}\left[(1 - Pm - \alpha)e^{\alpha_1 y} - (1 - Pm + \alpha)e^{\alpha_2 y}\right], \tag{8.54}$$

$$\frac{H_x(y)}{H_0} = -\frac{U_0\, Pm}{V_0\, \alpha}\left(e^{\alpha_1 y} - e^{\alpha_2 y}\right), \tag{8.55}$$

where

$$S = \frac{\mu_e H_0^2}{4\pi\rho V_0^2}, \qquad \alpha = [(1 - Pm)^2 + 4SPm]^{1/2},$$

$$Pm = \nu/\eta, \qquad \alpha_{1,2} = \frac{V_0}{2\nu}[1 + Pm \mp \alpha]. \tag{8.56}$$

It should be noted that the above solution is valid when $V_0 < 0$ and $S < 1$ so that both α_1 and α_2 are negative. The boundary conditions are

$$u = 0, \qquad v = -V_0, \qquad H_x = 0, \qquad H_y = H_0 \quad \text{at } y = 0,$$
$$u \to U_0, \qquad H_x \to 0, \qquad H_y \to H_0 \quad \text{as } y \to \infty. \tag{8.57}$$

To study the stability of the above flow, we assume that the basic flow **U** and the magnetic field **H** are perturbed such that the perturbed field becomes $(\mathbf{U} + \mathbf{u}, \mathbf{H} + \mathbf{h})$. For the perturbed flow we form the scalar product of (8.52) with **u** and of the induction equation (8.53) with $\mu_e \mathbf{h}/(4\pi\rho)$ and add them. The resulting equation is then integrated over the domain extending from the plate to infinity. Using the divergence theorem and the dimensionless quantities

$$\mathbf{u}' = \mathbf{u}/U_0, \qquad \mathbf{h}' = \mathbf{h}/H_0, \qquad \tau = U_0^2 t/\nu,$$
$$\mathbf{E}_1 = \mathbf{D}_1/m, \qquad \mathbf{E}_2 = \mathbf{G}/M_H, \qquad \nabla' = (\nu/U_0)\nabla, \tag{8.58}$$

we find that (after dropping the primes)

$$\frac{d}{d\tau}(K_1 + A^2 K_2) = \int_{D_0} [-\,Re\,\mathbf{u}\cdot\mathbf{E}_1\cdot\mathbf{u} + A^2\,Re\,\mathbf{h}\cdot\mathbf{E}_1\cdot\mathbf{h}$$

$$+ A^2 Q\,Re\,\mathbf{u}\cdot\mathbf{E}_2\cdot\mathbf{h} - \nabla\mathbf{u} : \nabla\mathbf{u} - (A^2/P_m)\,\nabla\mathbf{h} : \nabla\mathbf{h}]\,dV. \tag{8.59}$$

In (8.58), $- m$ and M_H denote respectively the least and greatest characteristic value of D_1 (the rate-of-strain tensor for the basic flow) and G (the corresponding tensor for the magnetic field), where D_1 and G have components

$$\frac{1}{2}(\partial U_i/\partial x_k + \partial U_k/\partial x_i), \quad (\partial H_i/\partial x_k - \partial H_k/\partial x_i).$$

In deriving (8.59), the boundary conditions $\mathbf{u} = \mathbf{h} = 0$ at the plate and $\mathbf{u} \to 0$, $\mathbf{h} \to 0$ at infinity are used together with

$$K_1 = \int_{D_0} \frac{\mathbf{u}' \cdot \mathbf{u}'}{2} \, dV, \quad K_2 = \int_{D_0} \frac{\mathbf{h}' \cdot \mathbf{h}'}{2} \, dV,$$

$$A = \left(\frac{\mu_e H_0^2}{4\pi\rho U_0^2}\right)^{1/2}, \quad Re = \frac{m\nu}{U_0^2}, \quad Q = \frac{U_0 M_H}{M H_0},$$

$$P_m = \nu/\eta, \tag{8.60}$$

where M is the greatest characteristic value of D and η is the magnetic diffusivity.

We confine our discussion here to disturbance functions f which are absolutely integrable for y in $[0, \infty]$ and are periodic in x and z. Let us denote this class by S_1. Equation (8.59) can be written as

$$\frac{dE}{d\tau} = - D + Re\, I \tag{8.61}$$

with

$$I = \int_{D_0} [- \mathbf{u} \cdot \mathbf{E}_1 \cdot \mathbf{u} + A^2\, \mathbf{h} \cdot \mathbf{E}_1 \cdot \mathbf{h} + A^2 Q \mathbf{u} \cdot \mathbf{E}_2 \cdot \mathbf{h}]\, dV \tag{8.62}$$

$$D = \int_{D_0} [\nabla\mathbf{u} : \nabla\mathbf{u} + (A^2/Pm)\, \nabla\mathbf{h} : \nabla\mathbf{h}]\, dV. \tag{8.63}$$

Here, $E = K_1 + A K_2$. It follows from (8.61) that

$$\frac{dE}{d\tau} \leq - (1 - Re/\overline{Re})\, D. \tag{8.64}$$

$\overline{Re}$ is obtained from the solution of the following variational problem:

$$(\overline{Re})^{-1} = \max_{S_2} \left(\frac{I}{D}\right). \tag{8.65}$$

In (8.65), S_2 is the set $\{\mathbf{u}, \mathbf{h} \,|\, \mathbf{u}, \mathbf{h}$ having continuous second partial derivatives with $\nabla \cdot \mathbf{u} = 0$, $\nabla \cdot \mathbf{h} = 0$, $\mathbf{u} = \mathbf{h} = 0$ on $y = 0$ and $\mathbf{u}, \mathbf{h} \in S_1\}$.

If $Re < \overline{Re}$ in the time interval $[0, \tau]$, it follows from (8.64) that

$$E(\tau) - E(0) \leq - \left(1 - \frac{Re}{\overline{Re}}\right) \int_0^\tau D\, dt. \tag{8.66}$$

If $E(0)$ is bounded, then (8.66) shows that $E(\tau)$ remains bounded in τ. Now $D \to 0$

as $\tau \to \infty$ in the sense that

$$\lim_{\tau \to \infty} \int_0^\tau D\, dt < \infty. \tag{8.67}$$

Following Joseph [81], we find an upper bound for I/D in the maximum problem (8.65). We introduce

$$(R_E)^{-1} = \sup\,(I/D), \tag{8.68}$$

where the supremum is taken over the class of functions $\xi = (u, v, w, h_x, h_y, h_z)$ in S_1 which are absolutely integrable in $0 \le y \le \infty$, and are almost periodic in x and z (z-axis is normal to the xy-plane in Fig. 8.1) with $\nabla \cdot \mathbf{u} = \nabla \cdot \mathbf{h} = 0$ and $\mathbf{u} = \mathbf{h} = 0$ on $y = 0$. Omitting the details of calculation, we find eventually that the magnetohydrodynamic suction profile is stable for finite amplitude disturbances when $R\,(= \alpha\, \alpha_1^2 d/F)$ satisfies

$$Re \le 5.81R \le R_E, \tag{8.69}$$

where

$$d = v/U_0, \qquad \mu_1 = A^2, \qquad \mu_2 = A^2 Q, \qquad a = 1 - Pm - \alpha,$$

$$b = 1 - Pm + \alpha, \qquad c = -\,U_0\, Pm \cdot \alpha \cdot V_0^{-1},$$

$$F = [(1 + \mu_1^2)(a^2\,\alpha_1^2 + b^2\,\alpha_2^2) + 8\alpha^2\mu_2^2 c^2(\alpha_1^2 + \alpha_2^2) + A_1]^{1/2},$$

$$A_1 = [(1 - \mu_1^2)^2\,(a^2\,\alpha_1^2 + b^2\,\alpha_2^2)^2 + 16(1 + \mu_1)^2\,\alpha^2\mu_2^2 c^2$$

$$\times\,(\alpha_1^2 + \alpha_2^2)\,(a^2\,\alpha_1^2 + b^2\,\alpha_2^2)]^{1/2}. \tag{8.70}$$

It is also found that the domain of sure stability increases with increase in suction (see Fig. 8.2).

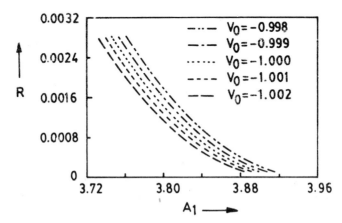

Fig. 8.2   Variation of R vs. A_1.

Thermal Instability of a Layer of Rotating Fluid

Investigations in hydrodynamic stability have led to eigenvalue problems in differential equations of high order. Here we present a variational method for solving the problem of a horizontal layer of an incompressible viscous fluid heated from below and subjected to uniform rotation about a vertical axis (see Chandrasekhar [60]).

Consider a horizontal layer of an incompressible viscous fluid (of depth d) which is heated from below and subjected to rotation with uniform angular velocity Ω about the vertical axis (taken as z-axis), the origin being in the central plane of the layer which is parallel to xy-plane. Heating from below leads to an adverse temperature gradient which is the cause of instability since such heating leads to a top heavy configuration. However, this instability does not always manifest itself in the form of convection because viscosity tries to resist such convection. It is only when the adverse temperature gradient exceeds critical value (measured in terms of a dimensionless number known as Rayleigh number $R = g\alpha\beta d^4/Kv$, where g, α, β, K and v denote the acceleration due to gravity, the coefficient of volume expansion of the fluid, the adverse temperature gradient, the thermal diffusivity and the kinematic viscosity, respectively), then the convection sets in the form of cells in which the liquid rises in the middle and descends near the boundary of the cells. Rotation is known to exert a stabilizing influence on the onset of convection so that the critical value of R increases with rotation. The dimensionless linearized equations of stability (corresponding to disturbances of small amplitude) in the normal mode analysis are

$$(D^2 - a^2 - i\sigma)Z = -\frac{2\Omega d}{v} \cdot DW, \tag{8.71}$$

$$(D^2 - a^2)(D^2 - a^2 - i\sigma)W - \frac{2\Omega d^3}{v} \cdot DZ = F \tag{8.72}$$

and

$$(D^2 - a^2 - iP\sigma)F = -Ra^2 W \tag{8.73}$$

subject to the boundary conditions

$$W = F = 0 \quad \text{at } z = \pm\frac{1}{2} \tag{8.74}$$

and either

$$DW = Z = 0 \quad \text{at } z = \pm\frac{1}{2} \quad \text{for rigid boundaries} \tag{8.75a}$$

or

$$D^2 W = DZ = 0 \quad \text{at } z = \pm\frac{1}{2} \quad \text{for free boundaries,} \tag{8.75b}$$

where $D = d/dz$, and a, σ, P denote the dimensionless wave number of a disturbance, the growth rate, and the Prandtl number v/K, respectively. Further, W and Z represent the dimensionless amplitudes of the vertical components of the velocity and vorticity of a disturbance, respectively. Now the growth rate σ is the parameter to be determined from the condition that the eigenvalue R is real. The solution of the physical problem requires the minimum (with respect to a^2) of these values of R for given values of the Taylor number $T(= 4\ \Omega^2 d^4/v^2)$ and P.

This double eigenvalue problem (double since both σ and R are to be determined) leads to the following variational principle: Multiplying (8.73) by F and integrating over the range of z and then using (8.72) and (8.74), we get

$$\int_{-1/2}^{1/2} [(DF)^2 + (a^2 + iP\sigma)F^2]\, dz = \int_{-1/2}^{1/2} W\left\{(D^2 - a^2)^2\, W\right.$$

$$\left. - i\sigma(D^2 - a^2)W - \left(\frac{2\Omega d^3}{v}\right)DZ\right\}\, dz.$$

After several integrations by parts and using (8.71) and the boundary conditions (8.75), we finally get

$$R = \frac{\displaystyle\int_{-1/2}^{1/2} [(DF)^2 + (a^2 + iP\sigma)F^2]\, dz}{\displaystyle a^2 \int_{-1/2}^{1/2} \{[(D^2 - a^2)W]^2 + d^2[(DZ)^2 + a^2 Z^2] \\ + i\sigma[(DW)^2 + a^2 W^2 + d^2 Z^2]\}\, dz} \tag{8.76}$$

It can now be easily shown that the variation of δR in R given by (8.76) due to variations δW and δZ in W and Z consistent with the boundary conditions on W, Z and F is given by

$$\delta R = -\frac{2}{a^2 I_2} \int_{-1/2}^{1/2} \delta F[(D^2 - a^2 - iP\sigma)F + R \cdot a^2 W]\, dz, \tag{8.77}$$

where I_2 denotes the integral in the denominator of the expression for R in (8.76). Accordingly, $\delta R = 0$ for all small arbitrary variations δF, provided that

$$(D^2 - a^2 - iP\sigma)F + Ra^2 W = 0,$$

which is (8.73). Thus (8.76) provides the variational basis for solving (8.71)–(8.73) for any prescribed a^2 and σ subject to the boundary conditions (8.74) and (8.75).

It may be noted that (8.76) does not express R as the ratio of two positive definite integrals. However, it is found that a simple trial function $F = \cos \pi z$ leads to very accurate determination of the eigenvalues provided that, for the chosen form of F, the functions W and Z are determined as solutions of (8.71) and (8.72).

Arnol'd's Stability Theorems

We consider steady inviscid flow of an incompressible fluid in a two-dimensional region V in the xy-plane which is simply connected and is bounded by a connected surface S on which the stream function Ψ for the flow vanishes (see Fig. 8.3). Here the vorticity ω is a function of $\Psi(x, y)$ and is normal to the plane of the flow. We can describe the flow by $\Psi = \Psi(\omega)$. When this steady flow is perturbed by

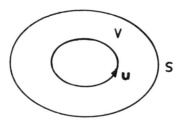

Fig. 8.3   A sketch of a topologically simple streamline pattern.

a two-dimensional disturbance, the perturbed stream function $\Psi_1(x, y, t)$ is given by

$$\Psi_1(x, y, t) = \Psi(x, y) + \varepsilon\phi(x, y, t), \tag{8.78}$$

where ε is a small parameter. Further, since $\Psi_1 = 0$ on S, it follows that $\phi = 0$ on S also. Since the flow is inviscid, we must have

$$\frac{d}{dt}(\nabla^2\Psi_1) = 0, \tag{8.79}$$

where d/dt is the material derivative following the motion. Arnol'd [82] showed that for this flow, the functional

$$A(\Psi_1) = \int_V \left[\frac{1}{2}|\nabla\Psi_1|^2 - C(-\nabla^2\Psi_1) \right] dV \tag{8.80}$$

is conserved by the flow for any function C (which is a function of the disturbed vorticity $-\nabla^2\Psi_1$). This means that $dA/dt = 0$. We can write (8.80) to $0(\varepsilon)$ as

$$A(\Psi_1) = A(\Psi) + \varepsilon \int_V [\nabla\Psi \cdot \nabla\phi + \nabla^2\phi \cdot C'(-\nabla^2\Psi)]. \tag{8.81}$$

It can be shown by using the divergence theorem that $A(\Psi_1)$ will be stationary at $\Psi_1 = \Psi$ if we choose C such that

$$C'(\omega) = \Psi(\omega). \tag{8.82}$$

Then it follows from (8.80) that

$$A(\Psi_1) = A(\Psi) + \frac{1}{2}\varepsilon^2 B(\phi) + o(\varepsilon^2), \tag{8.83}$$

where the functional $B(\phi)$ is given by

$$B(\phi) = \int_V \left[|\nabla\phi|^2 - \frac{d\Psi}{d\omega} \cdot (\nabla^2\phi)^2 \right] dV. \tag{8.84}$$

Since $A(\Psi_1)$ is conserved by the flow, it follows from (8.83) that $B(\phi)$ is equal to its initial value in the linear approximation. Now the magnitude of the disturbance ϕ can only increase if it can keep the value of $B(\phi)$ small. Thus an unstable mode of disturbance given by $\phi = \Phi(x, y)e^{\sigma t}$, with Re $(\sigma) > 0$ should satisfy $B(\phi) = 0$. Now if the basic flow (ω, Ψ) and the domain V are such that $B(\phi)$ is bounded away from zero for all $\phi(x, y, t)$, then this will also be the case for the restricted class of dynamically possible ϕ. Hence in this case any initial perturbation will not be able to grow. This gives Arnol'd's stability theorem which says that the flow is stable for all admissible functions ϕ vanishing on S, if either

$$B(\phi) > k \parallel \phi \parallel > 0 \qquad\qquad (8.85a)$$

or

$$B(\phi) < - k \parallel \phi \parallel < 0, \qquad\qquad (8.85b)$$

where k is a positive constant and ϕ has a suitable norm $\parallel \phi \parallel$ given by

$\left[\int_V | \nabla \phi |^2 \, dV \right]^{1/2}$, say. Arnol'd also showed that with a more stringent condition

on $B(\phi)$ than (8.85), the condition for nonlinear stability can also be derived. It is clear from (8.84) that if

$$d\Psi/d\omega \leq 0 \text{ throughout } V, \qquad\qquad (8.86)$$

then (8.85a) holds, and the flow is stable. This is Arnol'd's first theorem. Mestel [83] pointed out that for one-dimensional flow $\mathbf{u}$ ($u(y)$, 0, 0), (8.86) gives the well-known Rayleigh's inflexion point result

$$u \frac{d^2 u}{dy^2} \leq 0$$

for the stability of shear flow. For inviscid flow, it is known that the velocity profile must have an inflexion point for instability. For a circular flow with $\mathbf{u} =$ (0, $u(r)$, 0), the criterion (8.86) similarly gives the well-known result that the necessary condition for instability is that the vorticity gradient of the basic flow must change sign. When $d\Psi/d\omega \geq 0$ throughout V, the two terms in (8.84) are in competition. It can be shown that by a judicious choice of ϕ, the term with the higher derivative can be made the greater of the two. This stems from the fact that if ϕ is made to vary on very short length scales within V_- and on much larger ones outside V_-, then the high derivatives in V_- will dominate the integral in (8.84). Thus for certain suitable norm on ϕ, the functional $B(\phi)$ has no lower bound. However, a global maximum for B exists. Arnol'd's second theorem (8.85b) then applies if this maximum is negative.

8.6 Variational Formulation for Constrained Quasilinear Vector Systems

Variational formulations corresponding to boundary value problems for ordinary and elliptic partial differential equations have been of common use in continuum mechanics and other branches of physics. For non-elliptic equations (diffusion and wave equations), the Dirichlet problem is improperly posed and different conditions on parts of the boundary only have to be assigned.

In this section we present a variational formulation due to Geffen [84] for three-dimensional nonlinear initial and/or boundary value problems for a system of quasilinear conservation equations. Since the vector field envisaged in the problems is rotational, the formulation is applicable to flow problems involving non-isentropic processes and shock waves.

Consider a solenoidal vector field $\mathbf{A}(\mathbf{u}, \mathbf{x})$ satisfying

$$\nabla \cdot \mathbf{A} = 0, \tag{8.87}$$

where $\mathbf{u}$ and $\mathbf{x}$ are the vectors of dependent and independent variables. The rotationality condition is

$$\nabla \times \mathbf{u} = \mathbf{W} \tag{8.88}$$

and the initial-boundary conditions are

$$u_i \,|\, {\partial \Omega i} = g_i(\mathbf{x}) \tag{8.89}$$

prescribed on appropriate parts $\partial \Omega_i$ of the boundary $\partial \Omega$ of the region Ω where the solution is sought. Equations (8.87)–(8.89) constitute a first-order quasi-linear system of partial differential equations with initial/boundary conditions, assumed well-posed, for the solution vector $\mathbf{u}(\mathbf{x})$. The mathematical structure and properties of solutions of the system depend on the nature of the differential operator (8.87), i.e., on the explicit form of $\mathbf{A}(\mathbf{u}, \mathbf{x})$ which determines whether the system is elliptic, parabolic, hyperbolic or mixed. The precise way to prescribe the boundary conditions (8.89) for given operators (8.87) and (8.88) depends on the type of the operator. This in turn determines what conditions $u_i = g_i$, on which of its boundary Ω_i are to be specified (e.g., Dirichlet or Neumann boundary data on the whole boundary $\Omega \,(= \sum_i \Omega_i)$ for an elliptic operator, Cauchy data $u_i = f_i$ on a non-characteristic plane $\Omega_i \subset \Omega$ and the remaining $\Omega_M = \Omega - \Omega_i$ without prescribed conditions for a hyperbolic operator).

It is assumed that $\mathbf{u}(\mathbf{x})$ is twice continuously differentiable in all directions almost everywhere and that $\mathbf{A}(\mathbf{u}, \mathbf{x})$ is once continuously differentiable in all its arguments ($\mathbf{u}$ and $\mathbf{x}$) almost everywhere.

We now state without proof the following theorem due to Geffen.

Geffen's theorem.   (a) The functional

$$J = \int_\Omega [L(\mathbf{v}, \mathbf{x}) + \boldsymbol{\lambda} \cdot (\nabla \times \mathbf{v} - \mathbf{W})]\, d\Omega + \int_{\partial \Omega_M} (\boldsymbol{\lambda} \times \mathbf{v}) \cdot ds \tag{8.90}$$

defined for functions $\mathbf{v}$ satisfying the initial/boundary conditions (8.89) on $\partial \Omega_i$ (and $\sum (\partial \Omega_M + \partial \Omega_i) = \partial \Omega$) is stationary at the point $\mathbf{v} = \mathbf{u}$, where $\mathbf{u}$ satisfies (8.87) and (8.88) which form its Euler-Lagrange equations. Here, we have

$$\mathbf{A} = \nabla_u L, \quad \text{i.e., } A_i = \frac{\partial L}{\partial u_i}. \tag{8.91}$$

Mathematically, (8.91) ensures the symmetry of the Gateaux derivative of the operator in (8.87), which in turn is the condition for existence of a variational principle as explained in Section 7.2.

(b) The Lagrangian L exists iff

$$\nabla_{(\mathbf{u})} \times \mathbf{A} = 0. \tag{8.92}$$

(c) The vector Lagrange multiplier $\boldsymbol{\lambda}(\mathbf{x})$ is connected with $\mathbf{A}$ by

$$\mathbf{A} = -\nabla \times \boldsymbol{\lambda}. \tag{8.93}$$

Further, $\boldsymbol{\lambda}$ is held fixed or its increment $\delta\boldsymbol{\lambda}$ is kept proportional to $\mathbf{v}$ on the free boundary $\partial\Omega_M$.

Let us apply the above variational principle to small perturbation equation in three dimensions governing uniform transonic flow around a slender body given by

$$(a + c\phi_x)\phi_{xx} + \phi_{yy} + \phi_{zz} = 0.$$

Let the flow domain be

$$(|x|, |y|, |z|) \leq (|\bar{x}|, |\bar{y}|, |\bar{z}|),$$

where $\bar{x}, \bar{y}, \bar{z}$ may be infinite, with a hole (or slit), $Y = Y(x, z)$, $(x, z) \in A$, $y = 0$, describing the body. Boundary conditions are prescribed for the far field $(\bar{x}, \bar{y}, \bar{z})$, i.e. vanishing of potential ϕ and its derivatives, and partial boundary conditions on the body, e.g.

$$\nabla[X - Y(x, z)] \cdot (1 + \nabla\phi) = 0$$

or

$$a\phi_x + b\phi_y + c\phi_z + d = 0.$$

The first-order system in this case is

$$(a + cu)u_x + v_y + w_z = 0, \qquad \nabla \times \mathbf{u} = 0.$$

The variational formulation is

$$J = \int_{-\bar{z}}^{\bar{z}} \int_{-\bar{y}}^{\bar{y}} \int_{-\bar{x}}^{\bar{x}} \left[\frac{au^2}{2} + \frac{cu^3}{6} + \frac{1}{2}(v^2 + w^2) + \boldsymbol{\lambda} \cdot \nabla \times \mathbf{u} \right] dx\, dy\, dz + \int_{\partial\Omega_M}$$

where

$$\partial\Omega_M = Y(x, y = 0), \qquad d\mathbf{s} = (0, dx\, dz, 0),$$

$$\int_{\partial\Omega_M} = \int_{x,\,z} \int_{\in A} (\lambda_3 u - \lambda_1 w)|_{y=0}\, dx\, dz.$$

8.7 Variational Principles for Some Heat Transfer Problems

It is useful to recall some well-known results of the entropy analysis of thermo-fluid-dynamic processes, e.g., heat (or mass) transfer in fluid flows. The two principles which are of great interest in this context are the principle of least dissipation of energy and the principle of minimum rate of production of entropy.

The principle of least dissipation of energy, first formulated by Onsager (see [16]) says that for any non-equilibrium process satisfying certain reciprocity relations (such that $L_{ij} = L_{ji}$, where L_{ij} are the phenomenological coefficients connecting the fluxes J_i and the forces X_i by the relation $J_i = - \Sigma L_{ij}X_j$), the rate of energy dissipation is at its minimum. On the other hand, the principle of minimum rate of entropy production, formulated by Prigogine (see [16]) states that for a system in the stationary non-equilibrium state, the entropy production rate is at its minimum compatible with some constraints to be specified in each particular case. Gyarmati [85] established that for a stationary system, these two principles are equivalent.   .

It is, however, worth emphasizing the situations when the principle of minimum rate of entropy production is valid. Consider the generic flow of a viscous fluid under the influence of a pressure field, external force field, a temperature field, its own inertia and certain dissipative effects arising due to viscosity and thermal conduction. Beginning with the full momentum equations, if inertial terms or time-dependent terms are included, then the above principle is not valid although it may hold in some cases when these terms are absent. Further, it can be shown that the principle of minimum entropy production does not hold unless the phenomenological coefficients L_{ij} defined before are constants with $L_{ij} = L_{ji}$.

Dissipation is associated with entropy production. In recent years another thermodynamic quantity known as exergy is employed to describe non-equilibrium processes. This is defined by $e = h - T_0s$, where h is the enthalpy (work interactions) and s is the entropy (lost work and heat transfer) and T_0 is a reference temperature. Note that since the entropy production rate can only be positive, exergy can only decrease in a real process. Two noteworthy features of exergy are, (a) for a process which represents a pure work interaction with no dissipation and no heat transfer, the exergy change in the medium is equal to the work exchanged, and (b) for a process which represents an ideal reversible heat transfer at some constant temperature T with no work interaction, the exergy change in the medium is proportional to the heat exchanged, the constant of proportionality being $(1 - T_0/T)$. Thus exergy analysis is a synthetic way of combining the first and second laws of thermodynamics. Recently, Sciubba [86] showed that if one assumes that the unsteady flow of a viscous fluid assumes at any instant and at every point of the relevant domain a flow configuration such that the exergy destruction rate is minimum, then the solution of this variational problem gives a solution of Navier-Stokes equations compatible with suitable boundary and initial conditions.

There is   another approach to the above flow and heat transfer problem advanced by Biot [87] using the Lagrangian thermodynamics. This approach is not strictly variational and may be regarded as some sort of a quasi-variational principle.

Consider the energy equation with convection

$$\rho c_v \left(\frac{\partial T}{\partial t} + \mathbf{u} \cdot \nabla T \right) = \nabla \cdot (k \, \nabla T) \quad \text{in the region } V \tag{8.94}$$

subject to the boundary condition

$$k\mathbf{n} \cdot \nabla T + h(T - T_s) = 0 \tag{8.95}$$

on the boundary S of V and the initial condition

$$T = g(\mathbf{x}) \text{ in } V \quad \text{at } t = 0. \tag{8.96}$$

For convenience, we assume that physical properties are functions of position and not of temperature. We introduce the following functions: a total heat h and a heat flow vector $\mathbf{H}$ defined by

$$h = \int_0^T \rho c_v \, dT, \tag{8.97a}$$

$$h = - \nabla \cdot \mathbf{H} \tag{8.97b}$$

with

$$\mathbf{n} \cdot \frac{\partial \mathbf{H}}{\partial t} = k\mathbf{n} \cdot \nabla T \quad \text{on } S. \tag{8.98}$$

The thermal potential V_1 and the variational invariants $\overline{\delta D}$ and $\overline{\delta D}_s$ are defined by

$$V_1 = \int_V \int_0^h T \, dh \, dV,$$

$$\delta V_1 = \int_V T \, \delta h \, dV = - \int_V T \nabla \cdot \delta \mathbf{H} \, dV, \tag{8.99}$$

$$\overline{\delta D} = \int \frac{1}{k}\left(\frac{\partial \mathbf{H}}{\partial t} - h\mathbf{u} \right) \cdot \delta \mathbf{H} \, dV, \tag{8.100}$$

$$\overline{\delta D}_S = \int \frac{1}{h} \mathbf{n} \cdot \frac{\partial \mathbf{H}}{\partial t} \mathbf{n} \cdot \delta \mathbf{H} \, dS. \tag{8.101}$$

The quasi-variational principle is now expressed as

$$\delta V_1 + \overline{\delta D} + \overline{\delta D}_S = - \int_S T_s \mathbf{n} \cdot \delta \mathbf{H} \, dS. \tag{8.102}$$

Using divergence theorem, this equation can be written to show the Euler equation and the natural boundary condition

$$\int_V \delta \mathbf{H} \cdot \left[\nabla T + \frac{1}{k}\left(\frac{\partial \mathbf{H}}{\partial t} - h\mathbf{u} \right) \right] dV$$

$$+ \int_S \mathbf{n} \cdot \delta \mathbf{H} \left[T_s - T + \frac{\mathbf{n}}{h} \cdot \frac{\partial \mathbf{H}}{\partial t} \right] dS = 0. \tag{8.103}$$

It is clear that the divergence of k times the first term in brackets of (8.103) gives (8.94) while the second term gives the surface boundary condition (8.95). An application of this variational principle to the problem of finding heat transfer from the walls of a duct to an incompressible fluid flowing under fully developed laminar conditions can be found in Nigam and Agarwal [88].

Despite the fact that the principle reproduces the original equations, it is somewhat complicated as far as its application is concerned. One has to solve (8.97b) and (8.98) exactly after making good guesses for the temperature T. For two and three-dimensional problems, the solution of these partial differential equations may pose difficulty. Further, since no variational integrals are stationary, the usual advantage of variational principles is absent. A Galerkin method applied in terms of temperature alone without introducting h and $\mathbf{H}$ may prove to be simpler from the point of view of computations.

It may be noted that the above variational principles are valid for non-equilibrium systems. We shall now briefly discuss about variational principles for systems in thermodynamic equilibrium. For instance, let us consider the phenomena which occur near the surface separating two continuous media at rest. If the surface of separation is curved, the pressures on the two sides of the interface are different. To determine the equilibrium shape of this interface, we use the variational principle that in thermodynamic equilibrium, the total free energy is minimum along the path of constant temperature and volume. The internal free energy of an incompressible fluid depends only on the volume occupied by it. The change in the shape of the surface affects the surface free energy $\int \alpha\, df$, where α is the surface tension and df is an element of the surface as well as the energy in the external field (gravity, say) given by $g\rho \int z\, dV$, where z-axis is along the vertical and dV is an element of the volume of the fluid. Thus the equilibrium shape is given by the variational principle (see [89]) of the minimum of

$$\int \alpha\, df + g\rho \int z\, dV$$

subject to the constraint

$$\int dV = \text{constant},$$

which expresses the fact that the total volume of the (incompressible) fluid is constant.

8.8   The Concept of Local Potential

In Section 8.7, we have seen that the principle of minimum rate of entropy production (or for that matter the other principles described in that section) is valid only for restricted class of non-equilibrium systems. In fact, the restrictions are of such a nature as to preclude many problems of engineering interest. We now wish to develop a general criterion for describing the stationary state of a continuous system. To accomplish this we have to extend our notions of variational calculus.

To this end we follow closely the analysis of Glansdorff and Prigogine (Schecter [90]). The essential ideas of their study can be best explained by considering a simple example. Let us concentrate our attention on a solid body which is simultaneously heated and cooled on its boundaries. These boundary temperatures are independent of time.

The internal energy balance is given by

$$\rho c_v \frac{\partial T}{\partial t} = -\frac{\partial q_i}{\partial x_i},$$

(8.104)

where ρ, T, c_v and q_i denote the density, temperature, specific heat and the heat flux, respectively. Multiplying (8.104) by $\frac{\partial}{\partial t}(1/T)$, we can write this equation as

$$\rho c_v \frac{\partial T}{\partial t} \frac{\partial}{\partial t}\left(\frac{1}{T}\right) = -\frac{\partial}{\partial x_i}\left[q_i \frac{\partial}{\partial t}\left(\frac{1}{T}\right)\right] + q_i \frac{\partial^2 (1/T)}{\partial x_i \partial t}.$$

(8.105)

We now define a function Ψ as

$$\Psi = \rho c_v \frac{\partial T}{\partial t} \frac{\partial}{\partial t}\left(\frac{1}{T}\right) = -\frac{\rho c_v}{T^2}\left(\frac{\partial T}{\partial t}\right)^2 \le 0.$$

(8.106)

Clearly, Ψ is semi-negative definite since the heat capacity must be positive for thermodynamic stability. We also define a function ϕ as

$$\phi = \int_V \Psi \, dV = \int_V \left[-\frac{\partial}{\partial x_i}\left(q_i \frac{\partial}{\partial t}\left(\frac{1}{T}\right)\right) + q_i \frac{\partial^2}{\partial x_i \partial t}\left(\frac{1}{T}\right)\right] dV \le 0, \text{(8.107)}$$

where ϕ represents a global property of the system and is semi-negative definite. Further, ϕ tends to zero as the system approaches the stationary state, although the decay to this state need not be always monotonic. We can regard ϕ as a measure of the deviation from the stationary state.

Using the divergence theorem, we can write (8.107) as

$$\phi = -\int_S q_i \frac{\partial}{\partial t}\left(\frac{1}{T}\right) n_i \, dS + \int_V q_i \frac{\partial^2}{\partial x_i \partial t}\left(\frac{1}{T}\right) dV \le 0,$$

(8.108)

where S is the surface enclosing V and n_i denotes the normal to the surface. The surface integral vanishes because the surface temperature is independent of time. Then (8.108) gives

$$\phi = \int_V q_i \left(\frac{\partial}{\partial t} \frac{\partial}{\partial x_i} \frac{1}{T}\right) dV \le 0.$$

(8.109)

Now using the linear law of heat conduction, we can write (8.109) as

$$\phi = \frac{1}{2}\int_V L_{\theta\theta} \frac{\partial}{\partial t}\left[\frac{\partial}{\partial x_i}\left(\frac{1}{T}\right)\right]^2 dV \le 0,$$

(8.110)

where $L_{\theta\theta}$ is a phenomenological coefficient depending on temperature. We now assume that the system undergoes an infinitesimal displacement from the stationary state and define $T^0(x_i)$ as the temperature distribution in this state. We suppose that for such a displacement, $L_{\theta\theta}(T) \approx L_{\theta\theta}(T^0)$. Then (8.110) gives

$$\phi = \frac{\partial}{\partial t}\int_V \frac{1}{2}L_{\theta\theta}(T^0)\left[\frac{\partial}{\partial x_i}\left(\frac{1}{T}\right)\right]^2 dV \le 0.$$

(8.111)

Hence the volume integral

$$E^* = \int_V \frac{1}{2} L_{\theta\theta}(T^0) \left[\frac{\partial}{\partial x_i} \left(\frac{1}{T} \right) \right]^2 dV \tag{8.112}$$

can only decrease with time. This shows that E^* is minimum at the stationary state and can be regarded as the rate of entropy production in the stationary state. We call E^* as the local potential or a measure of generalized entropy production. Hence we find a structure not encountered in our previous studies on variational calculus. The problem now is to extremize E^* by a suitable choice of temperature. It is important to remember that we now have two classes of temperature entering in our variational principle. One of them is T which we can vary at our will and the second class of temperature is T^0 which is a specified function of position. This duality of temperature is to be maintained until the temperature T is identified as that occurring in the steady state. Hence the necessary condition for E^* to be minimum is obtained by using $(\delta E^*/\delta T)_{T_0} = 0$ with $T = T_0$ after the variation. It is essential to distinguish between T^0 and T until the process of variation is complete.

Let us now illustrate the above concept of local potential by studying the concentration distribution in an isothermal chemical reactor [90]. The reactor is shown in Fig. 8.4.

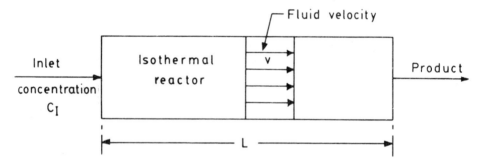

Fig. 8.4   A sketch of the plug flow reactor.

The concentration distribution $C(x)$ in the reactor satisfies

$$V \frac{dC}{dx} = D \frac{d^2 C}{dx^2} - kC^S, \tag{8.113}$$

where V and D denote the fluid velocity and the diffusion coefficient. Further, k and S are the reaction rate parameters. The boundary conditions are

$$C = C_I \quad \text{at } x = 0, \tag{8.114a}$$

$$\frac{dC}{dx} = 0 \quad \text{at } x = L. \tag{8.114b}$$

The transport equation (8.113) can be put in a variational form using the concept of local potential. In fact, it can be verified that the functional I given by

$$I = \int_0^L \left[VC \frac{dC^0}{dx} + \frac{D}{2} \left(\frac{dC}{dx} \right)^2 + \frac{k}{S+1} C^{S+1} \right] dx \tag{8.115}$$

is stationary and if C^0 is given by

$$C = C^0 \tag{8.116}$$

then (8.113) is satisfied. Assume

$$C = C_f(1 + a_1 x + a_2 x^2 + ... + a_n x^n) \tag{8.117}$$

satisfying (8.114a). The constants a_n are to be chosen so as to satisfy (8.114b). The concentration C^0 is not to be varied but must be known. We assume

$$C^0 = C_f(1 + \alpha_1 x + \alpha_2 x^2 + ... + \alpha_n x^n), \tag{8.118}$$

where α_n is determined such that $dC^0/dx = 0$ at $x = L$. We further suppose that α_i's are known and fixed but a_i's are to be found such that

$$\frac{\partial I_n}{\partial a_i} = 0 \quad (i = 1, 2, ..., n). \tag{8.119}$$

After performing this differentiation we set $\alpha_i = a_i$, which is equivalent to applying (8.116). Consider first a one-parameter approximation and assume

$$C = C_f(1 + a_1 x + a_2 x^2) \tag{8.120}$$

with a_2 chosen so that $(dC/dx)_L = 0$. This gives $a_2 = -a_1/2L$ such that

$$\frac{dC}{dx} = C_I a_1 \left(1 - \frac{x}{L}\right). \tag{8.121}$$

By the same reasoning,

$$\frac{dC^0}{dx} = C_I \alpha_1 \left(1 - \frac{x}{L}\right). \tag{8.122}$$

Using (8.120) and (8.122) in (8.115) and setting $(\partial I_1/\partial a_1)_{\alpha_1} = 0$, we get, on putting $\alpha_1 = a_1$ in the resulting equation (with $S = 1$), the relation

$$a_1 = \frac{-5kL}{\frac{15}{8} VL + 5D + 2kL^2}. \tag{8.123}$$

This gives the first approximation to concentration distribution inside the reactor with $S = 1$ for which the exact solution is known and is given by

$$C = C_I \left[\frac{P_2 \exp(P_2 L + P_1 x) - P_1 \exp(P_1 L + P_2 x)}{P_2 \exp(P_2 L) - P_1 \exp(P_1 L)}\right]. \tag{8.124}$$

Proceeding in the same way, we can find the higher order approximations. Table 1 gives a comparison of various approximations with the exact solution (8.124).

We conclude this section by applying the method of local potential to solve an unsteady heat transfer problem. Specifically, our aim is to calculate the rate of heat transfer to an incompressible fluid in ideal stagnation flow towards a flat surface. The phenomenon is time-dependent if we imagine that an eddy current suddenly sweeps fluid towards an interface (see Fig. 8.5).

Table 1   Comparison of Approximations with Exact Solution*

x	One parameter	Two parameters	Three parameters	Exact
0.1	0.9823	0.8670	0.7649	0.7642
0.3	0.9526	0.6279	0.4469	0.4478
0.5	0.9303	0.4300	0.2665	0.2664
0.75	0.9128	0.2486	0.1520	0.1511
1.0	0.9070	0.1928	0.1150	0.1159

*This table is adapted from "The variational method in Engineering" by R.S. Schechter (McGraw-Hill © 1967) and reproduced with permission of the McGraw-Hill companies.

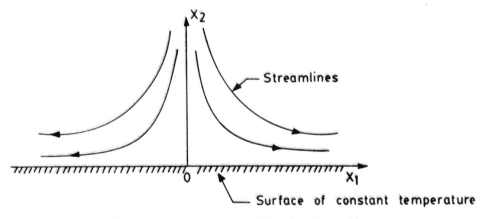

Fig. 8.5   An illustration of the physical problem.

The velocity field in ideal plane stagnation flow shown above is

$$v_1 = ax_1, \qquad v_2 = -ax_2, \tag{8.125}$$

a being a constant. The unsteady heat transfer equation is

$$\frac{\partial T}{\partial t} + v_1 \frac{\partial T}{\partial x_1} + v_2 \frac{\partial T}{\partial x_2} = \alpha \left(\frac{\partial^2 T}{\partial x_1^2} + \frac{\partial^2 T}{\partial x_2^2} \right), \tag{8.126}$$

where T is the temperature and α is the thermal diffusivity. The boundary and initial conditions are

$$T = T_\infty \quad \text{at } t = 0, \tag{8.127a}$$

$$T = T_w \quad \text{at } x_2 = 0 \tag{8.127b}$$

$$T \to T_\infty \quad \text{as } x_2 \to \infty, \tag{8.127c}$$

where T_w and T_∞ are the wall and the ambient temperature (assumed constant).

Defining l to be a characteristic length, we introduce the following dimensionless variables

$$\theta = \frac{\alpha t}{l^2}, \quad x = x_1/l, \quad y = x_2/l, \quad \phi = \frac{T - T_\infty}{T_w - T_\infty}. \tag{8.128}$$

This gives, from (8.126) and (8.128), the equation for $\phi(\theta, y)$:

$$\frac{\partial \phi}{\partial \theta} + 2Nx \frac{\partial \phi}{\partial x} - 2Ny \frac{\partial \phi}{\partial y} = \frac{\partial^2 T}{\partial x^2} + \frac{\partial^2 T}{\partial y^2} \tag{8.129}$$

subject to the initial and boundary conditions (see (8.127))

$$\phi(0, y) = 0, \tag{8.130a}$$

$$\phi(\theta, 0) = 1, \tag{8.130b}$$

$$\phi(\theta, \infty) = 0, \tag{8.130c}$$

where N is the Peclet number $al^2/2\alpha$.

It may be noted that a temperature distribution depending on θ and y (and not on x) can be found satisfying (8.129) with $\partial/\partial x = 0$ and the initial and boundary conditions (8.130).

A good approximation to the solution of the above system can be found by assuming

$$\phi(\theta, y) = \text{erfc} [f(\theta) \cdot y], \tag{8.131}$$

where erfc stands for the complementary error function. Clearly, ϕ given by (8.131) satisfies (8.130b) and (8.130c). The initial condition (8.130a) is satisfied provided that

$$f(\theta) \to \infty \quad \text{as } \theta \to 0. \tag{8.132}$$

It may be readily seen from above that a variational principle based on local potential is that the following functional is stationary:

$$L = \int_0^\varepsilon \int_0^\infty \left[\phi \frac{\partial \phi^0}{\partial \theta} - 2Ny\phi \frac{\partial \phi^0}{\partial y} + \frac{1}{2}\left(\frac{\partial \phi}{\partial y}\right)^2 \right] dy \, d\theta, \tag{8.133}$$

where ε is the upper limit of integration with respect to time θ. Here, ϕ^0 is a specified function of θ and y. Using (8.131), we get

$$\frac{\partial \phi^0}{\partial \theta} = -\frac{2}{\sqrt{\pi}} \cdot \frac{df^0}{d\theta} \cdot y \cdot \exp[-(f^0 \cdot y)^2],$$

$$\frac{\partial \phi^0}{\partial y} = -\frac{2}{\sqrt{\pi}} f^0 \cdot \exp[-(f^0 y)^2]. \tag{8.134}$$

Taking the variation of (8.133) and then utilizing (8.134), we find after integration with respect to y, the relation

$$\delta L = \int_0^\varepsilon \left[\frac{1}{2}\left(\frac{1}{f^3} \cdot \frac{df}{d\theta} - \frac{2N}{f^2}\right) + 1 \right] \cdot \frac{\delta f}{\sqrt{2\pi}} \, d\theta.$$

The condition of stationarity $\delta L = 0$ gives

$$\frac{1}{f^3} \cdot \frac{df}{d\theta} - \frac{2N}{f^2} + 2 = 0,$$

which gives, on integration, the relation

$$\frac{1}{f(\theta)} = \left[\frac{1}{N}(1 - e^{-4N\theta}) \right]^{1/2} \tag{8.135}$$

satisfying the boundary condition (8.132). It is indeed gratifying that (8.135) agrees with the exact solution. This stems from the fact that the original trial function (8.131) contains the exact solution. With ϕ known from (8.131) and (8.135), we can deduce the dimensionless heat transfer coefficient at the wall (the Nusselt number Nu) from

$$Nu = -\left(\frac{\partial \phi}{\partial y} \right)_{y=0} = 2\left[\frac{5}{2N}(1 - e^{-4N\theta}) \right]^{-1/2}$$

8.9   Variational Principles Applied to Heat Transfer by Radiation

It is worth pointing out that variational principles can also be applied to heat transfer by radiation. As mentioned in the introduction to this chapter, such problems are generally characterized by an integral equation (of Fredholm type)

$$z(x) = f(x) + \int_a^b K(x, y)z(y)\, dy, \tag{8.136}$$

where the kernel K is symmetric in x and y. This, of course, corresponds to the adjoint property of the equivalent differential equations.

We present now a simple example on radiation treated by variational methods by Sparrow [65].

Consider two plates of width L and infinite length placed at a distance h apart. Each plate is held at the same temperature T and the system loses heat by radiation through the sides which are exposed to black bodies held at zero temperature. Thus the flux of radiation is only to the surroundings and nothing is returned. The governing equation is an integral equation of the type (8.136) (with a symmetric kernel) given by

$$B(x) = \varepsilon\sigma T^4 + \frac{\rho h^2}{2} \int_{-L/2}^{L/2} B(y) \cdot \frac{dy}{[(y-x)^2 + h^2]^{3/2}}. \tag{8.137}$$

Here ε, σ and ρ ($= 1 - \varepsilon$), y and x denote the emissivity, the Stefan constant, the reflectivity, the coordinate perpendicular to the surfaces and the coordinate parallel to the surfaces, respectively. The origin is at the mid-point between the surfaces. Further, $B(x)$ represents the total radiation flux leaving area dA by emission and reflection. In dimensionless form, we write (8.137), with the aspect ratio $\gamma = h/L$, as

$$\beta(x) = 1 + \frac{\rho\gamma^2}{2} \int_{-1/2}^{1/2} \beta(y) \frac{dy}{[(y-x)^2 + \gamma^2]^{3/2}}. \tag{8.138}$$

We now make the following functional I stationary with respect to all continuous functions $\beta(x)$:

$$I = \frac{\rho\gamma^2}{2} \int_{-1/2}^{1/2} \int_{-1/2}^{1/2} \frac{\beta(x)\beta(y)}{[(y-x)^2 + \gamma^2]^{3/2}} - \int_{-1/2}^{1/2} \beta^2(x)\, dx + 2 \int_{-1/2}^{1/2} \beta(x)\, dx. \tag{8.139}$$

Due to the symmetry of the problem, a simple power series for $\beta(x)$ (even in x) is used as

$$\beta(x) = \sum_{i=1}^{N} c_i x^{2i-2}. \tag{8.140}$$

Table 2 shows the heat transfer to surroundings per unit width given by

$$\frac{Q/L}{\varepsilon\sigma T^4} = \left[1 - \varepsilon \int_{-1/2}^{1/2} \beta\, dx \right] \Big/ \rho.$$

Table 2   Values of Heat Transfer Rate to the Surroundings Per Unit Width with $N = 2$ and $\gamma = 0.5$

ε	$Q/L\varepsilon\sigma T^4$
0.1	0.858
0.3	0.669
0.5	0.549
0.7	0.467

The values of the successive approximations show that the variational method gives good results.

Remark.   It may be noted that the above variational formulation for the linear integral equation (8.138), as discussed in detail in Section 1.8, can also be extended to the following nonlinear integral equation due to Hammerstein (see [15]):

$$\alpha u(x) = \int_{a}^{b} K(x, \xi) f(\xi, u(\xi))\, d\xi,$$

where α is a constant. Here the kernel K is symmetric and positive semi-definite and its eigenvalues λ_j with eigenfunctions $\phi_j(x)$ are known. We introduce the kernel $L(x, \xi) = \sum_j \phi_j(x)\, \phi_j(\xi)\lambda_j^{-1/2}$ whose first iteration is K. Further, if we define the function $F(\xi, u) = \int_{u_0}^{u} f(\xi, s)\, ds$, then it can be shown that the Euler equation for the functional

$$I[v] = \frac{\alpha}{2} \int_{a}^{b} v^2(x)\, dx - \int_{a}^{b} F\left(x, \int_{a}^{b} L(x, \xi)v(\xi)\, d\xi\right) dx$$

is

$$\alpha v(x) = \int_{a}^{b} L(x, \xi)f\left(\xi, \int_{a}^{b} L(\xi, \eta)v(\eta)\, d\eta\right) d\xi.$$

By putting

$$u(x) = \int_{a}^{b} L(x, \xi)v(\xi)\, d\xi$$

in the above equation, we readily derive the foregoing nonlinear integral equation.

8.10   A Variational Problem Involving Optimal Design of Cooling Fins

It is well known that cooling fins are attached to radiators to increase the rate of heat transfer from the wall to the surrounding atmosphere [90]. The design of such fins is quite complicated since a designer must attend to such details as best material for construction, optimum number of fins per foot etc. In this section we will consider a simple design of cooling fins by using variational principles. The problem is stated as follows: if the mass of a rectangular cooling fin is specified, what is the optimum shape of the fin? An illustration of the physical problem is given in Fig. 8.6.

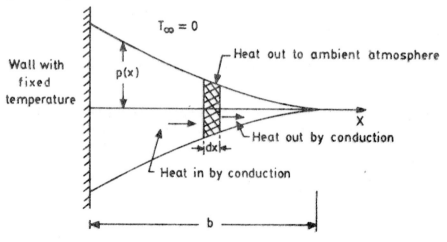

Fig. 8.6   A sketch of the cooling fin.

Without loss of generality we can assume the ambient temperature $T_\infty = 0$. Writing down the heat balance equation for an element of length dx for the fin, we get

$$\left(-kA\,\frac{\partial T}{\partial x}\right)_x = \left(-kA\,\frac{\partial T}{\partial x}\right)_{x+\Delta x} + hS(T - T_\infty), \tag{8.141}$$

where

T = temperature,
k = thermal conductivity,
A = cross-sectional area of the fin
  $= 2p(x)$ per unit width of the fin,
h = heat transfer coefficient,
S = surface area of the heat element
  $= 2(1 + (p'(x))^2)^{1/2}\,dx$ per unit width.

Thus with $T_\infty = 0$, we find, from (8.141), the heat equation

$$\frac{d}{dx}\left[p(x)\,\frac{dT}{dx}\right] = T\frac{h}{k}\left[1 + \left(\frac{dp}{dx}\right)^2\right]^{1/2}$$

If we assume that dp/dx is small as compared with 1, the above equation simplifies to

$$\frac{d}{dx}\left[p(x)\,\frac{dT}{dx}\right] = T\frac{h}{k}. \tag{8.142}$$

The total amount of heat dissipated by the fin per unit time is given by

$$H = 2\int_0^b hT\,dx, \tag{8.143}$$

where b is the length of the fin. Further, since the mass of the fin is specified, we have

$$M = 2\rho\int_0^b p(x)\,dx. \tag{8.144}$$

Our problem now is to maximize the dissipation (8.143) subject to (8.144). Thus, using a Lagrange multiplier λ, we make the following functional stationary:

$$I = \int_0^b [2hT + 2\lambda\rho p(x)]\,dx. \tag{8.145}$$

But in the above expression, $T(x)$ and $p(x)$ are connected by (8.142) which gives on integration the relation

$$-p(x)\,\frac{dT}{dx} = \frac{h}{k}\int_x^b T(y)\,dy, \tag{8.146}$$

where it is assumed that there is no heat flow at the end of the fin. Thus (8.145) and (8.146) lead to

$$I = 2 \int_0^b \left[hT - \frac{\lambda \rho h}{k} \left(\frac{dT}{dx} \right)^{-1} \int_x^b T(y) \, dy \right] dx. \tag{8.147}$$

Let us fix b temporarily and find the optimal temperature distribution. Finally, we shall select the best possible value of the fin length for a given mass. Define the variation as

$$T^*(x) = T(x) + \varepsilon \phi(x), \tag{8.148}$$

where $\phi(x)$ is continuously differentiable in $[0, b]$ and satisfies the boundary condition

$$\phi(0) = 0, \tag{8.149}$$

since the temperature is fixed at the wall. Substituting (8.148) in (8.147) and expanding to $0(\varepsilon)$, we get

$$\delta I = 2 \int_0^b \varepsilon \left[h\phi + \frac{\lambda \rho h}{k} \frac{\phi_x}{(T_x)^2} \int_x^b T(y) \, dy - \frac{\lambda \rho h}{k T_x} \int_x^b \phi(y) \, dy \right] dx, \tag{8.150}$$

where $\phi_x = d\phi/dx$ and $T_x = dT/dx$. Integrating (8.150) by parts gives

$$\delta I = 2\varepsilon \int_0^b \left[h + \frac{\lambda \rho h}{k} \frac{(d^2T/dx^2)}{(dT/dx)^3} \int_x^b T(y) \, dy + \frac{\lambda \rho h T}{k(dT/dx)^2} \right.$$

$$\left. - \frac{\lambda \rho h}{k} \int_0^x \left(\frac{dT}{dx} \right)^{-1} dy \right] \phi \, dx,$$

which yields for an extremum the following Euler equation:

$$h + \frac{\lambda \rho h}{k} \left[\frac{2(d^2T/dx^2)}{(dT/dx)^3} \int_x^b T(y) \, dy + \frac{T}{(dT/dx)^2} - \int_0^x \frac{dy}{dT/dx} \right] = 0. \tag{8.151}$$

It can be easily verified that

$$T(x) = 1 - \left(-\frac{\lambda \rho}{k} \right)^{1/2} x = 1 + ax \tag{8.152}$$

satisfies (8.151). Thus from (8.146) the shape of the fin is computed as

$$p(x) = - \left[\left(\frac{dT}{dx} \right)^{-1} \int_x^b T \, dy \right] \frac{h}{k} = \frac{h}{ka} \left(\frac{ax^2}{2} + x - \frac{ab^2}{2} - b \right). \tag{8.153}$$

The Lagrange multiplier λ related to a by $a = -\left(-\dfrac{\lambda\rho}{k}\right)^{1/2}$ is now determined

from (8.144) as

$$a = -\left(\frac{Mk}{\rho h b^2} + \frac{2b}{3}\right)^{-1} \tag{8.154}$$

The task of determining b still remains. It must be noted that $p(x) > 0$ for $0 < x < b$ for a physically meaningful solution. We now find b such that of all admissible values, it gives rise to maximum rate of energy dissipation. Substitution of (8.152) in (8.143) gives

$$H = 2h\left(b - \frac{3\rho h b^4}{3Mk + 2\rho h b^3}\right)$$

on using (8.154). For maximum dissipation rate, $\partial H/\partial b = 0$, which leads, on simplification, to

$$b = \left(\frac{3Mk}{\rho h}\right)^{1/3}$$

and this is the optimum value of b. This study can also be extended to fin design with radiative heat transfer.

APPENDIX

THE METHOD OF THE AVERAGED LAGRANGIAN

This is a very powerful method based on variational principles and is applicable to the study of nonlinear waves.

As a simple example, we follow Whitham [58a] and study the nonlinear Klein-Gordon equation

$$\frac{\partial^2 u}{\partial t^2} - \frac{\partial^2 u}{\partial x^2} + V'(u) = 0, \tag{A8.1}$$

where $V(u)$ is a nonlinear potential function and a prime denotes differentiation with respect to u. The Lagrangian density for (A8.1) is given by

$$L = \frac{1}{2}\left(\frac{\partial u}{\partial t}\right)^2 - \frac{1}{2}\left(\frac{\partial u}{\partial x}\right)^2 - V(u). \tag{A8.2}$$

An elementary progressive wave train is considered by setting

$$u = u(\theta), \qquad \theta = kx - \omega t, \tag{A8.3}$$

where k and ω denote the local wave number and frequency. Then (A8.1) gives

$$(\omega^2 - k^2) \frac{\partial^2 u}{\partial \theta^2} + V'(u) = 0, \tag{A8.4}$$

which gives on integration,

$$\frac{1}{2}(\omega^2 - k^2) \left(\frac{\partial u}{\partial \theta}\right)^2 + V(u) = E, \tag{A8.5}$$

E being the integration constant. Here

$$k = \frac{\partial \theta}{\partial x}, \tag{A8.6a}$$

$$\omega = -\frac{\partial \theta}{\partial t}. \tag{A8.6b}$$

Equation (A8.5) can be solved by a quadrature and has a solution periodic in θ given by

$$\theta = \left(\frac{\omega^2 - k^2}{2}\right)^{1/2} \int \frac{du}{(E - V(u))^{1/2}}. \tag{A8.7}$$

Here we assume that u is periodic with a period 2π so that

$$\frac{(\omega^2 - k^2)^{1/2}}{2} \oint \frac{du}{[E - V(u)]^{1/2}} = 2\pi. \tag{A8.8}$$

For the linear case with $V'(u) = u$, the solution is

$$u = \alpha \cos \theta, \tag{A8.9a}$$
$$\omega^2 - k^2 = 1, \tag{A8.9b}$$
$$\alpha^2 = 2E. \tag{A8.9c}$$

Here, (A8.9b) represents the linear dispersion relation. If $V(u)$ is cubic or quartic in u, (A8.7) reduces to elliptic functions.

It is interesting to note that slow variations of ω, k and E can be determined from the averaged Lagrangian. Using (A8.5), we obtain from (A8.2) the relation

$$L = (\omega^2 - k^2)\left(\frac{\partial u}{\partial \theta}\right)^2 - E. \tag{A8.10}$$

Averaging L over a period $[0, 2\pi]$ in θ, we get

$$2\pi \bar{L} = \int_0^{2\pi} L\, d\theta$$

$$= (\omega^2 - k^2) \int_0^{2\pi} \left(\frac{\partial u}{\partial \theta}\right)^2 d\theta - 2\pi E$$

$$= (\omega^2 - k^2) \oint \frac{\partial u}{\partial \theta} \, du - 2\pi E$$

$$= [2 \, (\omega^2 - k^2)]^{1/2} \oint [E - V(u)]^{1/2} \, du - 2\pi E, \tag{A8.11}$$

where use is made of (A8.5). The variation of $\bar{L}$ with respect to E, which is zero, (i.e., $\partial \bar{L}/\partial E = 0$), gives the dispersion relation (A8.8).

Now the Euler-Lagrange equation with respect to θ gives

$$-\frac{\partial}{\partial t}\left(\frac{\partial \bar{L}}{\partial \omega}\right) + \frac{\partial}{\partial x}\left(\frac{\partial \bar{L}}{\partial k}\right) = 0. \tag{A8.12}$$

This gives from (A8.11) the relation

$$\frac{\partial}{\partial t}(\omega F) + \frac{\partial}{\partial x}(kF) = 0, \tag{A8.13}$$

where

$$F = \left(\frac{2}{\omega^2 - k^2}\right)^{1/2} \oint [E - V(u)]^{1/2} \, du. \tag{A8.14}$$

The dispersion relation (A8.8), the amplitude equation (A8.13), and the consistency relations (A8.6) constitute the basic system of equations for the lowest order of approximation. Lighthill [92] gave a simple nonlinear stability analysis based on the determination of the averaged Lagrangian for small amplitude deep water waves. He found a critical value of the wave amplitude A (satisfying $(A/\lambda)_{cr} = 0.054$, λ being the wavelength) above which waves are stable. This is in keeping with the fascinating result of Benjamin and Feir [93] who found that waves of sufficiently small amplitude in deep water are unstable. A confirmation of the existence of this instability was made by Benjamin and Feir in the National Physical Laboratory experimental pool at Feltham (Greater London).

It may be finally noted that the present analysis is applied to the slow variation of a nonlinear periodic wave. Thus this variational method is applicable not only to weak nonlinear waves but also to fully nonlinear waves.

REFERENCES

[1] Elsgolts, L., *Differential Equations and Calculus of Variations*, Mir Publishers, Moscow, 1973.

[2] Lyusternik, L.A., *The Shortest Lines: Variational problems,* Mir Publishers, Moscow, 1976.

[3] Courant, R. and Hilbert, D., *Methods of Mathematical Physics, Vols. I and II*, Wiley-Interscience, New York, 1953.

[4] Schwinger, J., Selected Papers in Quantum Electrodynamics, Dover, New York, 1958.

[5] Yasue, K., *J. Functional Analysis,* **41**, p. 327, 1981.

[6] Young, L.C., *Lectures on the Calculus of Variations and Optimal Control Theory*, W.B. Saunders, Philadelphia, 1969.

[7] Morse, P.M. and Feshbach, H., *Methods of Theoretical Physics, Part I*, McGraw-Hill, New York, 1953.

[8] Figueiredo, D.G., Lectures on the Ekeland Variational Principles with Applications and Detours, Narosa Publishing House, New Delhi, 1989.

[9] Keller, J.B., Geometrical theory of diffraction, *Proc. of Symposia in Applied Math.*, **8**, McGraw-Hill, New York, 1958.

[10] Gelfand, I.M. and Fomin, S.V., *Calculus of Variations*, Prentice-Hall, Englewood Cliffs, New Jersey, 1963.

[11] Arthurs, A.M., *Complementary Variational Principles*, Clarendon Press, Oxford, 1970.

[12] Gardner, C.S., *Journal of Math. Phys.*, **12**, p. 1548, 1971.

[13] Landau, L.D. and Lifshitz, E.M., *Mechanics* (Vol. I in the series—A Course in Theoretical Physics), Pergamon Press, New York, 1960.

[14] Krasnov, M.I., Makarenko, G.I. and Kiselev, A.I., *Problems and Exercises in the Calculus of Variations*, Mir Publishers, Moscow, 1975.

[15] Myskis, A.D., *Advanced Mathematics for Engineers*, Mir Publishers, Moscow, 1975.

[16] Finlayson, B.A., *The Method of Weighted Residuals and Variational Principles*, Academic Press, New York, 1972.

[17] Gould, S.H., *Variational Methods for Eigenvalue Problems*, University of Toronto Press, Toronto, 1966.

[18] Diaz, J.B., Calculus of variations and its applications, *Proc. of Symposia in Applied Math.*, Vol. **8**, McGraw-Hill, New York, 1958.

[19] Aronszajn, N., *Proc. Nat. Acad.*, (USA), **34**, p. 474, 1948.

[20] Weinberger, W.F., *Proc. Amer. Math. Soc.*, **3**, p. 643, 1952.

[21] Payne, L.E., *J. Rat. Mech. Anal.*, **4**, p. 517, 1955.

[22] Kornhauser, E.T. and Stakgold, I., *J. Math. Phys.*, **31**, p. 45, 1952.

[23] Szego, G., *J. Rat. Mech. Anal.*, **3**, p. 343, 1954.

[24] Kantorovich, L.V. and Krylov, V.I., *Approximate Methods of Higher Analysis*, Fizmatgiz, Moscow, 1962.

[25] Djukic, Dj, S., *Trans. ASME* (USA), p. 822, Sept. 1974.

[26] Schulman, Z.P. and Berkovsky, B.M., *Nauka i Tehnika* (in Russian), Minsk, p. 100, 1966.

[27] Sengupta, S. and Gupta, A.S., *Publications de l'institute Mathematique*, Belgrade, Nouvelle Serie, **19**, p. 147, 1975.

[28] Prenter, P.M., *Splines and Variational Methods*, John Wiley & Sons, New York, 1975.

[29] Lax, P.D. and Milgram, A.N., *Ann. of Math. Studies*, **33**, Princeton, p. 167, 1954.

[30] Siddiqi, A.H., *Functional Analysis with Applications*, Tata McGraw-Hill, New Delhi, 1986.

[31] Synge, J.L., *The Hypercircle in Mathematical Physics*, Cambridge University Press, London, 1957.

[32] Hardy, G., Littlewood, J.E. and Polya, G., *Inequalities*, (Paperback edition), Cambridge University Press, London, 1988.

[33] Vladimirov, V.S., *A Collection of Problems of the Equations of Mathematical Physics*, Mir Publishers, Moscow, 1986.

[34] Komkov, V., *Variational Principles of Continuum Mechanics with Engineering Applications, Vol. 1*, D. Reidel Publishing Co., Dordrecht, Holland, 1985.

[35] Banerjee, M.B. and Gupta, J.R., *Studies in Hydrodynamic and Hydromagnetic Stability*, Silverline Publications, Shimla, 1989.

[36] Stampacchia, G., *C.R. Acad. Sc.* (Paris), **258**, p. 4413, 1964.

[37] Duvaut, G. and Lions, J.L., *Les inequations en mecanique et en physique*, Dunod, Paris, 1971.

[38] Vainberg, M.M., *Variational Methods for the Study of Nonlinear Operators*, Holden-Day, San Francisco, 1964.

[39] Rudin, W., *Functional Analysis*, Tata McGraw-Hill, New Delhi, 1973.

[40] Nirenberg, L., *Topics in Calculus of Variations* (edited by M. Giaquinta), p. 100, Springer-Verlag, Berlin, 1989.

[41] Mikhlin, S.G., *Variational Methods in Mathematical Physics*, Macmillan, New York, 1964.

[42] Rall, L.B., *J. Math. Anal. Applic.*, **14**, p. 174, 1966.

[43] Kato, T., *Math, Annalen,* **126**, p. 253, 1953.

[44] Gurtin, M.E., *Q. Appl. Math.,* **22**, p. 252, 1964.

[45] Tonti, E., *Annali di Matem. Pura. Appl.,* **45**, p. 331, 1972.

[46] Magri, F., *Int. J. Engineering Sci.,* **12**, p. 537, 1974.

[47] Tonti, E., *Int. J. Engineering Sci.,* **22**, p. 1343, 1984.

[48] Langhaar, H.L., *Energy Methods in Applied Mechanics,* Wiley, New York, 1962.

[49] Oden, J.T. and Reddy, J.N., *Variational Methods in Theoretical Mechanics,* Springer-Verlag, Berlin, 1976.

[50] Yourgrau, W. and Mandelstam, S., *Variational Principles in Dynamics and Quantum Theory,* Pitman, London, 1956.

[51] Lundgren, T.S., *Phys. Fluids,* **6**, p. 898, 1963.

[52] Greene, J.M. and Karlson, E.T., *Phys. Fluids,* **12**, p. 561, 1969.

[53] Wenger, N.C., *J. Fluid Mech.,* **43**, p. 211, 1970.

[54] Wasserman, M.L. and Slattery, J.C., *AI ChE J.,* **10**, p. 383, 1964.

[55] Nakano, Y. and Tien, C., *AI ChE J.,* **14**, p. 145, 1968.

[56] Keller, J.B., Rubenfeld L.A. and Molyneux, J.E., *J. Fluid Mech.,* **30**, p. 97, 1967.

[57] Luke, J.C., *J. Fluid Mech.,* **27**, p. 395, 1967.

[58a] Whitham, G.B., *Linear and Nonlinear Waves,* John Wiley & Sons, New York, 1974.

[58b] Seliger, R.L. and Whitham, G.B., *Proc. Roy. Soc.* (London), **A305**, p. 1, 1968.

[59] Simmons, W.F., *Proc. Roy. Soc.* (London), **A309**, p. 551, 1969.

[60] Chandrasekhar, S., *Hydrodynamic and Hydromagnetic Stability,* Oxford University Press, London, 1961.

[61] Cercignani, C. and Pagani, C.D., *Phys. Fluids,* **9**, p. 1167, 1966.

[62] Rao, G.V.R., *Jet Propulsion,* **28**, p. 377, 1958.

[63] Kraiko, A.N. and Osipov, A.A., *J. Appl. Math. Mech.,* **32**, p. 617, 1968.

[64] Guderley, K.C. and Armitage, J.V., *Theory of Optimum Aerodynamic Shapes,* Academic Press, New York, 1965.

[65] Sparrow, E.M., *J. Heat Transfer, Trans. ASME, Series C,* **82**, p. 375, 1960.

[66] Howard, L.N., *J. Fluid Mech.,* **17**, p. 405, 1963.

[67] Busse, F.H., *J. Fluid Mech.,* p. 457, 1969.

[68] Truesdell, C. and Toupin, R.A., Handbuch der Physik (Ed. S. Flügge), Vol. III/1, Springer-Varlag, Berlin, 1960.

[69] Lush, P.E. and Cherry, T.M., *Quart. J. Mech. Appl. Math.,* **9**, p. 6, 1956.

[70] Bateman, H., *Proc. Roy. Soc.* (London), **A125**, p. 598, 1929.

[71] Batchelor, G.K., *An Introduction to Fluid Dynamics*, Cambridge University Press, London, 1970.

[72] Hill, R., *J. Mech. Phys. Solids,* **5**, p. 66, 1956.

[73] Happel, J. and Brenner, H., *Low Reynolds Number Hydrodynamics*, Prentice-Hall, Englewood Cliffs, New Jersey, 1965.

[74] Lamb, H., *Hydrodynamics,* 6th ed., Cambridge University Press, London, 1953.

[75] Serrin, J., *Handbuch der Physik* (S. Flugge, Ed.), *Vol. VIII/1*, Springer-Verlag, Berlin, 1959.

[76] Taylor, G.I., *Phil. Trans. Roy. Soc.* (London), **A223**, p. 289, 1923.

[77] Joseph, D.D., *Archive for Rational Mech. and Analysis*, **22**, p. 163, 1966.

[78] Rajagopal, K.R., Gupta, A.S. and Dandapat, B.S., *Archive for Rational Mech. and Analysis* (USA), **83**, No. 1, p. 91, 1983.

[79] Gupta, A.S., *Zeit. ange. Math. und Physik*, **11**, p. 43, 1960.

[80] Kakutani, T., *Zeit. ange. Math. und Physik*, **12**, p. 219, 1961.

[81] Joseph, D.D., *Stability of Fluid Motions, Vol. II*, Springer-Verlag, Berlin, 1976.

[82] Arnol'd, V.I., *Doklady Akad. Nauk SSSR*, **162**, p. 975, 1965.

[83] Mestel, A.J., *J. Fluid Mech.*, **200**, p. 19, 1989.

[84] Geffen, N., *Quart. Appl. Math.*, p. 375, October 1977.

[85] Gyarmati, I., *Ann. Phys.*, **23**, p. 353, 1969.

[86] Sciubba, E., *Jour. Math. Phys. Sci.*, **25**, p. 61, 1991.

[87] Biot, M., *J. Aerospace Sci.*, **29**, p. 568, 1962.

[88] Nigam, S.D. and Agarwal, H.C., *J. Math. Mech.*, **9**, p. 869, 1960.

[89] Landau L.D. and Lifshitz, E.M., *Fluid Mechanics* (Vol. 6 in the series—A Course in Theoretical Physics) Pergamon Press, New York, 1960.

[90] Schechter, R.S., *The Variational Method in Engineering*, McGraw-Hill, New York, 1967.

[91] Razumikhin, B.S., *Classical Principles and Optimization Problems*, D. Reidel Publishing Co., The Netherlands, 1987.

[92] Lighthill, M.J., *Proc. Roy. Soc.* (London), **A299**, p. 1, 1967.

[93] Benjamin, T.B. and Feir, J.E., *J. Fluid Mech.*, **27**, p. 417, 1967.

INDEX